The politics of technology

The politics of technology

Edited by
Godfrey Boyle, David Elliott and Robin Roy
at The Open University

Published by
Longman in association with
The Open University Press

Longman Group Limited London

*Associated companies, branches and representatives
throughout the world*

*Published in the United States of America
by Longman Inc., New York*

Selection and editorial material
copyright © The Open University 1977.

First published 1977

Library of Congress Cataloging in Publication Data
Main entry under title:

The Politics of technology.

   Includes bibliographical references and index.
   1. Technology – Social aspects – Addresses, essays,
lectures.   I. Boyle, Godfrey.   II. Elliott, David.
III. Roy, Robin.
T14.5.P64   301.24′3   77-5678
ISBN 0-582-44373-3

Set in 10/11pt. Times New Roman
and printed in Great Britain by
Richard Clay (The Chaucer Press) Ltd, Bungay, Suffolk

Contents

Section 3   Public involvement in technology

Section 4   Decentralisation and community technology

Section 5   A guide to the literature

Preface

This reader has been produced as an integral part of an Open University third-level course, T361 *Control of Technology*.

The starting point for the course is the many problems, crises and dangers that have come to be associated with rapid technical and technological change in both the developed and developing world – themes which were discussed in earlier Open University courses such as *The Man-made World: A Foundation Course*[1] and *Man-made Futures: Design and Technology*.[2]

These problems have led to demands on the one hand for more regulation of technology and on the other for the positive redirection of technical and technological change to take more account of social, environmental and human needs.

The course adopts a broad interdisciplinary approach, and emphasises that there are many divergent views on how social control of technology may best be achieved. One of the aims of the course is to help students to assess the desirability and viability of the various prescriptions and strategies currently being put forward. Consequently, it should be of interest not only to students of technology and social science but also to anyone concerned with the effects on their lives of technological developments which are so often, seemingly, beyond their control.

In the context of the *Control of Technology* course this Reader is aimed at providing students with access to some of the recent theoretical and political literature on various means of bringing technology under social control – including government intervention, technology assessment, accountability and public participation, and the development of decentralised community technologies.

We are very grateful to Ernie Taylor for the considerable help he gave us in preparing this Reader and to Sue Stickland and John Taylor of the Open University Publishing Division for their advice and

---

1. The Open University (1971), T100 *Technology Foundation Course*, The Open University Press.
2. The Open University (1975), T262 *Man-made Futures: Design and Technology* The Open University Press.

assistance. Thanks are also due for their help to Kitty Gleadell and to Caryl Hunter-Brown.

Further information on the course materials associated with the Reader is available from:

Open University Educational Enterprises Ltd,
12 Cofferidge Close,
Stony Stratford,
Milton Keynes MK11 1BY

Godfrey Boyle
David Elliott
Robin Roy
Milton Keynes,
January 1977

Acknowledgements

We are grateful to the following for permission to reproduce copyright material:

American Society for Public Administration and the author for an article entitled 'Why Public Participation is Essential in Technology Assessment' by Joseph F. Coates from *Public Administration Review* January–February 1975; The Bulletin of the Atomic Scientists for an article entitled 'Technical Power and People' by A. Benn from *Bulletin of the Atomic Scientists*, December 1971; Author's Agents and Alfred A. Knopf Inc. for an extract from 'Social Aspects of the Environment Crisis' in *The Closing Circle* by Barry Commoner. Publ. by Jonathan Cape Ltd; Council for Science and Society for an adapted version of the article 'The Council for Science and Society (1976) Monitoring Technical Projects' from *Superstar Technologies*. Publ. by Barry Rose (Publishers) Ltd; Elsevier North-Holland Inc. for an adapted version of the article entitled 'Is Greater Citizen Participation in Planning Possible and Desirable?' by S. A. Umpleby in *Technological Forecasting and Social Change* Vol. 4, Part 1, 1972; The Author for his article entitled 'The More Effective Political Control of Technical Change' by Roger Williams in *Technology And Society* Vol. 8, No. 2, 2nd July 1973; Gordon & Breach Science Publishers Ltd. for an article entitled 'The Politics of Selecting Candidate Technologies for Assessment' by M. Blissett in *Technology Assessment* Vol. 2, No. 3, 1974; Granada Publishing Ltd. for an extract from the article 'Science, Technology and Democracy' by L. Skair in *Organized Knowledge*. Publ. by MacGibbon & Kee Ltd/Granada Publishing Ltd; The Institute of Economic Affairs for an adapted extract from *Occasional Paper* No. 37 by Professor J. Jewkes; Macmillan London and Basingstoke for an adapted version of the article entitled 'Contradictions of Science and Technology in the Productive Process' in *The Political Economy of Science* edited by H. Rose and S. Rose, 1976; Minerva for an article entitled 'Legal Frameworks for the Assessment and Control of Technology' by L. H. Tribe in *Minerva* October 1971; Organisation for Economic Co-Operation and Development for an article entitled 'Technology on Trial' by F. Hetman in *Society and the Assessment of Technology* 1974; Penguin Books Ltd. for an adapted extract from *The Economics Of*

Industrial Innovation by Christopher Freeman (c) Christopher Freeman, 1974. Reprinted by permission of the Publisher; The Royal Town Planning Institute for an adapted article entitled 'A Ladder of Citizen Participation in the U.S.A.' by Sherry R. Arnstein in *Journal of the Royal Town Planning Institute* April 1972; Sage Publications Ltd. for an article entitled 'The Political Impact of Technical Expertise' by D. Nelkin in *Social Studies of Science* Vol. 5, No. 1, 1975; American Association for the Advancement of Science and the author for the article entitled 'Technology Assessment and Social Control' by Prof. Michael S. Baram in *Science* Vol. 180, 4th May 1973, No. 4085; Science for the People for an article entitled 'Alternative Technology – Possibilities and Limitations' by the Boston Science for the People Collective in *Science for the People* September–October 1976; Science Policy Foundation for an article entitled 'Social Control and Social Responsibility' by S. Lal in *Science and Public Policy* October 1974; Spokesman Books for an article entitled 'Needs' by K. Coates from *Resources and the Environment: A Socialist Perspective* ed. by M. Barratt Brown, A. Emerson and C. Stoneham 1976; UNESCO for an article entitled 'The Consumer Movement And Technological Change' by J. Mitchell in *International Social Science Journal* Vol. XXV: 3, (c) UNESCO 1973. Reprinted by permission of UNESCO; The Author for his Appendix to Chapter 3 of *Fields, Factories & Workshops Tomorrow* by Kropotkin; Wildwood House Ltd. and Random House Inc. for extracts from *Radical Technology* ed. by Harper and Boyle; Working Papers for a New Society for an article entitled 'Neighbourhood Technology' by D. Morris and K. Hess from *Working Papers for a New Society* Vol. III, No. 1, Spring 1975. Copyright 1975 by the Centre for the Study of Public Policy. The artist for the figures on pages 284, 314 and 315, (c) Clifford Harper, 1975.

Whilst every effort has been made to trace the owners of copyright in a few cases this has proved impossible and we take this opportunity to offer our apologies to any authors whose rights may have been un-wittingly infringed.

Introduction

In the late 1960s and early 1970s long-established assumptions about the social benefits to be obtained from scientific and technological advance were called into question. Uncontrolled technology came to be associated with a variety of contemporary problems, among them hazards to health and safety; pollution and the depletion of resources; structural unemployment and the deskilling of labour; conflicts between amenity and commerce; mismatches between innovation and social need. Moreover, the number of obstacles to the democratic participation of ordinary people in decision-making increased in the face of technical experts and powerful industrial and government bureaucracies.

By the mid-1970s, when we came to compile this collection of readings, attention had begun to turn from the analysis of these problems to a search for possible solutions. The political implications of the problems began to become clearer. A 'technical fix' was clearly not enough to ensure that technological change better served social and human needs and did not pose a serious threat to the natural environment. Solutions seemed to lie more in political, social and economic change than in more or better technology, although the Alternative Technology movement had shown that a combination of social, political and technical change offered a possible path for development.

Section 1 of this book discusses various approaches to the problem of controlling technology to better meet social needs and their political implications. Two of the readings are in the main analytical. The concept of social need as a mechanism for controlling technology is analysed by Ken Coates. And in the first of three extracts from their book *The Control of Technology* David Elliott and Ruth Elliott outline several political mechanisms for ensuring the social control of technology.

The remaining readings in this section combine analysis with prescription. Shivaji Lal contrasts the social responsibility movement with the movement for social control of technology and finds the former lacking in understanding of the realities of power in modern industrialised societies. Mike Cooley also argues that fundamental social and political changes are required in order to bring technology under social control. François Hetman and Roger Williams offer less radical approaches and argue for more responsible and accountable control of technology by government. Barry Commoner, on the other hand, sees the forces for social control of technology coming, not from government, but from ordinary citizens in alliance with socially responsible scientists. Support for this comes from Hazel Henderson who argues that in the 'entropy state' central governments are incapable of managing the complexity of modern technical societies – successful control can only come from decentralised communities of citizens.

Clearly, social control of technology is a highly contentious issue. The means for achieving it advocated by the various contributors to this book differ widely, reflecting a broad range of political opinion – conservative, liberal, socialist, anarchist. For some, more comprehensive legislation and more effective government controls would be sufficient. For others, those who make decisions about technology must be made more accountable to the public. For others again, the public must be able to influence technological change more directly, through some form of participation. Finally, there are those who argue that existing technology and existing forms of social organisation must both be radically changed. Sections 2, 3 and 4 of the book are concerned with these different approaches to social control of technology.

Section 2 discusses the role of government in the social control of technology. Jewkes argues that the development of high technology is best left to private enterprise, if publicly financed technological 'white elephants' such as Concorde, are to be avoided in the future. Freeman agrees, but argues that more government controls are required to ensure that technological innovation is geared more to the interests of consumers and less to those of manufacturers.

The remaining readings in this section deal with various aspects of technology assessment and the monitoring of technical change. The Council for Science and Society describes, from a British perspective, the agencies it believes are appropriate for monitoring a technical project (e.g. a new steel plant) as it proceeds from conception to operation. Laurence Tribe, Marlan Blissett and Michael Baram discuss the theory and the practical experience of recent American legislation on technology assessment and environmental protection. David Elliott and Ruth Elliott cast doubts on the ability of official agencies for technology assessment to undertake the task of curbing the activities either of other government agencies or of private industry.

Section 3 considers the aims, problems and potential of public involvement in technical and technological decision-making. Direct participation, as opposed to mere consultation, is an ideal subscribed to by most of the contributors to this section. However, actual prescriptions for change differ considerably.

Tony Benn and Leslie Sklair present some forthright views as to the iniquities of the present situation, and make some fairly radical recommendations for grass-roots involvement in technological decision-making. Joseph Coates, on the other hand, displaying a belief in political pluralism, hopes that citizen activists will 'co-operate with those in control of the bureaucracies', rather than oppose them. Dorothy Nelkin looks in detail at the problems faced by developers, technical experts and citizens in conflict situations created by large-scale public projects. David and Ruth Elliott analyse the influence of organised labour and Jeremy Mitchell discusses the impact of the consumer movement on production and product-related decisions in industry. Stuart Umpleby describes some technical aids to participation and then analyses some differing attitudes to the idea of participation.

Sherry Arnstein's 'ladder of participation', although not directly related to technical issues, provides a useful classification of various forms of citizen participation – ranging from those in which public acceptance of official plans is won by manipulation, to those in which citizen groups attempt to take over control.

The most common sort of public involvement lies somewhere in between manipulation and citizen control and is typified by defensive campaigns aimed either at halting or harassing some project deemed not to be in the interests of the intervening group or at promoting a cause. Such campaigns tend to be reactive and negative. In Section 4 another, as yet much less common, approach to social control of technology is discussed. That is the development and demonstration by community groups of positive, creative alternatives.

Rather than simply reject proposals made by existing decision-makers, groups adopting this approach tend to go it alone and, through local initiative and self-help, create embryonic community-level examples of alternatives to the existing patterns of social and technological organisation. Not all such groups 'drop out' of existing society to experiment with alternative technology in rural isolation.

David Morris and Karl Hess describe how some groups are trying to relate to existing communities in the hope of aiding them to develop their own 'neighbourhood technologies'. Although these experiments are often fragile and are, as Peter Harper points out, so far mainly limited to experiments in domestic-scale self-sufficiency, there are a growing number of groups exploring the possibility of neighbourhood-scale, self-managed community enterprises, run co-operatively and utilising technologies which are easily understood and controlled. Some feel that these experiments might make an important contribution to the process of transforming our current large-scale, capital-intensive, advanced technology society to one in which direct social control of technology is possible. Their critics range from those who say that such a transformation cannot be accomplished by local self-help alone, but will require collective political action to oppose and ultimately eliminate the existing power structure, to those who say that a decentralised utopia is simply not technically, economically or socially feasible, or even desirable. The latter issue is tackled by Barry Stein who argues that small-scale, self-managed industrial units, of the sort described by Colin Ward, are viable. The role of such experiments in aiding wider social change is discussed by Entemann et al. who analyse what they see as the strategic significance of the various attempts to implement, or at least demonstrate, radical technologies of the sort outlined by Harper.

This book clearly cannot provide final answers to any of the questions it raises – for the answers will only emerge from practice. Our aim rather has been to present an overview of the ideas being offered on how best to proceed. That there is a need to control technical and technological development by some means seems to be widely accepted. That confidence in centralised, expert-dominated forms of control is waning is demonstrated by the large number of campaigns by citizens aimed at influencing technical and technological decisions both at work and in the community. Whether this will result in a radically different society, based on a radically different pattern of political, economic and technological organisation, remains to be seen.

Social control of technology

Technology on trial

François Hetman

Disenchantment with technology and 'technological progress'

Perhaps the most revolutionary event of the last third of this century
is the claim for social responsibility of science and technology. Up to
now, technologies have been hailed and accepted as irresistible forces
bringing unquestioned technical advantages and intrinsically containing
seeds of economic and social progress. Now, at the beginning of the
1970s, for the first time, new technological developments are being
rejected – allegedly on social grounds.

Two most significant cases, the first in the United States and the
second in the United Kingdom, different in scope and technology
contents, illustrate this important turning point.

The first is the decision of the United States Congress against the
development of supersonic transport (SST).

> *The unexpected Senate vote 52 to 41, against the SST on December
> 3rd (1970) was a political victory for the supporters of purer environment,
> but it was a battle that they won largely by default. Arguments about the
> pollution that would have been created by a supersonic airliner could have
> been shot down quite easily if anyone had had the heart to do so. The
> Senate victory was won because they had not. The temporary stay of
> execution wrung from the House of Representatives on Tuesday was
> achieved only by frantic rearguard lobbying, especially by a President
> very much concerned with unemployment in Boeing country.*
>
> *The majority of advocates for an American SST cannot honestly argue
> that they want the aircraft for its own sake; their case for building it has
> rested on fears of what might happen to the American economy should
> the project die. These fears are concerned with unemployment and with
> the balance of payments, and such largely defensive arguments are not
> the kind from which battle-cries are made.[1]**

The second case is the decision taken in April 1971 by the Govern-

---

Extracts from Chapter 1 of François Hetman, *Society and the Assessment of
Technology*, OECD, 1973.
* Superior numerals apply to Reference at the ends of the readings.

ment of the United Kingdom to rule out any inland site for a new London airport. This decision was

a stark victory for environment over economics – probably the most significant in Britain so far. The Government was simply not prepared to handle the political storm that would have been aroused by an inland choice. The location of the airport had been debated for years by experts, politicians and the public. The outcome was the more remarkable because it precisely reversed the recommendations of a high-level commission.[2]

The commission suggested, after an important series of studies, a site north of London, near Cublington. People in that area protested very strongly against what they called 'destructive progress'. Finally, the choice fell on Foulness, a sparsely populated area on the east coast of England, farther from London than other sites that were considered: an airport there will cost about £140 million more than the alternatives.

The first example concerns the development of a new technology, the second is an application of existing technologies which cause a certain amount of nuisance. In both cases, studies have been made with a view to consider some possible costs and benefits other than of a purely technical or economic nature, particularly in the field of environment.

However, the final outcome of the political debate shows that:

(a) the decision was finally taken on grounds other than those resulting from the analysis, mainly under the pressure from new ad hoc groups representing strongly polarised currents of opinion;
(b) the Government yielded to these pressures, because they were unprepared and unable to explain or justify their proposals in terms of 'social costs and benefits';
(c) the underlying studies were carried out in the traditional form of techno-economic evaluation, though giving some thought to primary effects on environment;
(d) these studies did not take into account social, cultural or political aspects, or include any analysis whatsoever of affected groups, their strength or behaviour;
(e) the public discussion was restricted to technical and economic figures on the one side, and to highly emotional reactions on the other; this was due to a real information gap and to the failure to discern – at both the level of analysis and of decision-making – new wants of understanding the social impact of technology.

[. . .] Technology is fully involved in human activities, it is a permanent component of socio-economical pattern of modern societies. Like other sub-systems, it can be geared to certain social ends. The choice, determination and implementation of these ends and technological ventures which are linked to them are matters of general policy.

Technology cannot escape the process of value judgment resulting from political struggles and orientations of society.

It can be said in general that technological change is widely accepted as an essential element of economic development. Economic growth is based on gains in productivity which can be realised only through the infusion of new knowledge and technology. As on the productive side, technology has enormously increased the range of opportunities open to consumers. In all sectors of human life, advances in communication technology have led to rapid information, advances in transport technology to greater mobility and easy access to any place on the planet, advances in medicine and health technology have led to substantially greater life expectancy and relief from suffering.

Nevertheless, the uncontrolled introduction of new technologies is not an unmitigated blessing. The accumulation of technology seems to produce a rapidly extending array of negative side-effects. There is a growing awareness of disruptive impacts of technology which tend to be identified with causes of individual dissatisfaction and social disillusionment.

Demand for control of technology

[. . .] These negative influences are not necessarily inherent in science and technology, but rather in the objectives at which science is aimed and in the way in which technology is used.

Be that as it may, science is no longer accepted as a sacred cow: its claims are challenged, its demands for resources much more carefully (but not always wisely) scrutinised than in the past. Many people resent the apparently privileged positions of scientists as an apparently elitist group with technocratic leanings. While it is obviously right that science should be questioned and be forced publicly to justify its demands, there is a real danger that this can go too far. Science and technology have been immensely successful and have made possible the rise of man from subsistence level, have created the resources for the building of prosperous societies, have through medicine contributed greatly to health and longer life, and the promise they hold for the creation of better societies and the abolition of poverty is enormous. The problem is essentially a political one of how to guide and manage technological progress for the well-being of society, a matter as yet seldom explicitly tackled by governments or debated in parliaments.[3]

(a) Food and robins
Science and technology are blamed because society itself is at a loss, largely because of the power of modern science which has enabled society to reach goals that were formerly only vague aspirations but whose achievement has revealed new problems and has stirred expec-

tations that go beyond the possibilities of the economic and social system. It is against this background that the limitations and relative failures of science policies can be understood most clearly. 'A crisis of growth and a crisis of the linkage of science policy to social aspirations seem to be two closely related aspects of the same problem: the aim of science policy cannot be solely the expansion of science and technology but must include the management and direction of technological progress for the service of other ends.'[4]

Theoretically, three main courses of action seem to be possible:

1. Continuation of uncontrolled scientific and technological development. This appears unacceptable given the growing awareness that present imbalances are not self-correcting and risk becoming irreversible if certain thresholds are transgressed without remedial action.
2. Stopping of scientific and technological advancement. This is advocated as a complementary measure to the 'no-growth economy' or the prevention of economic growth on the grounds that further economic growth endangers both the environmental and social quality of life and constitutes a major menace of depletion of natural resources. It would mean that the present state of affairs has to be accepted without hope of modifying its unpleasant sides. Absence of scientific and technological effort could but lead to a mere exacerbation of such an unbalanced society.
3. Socially responsible management of scientific and technological innovation. To fulfil the promises of improvement of human condition, science and technology will be needed still more than before, not only to solve the problems that technology has caused by its precipitation or inadvertence but essentially to strike new directions for a more harmonious social development.

This last strategy seems to be the only reasonable choice. It is not an easy one. It will have far-reaching implications for decision-makers and society and for scientists themselves. Science and technology policy will have to be open to public discussion and ready to take measures concerning the opportunity of new research in science and new developments in technology. 'In science policy the hand must be visible.'[5]

How can scientists and technologists respond to these new demands which break with the easily accepted dogma of unrestricted freedom for search?

In principle, the answer seems to be simple: they must share the common concerns of society. They must be more thoughtful about the applications of the results of their research. 'They must try to find better institutional forms in which their co-responsibility for the consequences of their discoveries and inventions can be explored and negative ones guarded against and corrected. They must above all not regard themselves as the chief custodians of the future of mankind.'[6]

The technologies that have been made possible by modern science are 'tainted':

> the automobile is at once a convenient mode of transport and a death-dealing device as well as a pollutant of the atmosphere; the large tanker softens the political consequences of closing the Suez Canal, but it can ruin our beaches; persistent insecticides increase our food supply but still the robins. Is it not clear that the social responsibility of the technologist and his scientific supporter lies in removing the taints that now mar the modern technologies of abundance? Rather than ending technological development we must invent new technologies, or improve the old, so as to have both food and our robins, our cars and clean air.[7]

These striking images show that the emphasis shifts from the implacable hunt for feasibility to choosing the most desirable developments out of alternatives provided by scientific research. It is up to science itself to develop, at least partly, the criteria of selection and to clarify the implications of technological choices for various economic and social objectives.

(b) Community's interest in technology

However, many of the problems which arise from the interaction between science and technology on the one side and society on the other hang on the answers to questions which can be asked of science and yet which cannot be answered by science. Alvin M. Weinberg proposes the term trans-scientific for these questions since,

> though they are, epistemologically speaking, questions of fact and can be stated in the language of science, they are unanswerable by science: they transcend science. In so far as public policy involves trans-scientific rather that scientific issues, the role of the scientists in contributing to the promulgation of such policy must be different from his role when the issues can be unambiguously answered by science.[8]

In simple terms, this is the recognition of the fact that fundamental problems of society are common to the whole community and may call for political decisions even against the opinion of scientists and technologists. It implies that technology, in particular, must be brought under control if serious perils are to be avoided. Control of technology requires a systematic effort to maximise its benefits and minimise its harmful effects in the context of social purposes and objectives. It also requires analytical insight into the nature of technological impact and the existence of appropriate institutions capable of generating and implementing policies that can take into account real social concerns in all their breadth and importance.

The control and management of technology, has several dimensions.

First of all, it conflicts with individual interests. Up to now, decisions in the field of new technologies have been taken on the basis of an ad-hoc and self-interested analyses.

In their pursuit of benefits for themselves or the segment of the public that they represent, those who make the relevant decisions often have little incentive, responsibility or authority to consider the possibility that a technological application might have undesirable consequences. For the same reasons they may fail to pursue technological opportunities that, from a broader perspective, might clearly deserve exploitation.[9]

This attitude has led to a loss of trust in those who controlled the advance of technology in their own way and sphere of interest. There is a growing dissatisfaction with such narrow assessments that do not take sufficient account of social and human consequences which may prove more important than any short-term purely economic analysis can reveal.

A fundamental element of social control of technology is the necessity for full and candid disclosure and discussion of potential costs and benefits. One cannot expect that those who are sponsoring the development of a new technology will indulge in listing its undesirable social consequences, since an inherent feature of the promotion process is to minimise these consequences and to argue that they can be technologically overcome.

The awareness that technology may have second-order consequences, both adverse and beneficial, is not new. What seems to be new is:

1. Technology is becoming both more voluminous and more complicated.
2. The complexity of much new technology makes it more difficult to anticipate how it will do its primary job and what its second-order consequences will be.
3. As our understanding of biological, ecological, economic and social processes improves, we are struck with the complexity of the consequences which technology can produce.
4. We have a growing determination and belief in our capacity to evaluate the second-order consequences of all our actions including the use of technology and to include their costs in our policy-making process.[10]

The call for public control of technology is stimulated by the idea that evaluation of possible impacts of technology can enable public or social authority to introduce new technologies only after a deep examination of all envisageable effects in the long run.

(c) Control without stifling

So far however, the mission-oriented research undertaken by governments was not directed to this objective. The mutual interaction of separate programmes of research has been given little attention as has the problem of the inherent cost-benefit structure of resulting technologies. The problems of the industrial societies are, however, increasingly inter-related. It is therefore necessary to understand **better** the operation of society as a whole before action on constituent elements can be meaningful. This will require new ways of thinking both of ethical and institutional character before methods of effective social management of technology can be devised.

The fundamental question is to what extent the future development of technology can be guided into desirable directions without stifling innovation. 'Constraints on innovation are all too likely to become coercive restraints on progress.'[11] Great care will have to be taken that the system of control is not so rigid as to discourage technological change and hence inhibit in other ways the progress of society.

There are some precedents to the concept of technology assessment. In many fields, restrictive and normative legislation had apparently similar aims. However, these were mostly remedial, fractional, and generally concentrated on the immediate effects of one aspect of technology.

The new mechanisms which are needed now would embrace the evaluation of the technical, economic, social, cultural and individual effects of particular technological options.

Such a mechanism would be an obligatory checkpoint to be consulted in the process of preparing decisions on research, development, innovation and the major social and economic equilibria. It would, among other tasks, have the function of predicting the short and long term effects of potential new technologies on the natural and social environment. It would evaluate costs and benefits in societal as well as economic terms and anticipate detrimental effects so as to provide the basis of an early warning system.[12]

The institution of mechanisms for the control and management of technology raises enormous issues which concern the whole political, economic and social system, both its basic values and its fundamental rules of functioning.

While economic growth remains an objective, technology is needed to produce it. Even if it were decided to stop economic growth, technology would be still needed, but a new kind of technology. Thus, technology as an agent for the achievement of the goals of society appears as an intrinsic necessity.

Modern societies are very complex economic and social systems with multiple units which pursue some immediate effects of technology and appraise quite differently its long-term impacts. It seems extremely difficult to find an objective denominator to clarify the issues of new technologies at the level of society or nation.

Science and technology have contributed to a rapid integration of the world economy, particularly through the influence of technology on production and consumption patterns. The rapid diffusion of new technological developments makes the proliferation of new techniques a planetary phenomenon. To halt or to prevent socially undesirable new technologies at national level is practically impossible. Since the impact tends to be global, control and management of technology are likely to be effective only if they can be organised on a world-wide scale. This is a vast objective, the full achievement of which is probably beyond immediate reach. Nevertheless, there is a growing consensus that even partial agreements would be highly valuable.

References

1. 'The friendless SST', *The Economist*, 12.12.1970, p. 73.
2. 'U.K. rules out inland site for new airport', *International Herald Tribune*, 26.4.1971, p. 2.
3. Alexander King, 'Report on the first theme', *Parliamentary Democracy in the Scientific-Technological Age*, Council of Europe, Third Parliamentary and Scientific Conference, Lausanne, 11–14.4.1972, p. 3.
4. *Science, Growth and Society*, OECD, Report of the Secretary General's Ad Hoc Group on New Concepts of Science Policy, Paris, 1971, pp. 38–9.
5. Staffan Burenstam Linder, 'The unbalanced progress of progress', *Panel on Science and Technology*, Committee on Science and Astronautics, US House of Representatives, 26–8.1.1971, p. 303.
6. Eduard Shils, 'Anti-science', *Minerva*, Oct. 1971, p. 449.
7. Alvin M. Weinberg, 'In defense of science', *Science*, 9.1.1970, p. 146.
8. Alvin M. Weinberg, 'Science and trans-science', *Minerva*, Vol. X-2, April 1972, p. 209.
9. Harvey Brooks and Raymond Bowers, 'The assessment of technology', *Scientific American*, Vol. 222, No. 2. Feb. 1970, p. 13.
10. *Toward Balanced Growth, Quantity with Quality*, Report of the National Goals Research Staff, 4.7.1970, pp. 119–20.
11. Robert U. Ayres, Jack W. Carlson and Susan C. Simon, 'Technology assessment and policy-making in the United States', United Nations, Economic Commission for Europe, *Seminar on Technological Forecasting*, Working Paper 16, p. 3.
12. Science and the society of the seventies', Theme 2 of the Fourth Ministerial Meeting on Science, OECD document SP(71)6, p. 20.

Social control and social responsibility in science and technology

Shivaji Lal

How can science and technology be best controlled in a society that is both industrial and democratic? One can advocate a policy based on social responsibility, or a policy based on social control. But for the moment these phrases can be taken as shorthand labels for two very different kinds of positions that can be taken up vis-à-vis the social misuse of science and technology.

Simplifying a complex argument, it might be said that the advocates of social responsibility believe, or at least tend to believe, that the social abuses of science and technology can be attributed to: (*a*) the failure of individual scientists to discharge their ethical responsibilities; (*b*) the failure of the scientific and technological community to develop a social ethic for regulating the activities of its members in relationship to the wider community; and (*c*) the unwillingness of scientists and technologists to consider the possible social impact of their discoveries and inventions, and to communicate their anticipations and apprehensions about these matters to the public.

Simplifying once again, it might be said that their opponents, i.e. those who advocate social control, subscribe to the view that the social misuses and abuses of science and technology are an inevitable by-product of the politico-economic and ideological function that the scientific and technological order plays in industrial societies.

The primary aim of this essay is to explore and elucidate some aspects of this important argument. It hardly needs saying that the two view-points examined are highly simplified idealisations of a family of positions held by a number of individuals: they are thus ideal types put forward to sharpen distinctions, raise questions, expose conflicts, and reveal possible dilemmas.

In order to carry out this enterprise of unmasking and illuminating some of the fundamental differences that separate the two groups, I shall examine the sorts of accounts and answers they give to the following three questions. What are the most important kinds of harmful effects engendered by science and technology? How can such harmful effects be best avoided and what contributions can scientists and

From Shivaji Lal, 'Social control and social responsibility', *Science and Public Policy*, October 1974.

technologists make towards defining and implementing a social policy for tackling such harmful effects?

What are the most important harmful effects?

The upholders of social responsibility operate with a narrower definition of 'harmful effects' than their opponents. They tend to restrict it to two main areas: war and the environment. Many of them admit that science and technology have been systematically employed to develop weapons of a particularly horrifying kind – nuclear bombs, napalm, defoliants, antipersonnel devices, poison gas; and that many scientists and technologists have not been averse to lending their efforts to this kind of work.

They will further admit that the scientific and technological communities have never collectively tried to do anything about this state of affairs. Like Pontius Pilate, they have washed their hands and served whichever master has held the reins of financial and political power; and they have assuaged their conscience by pointing out the contribution that science and technology have made to the welfare of mankind, and by asserting that they could not control the uses to which the products of scientific and technological activity are put by states, agencies, and individuals.

It is interesting to note here a certain contradiction in the position of biomedical scientists who support the idea of social responsibility. Virtually all of them would be outraged to be asked to support a proposed study on the physiology of torture; and many consider this a matter requiring collective militant action by the biomedical community. Yet what is the moral difference between tacitly allowing particular members of the biomedical community to do research on 'improving' napalm, or finding a 'better' substitute for it, and tacitly supporting a research programme on the 'physiology of torture'?

The other area in which believers in social responsibility are uneasy over the role of science and technology is the environment. Here some of them seem all too eager to ascribe the emergence of environmental degradation, pollution, wasteful consumption of non-renewable resources to the development and deployment of inappropriate technologies. And they see the answer to these problems – the technological price of progress – in the development of a more appropriate technology.

Thus, the social responsibility movement, or rather one particular kind of social responsibility movement. For many social responsibility groups are better described as belonging to the movement that I have called social control.

The advocates of social control include in their notion of harmful effects both ideological and material impacts of science and technology, and the range of material impacts which they cite is drawn from a far wider area than that of their opponents. It includes effects on the political, social and economic experience and conditions of the majority of the population. For example, they allude to the effects that technological innovation has had on the work conditions and work experience of the labour force. They point out that the introduction of scientifically managed, capital intensive, production lines has led to a formalisation and routinisation of work, to the gradual restriction of the amount of discretion and freedom enjoyed by the individual worker.

In recent years, while working conditions in an ergonomic and an environmental sense may have improved, the quality of the work experience has declined, as has the power of the worker to control his manner of work. Besides increasing alienation, the relentless pursuit of technological innovation for the sake of profit is creating structural unemployment. Yet the scientific and technological community has never deemed it worth while to comment or criticise or oppose these processes.

Two other kinds of influence exerted by advances in science and technology that are commented on by believers in social control are worth mentioning here, partly because of their direct political reliance, and partly because they indicate what some would call sweeping, and others radical, nature of the critique that the social control movement mounts against the scientific and technological establishment. These are: the use of psychiatric and social techniques to treat deviants and dissidents, and to control protest movements, and the use of technology transfer as a means of creating dependency and exerting control over the countries of the Third World. Both these processes, or so the movements for social control argue, exhibit the extent to which science and technology, under the guise of a benevolent helping hand, are actively used for coercive and exploitative political purposes: they provide the means whereby the rich and powerful maintain their position.

Here at least would seem to be areas on which one would expect the scientific and technological community to mount a serious and meaningful collective debate, rather than to leave it to the individual conscience of particular members. Even if no common position could be articulated by the scientific and technological constituencies, yet surely these are, and ought to be, matters that warrant the serious attention of the membership. Controversial though such a debate would be, unpleasant and socially divisive as it would be, it would still be preferable to bland indifference.

The most controversial aspect of the radical critique – if one might so label the line of thought I have termed social control – is its criticism of the pernicious 'ideological' influence of science and technology: its mechanistic and reductionistic view of man and nature – a view that leads to the repression of the moral and religious sensibilities. Man is no longer, in this view, a moral agent with powers, inescapably involved in social, and hence moral, choice and conflict, but a cognitive machine among other machines, differing only in the subtlety of its programming.

The other prong attacks the false legitimacy bestowed on the procedures and results of the policy and management disciplines, and of the social sciences, by the adoption of a scientistic vocabulary, methodology and ontology. Further, the physical and biological sciences are used to accredit ideologically constituted social policies and programmes, particularly in education and employment.

There are other critiques of the 'ideology of science' e.g. the critiques of objectivity and value neutrality. But I shall not attempt to deal with these issues here, since they raise complex and subtle problems which are already the subject of far too much opaque and philosophically confused comment. In fact, so muddled is the conflict on these topics that it is difficult, at times, to discern exactly what the problem at issue actually is: especially since the contestants, on the whole, eschew any attempt to put forward coherent, reasonably clear theses, relying instead on propaganda, slogans and the argument *ad homineum*.

Why have harmful effects arisen?

The rather different definitions and identifications of harmful effects espoused by the two groups spring from very different socio-political commitments. The upholders of social responsibility are basically liberal individualists, subscribing to a consensualist view of society. There is nothing fundamentally wrong with the social order, in their opinion. They construe science and technology as politically neutral activities. Thus, the abuses and misuses of science and technology are unintended and accidental side-effects. They are due to inadvertence, lack of foresight, lack of planning, lack of wisdom, failure to communicate and consult, and insufficient information.

These causes have been compounded by a lack of responsible behaviour by the scientific and technological professions: not only have they failed to disseminate information about the kinds of work that they do, and about the implications it has, but they have also failed to deploy moral and statistical argument in order to mobilise public opinion in favour of more responsible policies. Ultimately, of course, it is the politicians and businessmen, in pursuit of their private interests, who have corruptly used science and technology, and this was a process over which scientists and technologists had no control.

The believers in social control have a radically different view of the social order. They operate with a social conflict model of society in which social dynamics is a function of conflict of interest. Their viewpoint is best labelled as structuralist. They are usually, but by no means inevitably, of a Marxist persuasion. They see science and technology as providing the means – intellectual, ideological, material – whereby a power elite or a ruling class maintains its power and privilege. For them, science and technology are inescapably political activities involving social decisions and choices that serve definable and locatable economic and political interests.

Science and technology, they argue, can never be independent of the politico-economic milieu in which they operate. In social systems that thrive on profit, inequality, exploitation, militarism, the scientific and technological order can be an instrument of dehumanisation and oppression. The radicals ask such questions as: who controls the funding and priority systems of scientific and technological research? Why are most of the resources for carrying out research and development situated in the corporate agencies of government and big business? Who benefits most from the discoveries and inventions of science and technology? Why is so little effort expended on research to meet the needs of the poor and powerless? Why should science and technology be used to produce alienating work conditions? In whose interest is commercial and military R & D carried out?

Why is it that, granted our present-day level of science and technology, 30 million children had to die of starvation and malnutrition in 1972? Why is it that in 1968 in the USA – which has a GNP per capita of nearly 5,000 dollars, and which produces 360 million tons of garbage a year – an estimated 30 million people went hungry? Why is it that scientists and technologists seem so eager to offer their services to the $150 billion a year military programmes of the USA and USSR? Why is it that the world's GNP continues to increase, but the proportion going to the poor of the underdeveloped countries continues to decline?

Reflection on the possible answers to these questions, the radicals argue, must lead to the inevitable realisation that science and technology cannot be considered in isolation from an historically-conditioned politico-economic context, and that scientists and technologists are accomplices of corrupt and coercive social systems. Science and technology are not, as is often claimed, vehicles for meeting the social needs of the poor and powerless, and of enabling them to control their own lives, but rather, they are ideologically-shaped instruments that provide power for the already powerful, that enable the social surplus product created by the many to be expropriated by the few for the benefit mainly of these few.

How can such harmful effects be best avoided and what can scientists do?

The answers to these questions follow from the analyses offered. By virtue of their particular analysis, the supporters of social responsibility are committed to a strategy based on piecemeal reform of certain limited aspects of the practice of science and technology, the interface these disciplines have with society, and the education and attitudes of scientists and technologists. This strategy would be realised in a series of specific campaigns designed to correct particular evils and abuses that have arisen out of the unconsidered manner in which science and technology have been perceived and used, both by scientists and by the community.

Responsible behaviour in the scientific and technological communities would be encouraged through the fostering of discussion among its members on the possible implication of their work. Through appeals to scientists and technologists asking them to accept moral responsibility for their work, through a change in the methods and contents of science education – a change that would lead to an emphasis being placed on the imaginative structure of scientific and technological thinking, on the contribution that science and technology can make to the solving of social problems and to the welfare of mankind, and on the social and philosophical contexts within which scientific knowledge has developed.

But, besides this, the scientific and technological communities need to redirect their research effort – that is, make it more 'socially relevant'. For solutions to many of the problems engendered through the abuses and misuses of science and technology require a greater mission-oriented research effort aimed at developing new technologies, improving data acquisition and communication systems, creating sophisticated analytical tools for the new planning systems required, constructing a better skill and information base for social, economic and science policy decision-taking.

Thus, the basic policy of the social responsibility movement seems to be founded on: (1) the mobilisation of scientists and technologists to provide and disseminate information, knowledge, and techniques for the making of informed public choices by the community; and (2) the arousing of the moral and social conscience of the individual scientist and technologist.

To the social control movement, such a policy is totally inadequate. It neglects the power-political aspects of social systems, the way in which ruling classes or power-elites deploy; administrative and legal systems to control the flow of information and the processes of decision making; the media and the educational system to shape ideology, values and consciousness; and the police and military to suppress mass protest movement. In such social systems, based as they are on false consciousness, inequality and exploitation, there can only arise socially irresponsible forms of science and technology that service the few at the expense of the many.

The present-day institutional irresponsiblity of science and technology can ably be solved through a radical change in the politico-economic conditions that have created it. In other words, to quote a pamphlet from the British Society for Social Responsibility in Science: 'Because science is embedded in society as a whole, major changes in the role of science can only be achieved through cultural and political changes in the whole of society, as well as radical transformation in the consciousness of its members. This is the only way to a socially responsible science.'

Granted this, it necessarily follows that scientists and technologists need to be actively involved in the ideological and political struggles of the exploited and oppressed, as they strive to change the conditions under which they live and work, as they strive to regain – as men – their right to 'choose' their own lives. But as well as putting their skills and expertise at the service of the deprived and oppressed and participating in their struggles, scientists and technologists need to develop new social forms within which science and technology can be used and controlled by the people as a whole rather than the massive corporations of industrial society.

A non-elitist general education has also to be developed, one that, as well as pointing out the conventional social implications of science and technology, raises questions about the social definition, production, distribution and utilisation of knowledge and the relationship these processes have to the distribution of power and advantage. The military-industrial complex has to be challenged, and its R & D activities unmasked and criticised. The ideologies of social planning, of education, of much that passes for social science, have to be exposed.

The purpose of these and many other such activities is not so much to correct immediate, specific – though this consideration obviously must play a part – but to change the conditions that bring about these evils, and to create the conditions for the existence of a truly moral community. For the necessary, though not sufficient, condition for the existence of a socially responsible science and technology is the existence of a responsible society. And the necessary, though not sufficient, conditions for the existence of a responsible society are the existence of participatory democracy, socio-economic equality, the equality of dignity and respect, and a sense of organic sympathy between man and nature.

Social control of technology

David Elliott and Ruth Elliott

Those who carry on great public schemes must be proof against the presumptuous judgements of the ignorant upon their designs.
Edmund Burke.

If we want to create a technology dedicated to goals which may be unprofitable in terms of money and power, but important for the 'quality of life' rather than the 'quantity of goods' at our disposal, then the people should have more opportunities to be consulted about the future technology they want and the future technology they would rather reject.
C. R. Jungk 'Technological forecasting as a tool of social strategy', in R. V. Arnfield (ed.), *Technological Forecasting*, Edinburgh UP, 1969.

1. Towards social control

The control of technology
In many ways, the notion of controlling technology at all towards *any* ends is comparatively recent.

Laissez-faire philosophies of the eighteenth and nineteenth centuries resulted in a heavy reliance on the fortuitous discoveries of industrial 'inventors' and on the 'free play of market forces' within a competitive free enterprise economy to ensure the rational and beneficial development and application of these 'inventions'.

Decisions concerning investments, production, research and development are, according to the theory of the 'free-play of market forces', responsive to the consumer market, the labour market and the overall economic conditions. Thus decisions are supposed to reflect not only the shareholders' concern for profit and managements' concern for growth or security, but also the customers' interests and the 'national interest'. Competing claims and demands are balanced out through the impersonal market mechanism. But, as has been previously pointed out, we no longer have a 'free market' of this type. As Galbraith has

From Chapter 5, 'Social control of technology', in David Elliott and Ruth Elliott, *The Control of Technology*, Wykeham, 1976.

illustrated, markets have to be, and to a considerable extent are, controlled by industry, consumer sovereignty is being replaced by 'producer' sovereignty. Of course in spite of growing industrial concentration and the increase in oligopolies, competition is not dead. However, there is slightly *less* faith today that competition can be relied upon as the prime mechanism for controlling technological development. There are many who would argue that market forces in fact *distort* these developments, and that

while competition certainly enhances economic efficiency and optimizes the division of labour both within national societies and in world trade, it sometimes leads to excessive differentiation of products and services or built-in obsolescence for rather marginal social gains, and in doing so may divert a substantial amount of technical effort in directions having only marginal social return . . . Also, competition sometimes rewards the least responsible corporate behaviour, while exacting a large social cost in regulation and alleviating the disbenefits – a cost borne by the firms themselves, by their consumers, and by the social system.[1]

Certainly industrial organizations themselves are no longer content to adopt a laissez-faire attitude to technological developments. The huge amounts of capital involved make it imperative, in their own interests, that they evolve long-range plans. Similarly, within government the trend is, as we have noted, towards a 'managed' science and technology.

In general then it seems that 'the pressures in the future will be towards a society marked by a much greater degree of organization and deliberate control'.[2]

The crucial issue, which we have emphasized throughout this book is *who* should do the controlling, and towards what ends. At present control is vested in the hands of a minority, and is frequently directed towards *sectional* interests. Certainly the majority of people have little chance to influence policy, even if they wished to do so.

Frequently the only channel of influence open to the public is pressure group activity, campaigning often in a *negative* way against certain policy decisions.

However, as one commentator has remarked, in view of the scale and rapidity of change, 'Our present method of depending on the alertness of individuals to foresee (technological) danger and to form pressure groups that try to correct mistakes will not do for the future'.[3] Furthermore, pressure group activity is likely to lead to piecemeal changes rather than to coherent planning. The crucial problem facing us is essentially how to bring technology 'with all its social consequences under *deliberate* social control'.[4]

To achieve this within our present social structure, it would seem to be necessary to set up more *formal* channels of accountability, influence and participation, which might enable the emergence of some 'countervailing force' to challenge the existing power structure's virtual monopoly control over choices of policy, goals and values.

Some people, who might be labelled 'technological determinists', argue that people do not *really* have much choice about the technology they want, or indeed the society they want, once the basic decision to opt for a high level of industrialization has been taken. For example, Galbraith has suggested that while man 'could conceivably decide whether or not he wishes to have a high level of industrialisation'; thereafter 'the imperatives of organisation, technology and planning operate similarly . . . to a broadly similar result, on all societies. Given the decision to have modern industry much of what happens is inevitable and the same'.[5]

The determinist assumptions behind this approach, with its implication that the autonomous momentum of technology defines irrevocably all forms of social and economic organisation, have already been criticized. Such arguments can be used to deny the need for more democratic social control over decisions and choices on the grounds that no *important* 'choices' are really being made, and that those in power are merely obeying, as everyone else must, the imperatives of technology. True, opting for a high level of industrialization does have far-reaching implications on all aspects of life and social organization. But 'industrial society' is not a 'package deal' that has to be accepted in its entirety; we are not confronted with one simple dichotomous choice of high-technology and industrialized society, with all its pleasant or unpleasant connotations, or low-technology pre-industrial arcadia or subsistence-society. 'Technology' is not some total monolith, but rather consists of a variety of discrete, albeit closely related technologies. Throughout history, *choices* have been made to develop certain technologies rather than others, and to direct them towards certain goals rather than others. 'Mankind has selected an array of technologies that currently form its technological order.[6] True, many developments may have occurred in the past by chance rather than design. But it might be argued that with the techniques of forecasting and assessment available to us now, it is increasingly possible for conscious *choice* rather than *chance* to govern our future.

If this is so, what mechanisms are there for ensuring that these 'choices' reflect not only the values and priorities of those in positions of power, but also the values and priorities of the majority of men and women who will have to live with the consequences of these decisions?

2. Types of social control

Three basic types of social control can be identified for the purpose of the present analysis although they are not always in reality discrete and easily separable.

(*a*) Accountability
(*b*) Representation
(*c*) Participation.

Accountability

Industrial organizations, governments or ministries are usually expected to be *accountable* to the public in some way – that is their action and policies must be open to scrutiny by the citizen, and responsive to his views where possible, although there is usually little direct involvement by the public. It is expected that the company or organization can justify its actions if required – either in ethical terms or in law. The organization may *voluntarily* select 'socially responsible' policies or be *required* to operate within the framework of the law, which sets certain minimum standards or requirements. The basic idea is that the organization or institution must be open to public scrutiny and 'investigation by the public or its agents'.[7] This approach is not particularly concerned with giving individuals the chance to be involved in decision-making or to exert control over their own lives. The main object of making an organization open to potential public scrutiny is to encourage it to behave in a manner consistent with its own rules – and with the law of the land.

> ... *the importance of public scrutiny* ... *lies not only or even mainly in the opportunity it provides, for the participants to press their own interests or for individuals to find personal fulfilment in civic authority* ... *it is a condition of its openness to contradiction, that is, it is an essential condition of the very rationality of the behaviour and beliefs of the bureaucracy itself.*[8]

This indirect form of control is relatively weak, particularly if the citizen wishes to oppose some aspect of what the bureaucracy may see as 'rational', or some policy which is in the interest of a powerful group. The existence of laws which set certain minimum requirements does not mean that these requirements are *necessarily* met. Hence 'inadequate performance is not always the result of inadequate legislation *per se*, but often is the result of unenforced, unutilized, or misused powers. Special interests, usually economic, often have the skills, power and organization to thwart the public interest'.[9]

Furthermore, since some of the most crucial activities in organizations are the least visible, it is hard to see how such organizations could be fully open to public scrutiny and public pressure. Recent moves were made in the Industrial Relations Act to compel employers to reveal certain types of information about company affairs to employees. But this only applied to information deemed necessary for adequate collective bargaining, and a considerable amount of discretion was left to employers and the courts in deciding what information might fall into this category. Moreover, information that might damage a company's competitive position, if disclosed, was exempted.

A move towards more effective accountability in Government has occurred with the recent announcement by Mr Tony Benn, Minister for Trade and Industry in the 1974 British Labour Government, that the books of the Department of Trade and Industry are to be open to the public.

The Minister intends that: 'Policy making will also be done as much as possible in the open'.[10] The rationale behind Mr Benn's action is his belief that:

Secrecy allows those in power to reach their decisions without being forced to publish the facts available to them which might lead the public to prefer an absolutely different policy to be pursued. If the secrecy is complete enough, the public will not even learn about the decision until it is too late to change it. Many technological decisions are virtually irreversible once they have been reached, and until we strip away unjustifiable secrecy we can have no real democracy.[11]

However, it might be argued that even given such disclosure of information, unorganized, uncoordinated members of the public, lacking in the advice of experts, are not in a strong position to forcefully express their views. Consequently it has been suggested that '. . . there is a need for countervailing forces which can compel a regulatory or administrative agency to perform its task well.'[12] One suggestion has been '. . . the institution of permanent independent organs of inspection and criticism, accessible to the public, with processes as sophisticated and authority as high as the bureaucratic organizations to be brought under surveillance.'[13] We consider in later sections a number of attempts to set up regulatory agencies of this type – for example in the 'Technology Assessment' organizations.

One problem is that these agencies can take on a life of their own – they do not *necessarily* reflect the interests of the citizens. And once again the citizen is reduced to a state of helpless dependence on 'experts'.

The full-time officials of the 'assessment' or regulatory agencies may or may not operate benevolently on behalf of the interests of the citizens. One way to attempt to regulate the behaviour of the full-time officials is to have them *elected* so that they formally represent the interests of those who elect them.

Representation

Social control through 'representation' places more emphasis on the positive democractic virtues of enabling people to participate, albeit indirectly, in the processes of government and administration.

In the case of democratic government, this indirect participation is, in theory, ensured by the election of representatives. The public delegates its authority and relies on its representatives to act on their behalf.

Representation is really a special type of 'accountability' in which the representative is subject to 'recall' and 'dismissal' by those who elect him, although this process may occur only occasionally, as in parliamentary government.

This is clearly a relatively indirect form of control, since the citizens' influence is limited to occasional elections. As Pateman puts it:

The electorate do not 'normally' control their leaders except by replacing them at elections with alternative leaders.[14]

Thus ... 'participation', so far as the majority is concerned, is participation in the choice of decision makers ... although, ... decisions of leaders can also be influenced by active groups bringing pressure to bear during inter-election periods.[15]

Forms of control which rely on elected and accountable 'delegates' and 'representatives' are common in most democratic organizations – in parliamentary and local government, the trade unions and many voluntary clubs and societies.

It is, however, not always the case that the decision-makers charged with 'representing the interests of the public' are *elected*. In some forms of representative control, experts or officials are simply *appointed* to serve public interests. In theory they should respond to the public's interests and be accountable to the public for their actions. In practice (as in the case of civil servants) this is achieved by making them responsible (and accountable) to the elected political representative – the minister. In this situation the citizen may have much less control – whether in terms of representation or accountability over the day-to-day actions of the organization concerned.

Participation[16]

In this third form of social control the citizen plays a much more direct role in the decision-making process.

'Participation' experiments are now widespread in industry, local government, planning and so on.

Of course, the word 'participation' has a number of meanings. In general it suggests that individuals or groups are in some way able to directly influence and be involved with decision-making.

As we have seen some forms of participation are much less ambitious than this and indeed some have been criticized for being no more than manipulative mechanisms for inducing acceptance of goals already chosen by those actually in control. In this situation the aim of those in control seems to be to give people a *feeling* of participation without actually allowing them any actual influence. Such approaches have been labelled 'pseudo-participation'.[17]

In some situations it may be possible for those in control to allow considerable freedom to subordinates without actually altering the 'balance of power' between superior and subordinate, or without changing the authority structure, for example, in industry 'when a superior is indifferent to several alternatives so that employees can choose between them'.[18] The superior may be 'influenced' by the subordinates, but does not subordinate his wishes to those of his subordinates; he still has the power to make the ultimate decision. This form of participation has been called 'partial participation'.[19]

The definition of the superior's responsibilities is unchanged; the superior still defines the crucial overall aims of the operation. Subordinates have little control of the ends, goals or values chosen by those in control. Such 'partial participation' might be thought to amount to no more than 'pseudo-participation', being no more than a device to ensure acceptance of the existing goals of the controlling authority.

'Full participation' involves much more direct control over the 'ends' as well as the 'means'. It implies a basic change in the balance of power between superior and subordinate; 'a modification to a greater or less degree, of the orthodox authority structure'.[20]

Subsequent sections take up the question of the extent to which participation within our existing institutions *can* modify the orthodox authority structures, and *how much* power, influence or control can in fact be exerted by subordinate groups, particularly over higher levels of policy and decision-making. It is easy to imagine situations in which groups of workers or citizens can influence low level decisions concerning local, immediate affairs, but more difficult to find cases where higher levels of policy – at national or regional level – for example, can be so controlled. Given the technological and economic complexity of modern society, and hierarchical organization, it seems less easy to have direct participation in the decisions made at the higher levels of the hierarchy of control. It is for this reason that some of those who support the ideal of direct democracy argue for a restructuring of the control system and the abolition of hierarchies.

In its most developed form participation thus means that the citizen is *directly* concerned with every level of the decision-making process. This implies a considerable *devolution* of power, and consequently the decentralization of the decision-making process, in an attempt to enlarge the democratic and self-determining powers of the individual or group.

References

1. H. Brooks, 'Science, growth and society', OECD Report 1971, in N. Cross, D. Elliott and R. Roy (eds) *Man-Made Futures*, Hutchinson, 1974, p. 143.
2. R. Heilbroner quoted in Brian Wynne, 'Technology assessment: superfix or superfixation', *Science for People*, No. 24, Nov./Dec. 1973.
3. O. Solandt, Science Council of Canada, quoted in A. Toffler, *Future Shock*, Bodley Head, 1970.
4. R. Heilbroner, *The Future as History*, Harper and Row, 1959.
5. J. K. Galbraith, *New Industrial State*, André Deutsch, 1972.
6. R. J. Forbes, *The Conquest of Nature*, Praeger, 1968.
7. See R. Williams, 'The more effective political control of technical change', *Technology and Society*, Vol. 8, No. 2, July 1972, Bath U.P.
8. N. Dennis, *Public Participation and Planners Blight*, Faber and Faber, 1972, p. 281.
9. J. D. C. Little, 'Citizen feedback components and systems', NTIS PB-216 517. National Science Foundation/Ford Foundation Urban Grant, June 1972.
10. *Guardian*, 22.5.1974.
11. 'Technology assessment and political power', *New Scientist*, 24.5.1973.

12. J. D. C. Little, op. cit.
13. H. Wheeler, *Democracy in a Revolutionary Era*, Centre for the Study of Democratic Institutions, 1970.
14. C. Pateman, *Participation and Democratic Theory*, Cambridge UP, 1970, p. 5.
15. Ibid., p. 14.
16. For a full discussion of participation theory see C. Pateman, *Participation and Democratic Theory*, Cambridge UP, 1970.
17. Ibid.
18. Ibid.
19. Ibid.
20. Ibid., p. 68.

The more effective political control of technical change

Roger Williams

While for many life remains nasty, brutish and short, for many others among the populations of contemporary industrial societies it now displays also other rather different, and more immediately important, characteristics, not least its complexities, frustrations and uncertainties, and its paradox of increasing order and decreasing purpose. The point of departure of the present essay is best indicated by quoting Gould's[1] diagnosis: 'Much of (our) sickness comes from technology. We have at this point in our history become enmeshed in the results and dilemmas of technological progress . . .', and Habermas'[2] question: '. . . how can the power of technical control be brought within the range of the consensus of acting and transacting citizens?' One is concerned here, in other words, with the already much-discussed problem of social control over the direct and indirect effects of scientific discovery and technological innovation, but also, and rather more specifically, with certain aspects of politics in societies experiencing rapid technical change.

It is easy to sympathise with the widely-held view that technology is, as it were, 'out of control'. Its accomplishments in recent decades have more than once exhausted superlatives. This is the era of mass rapid transport and of mass instant communication: in a very real sense, all the world is now a stage, especially its trouble spots. The developed world has provided itself with the nuclear equivalent of several tons of TNT for everyone on earth, with an ever-growing stream of material goods, with computational facilities which for this purpose makes redundant the human brain, and with remarkable medical techniques for reducing disease and prolonging life. Well-known ills have followed: overpopulation, pollution, diminished amenity, the psychological problems of urban life. Possibly one should be more surprised that most pre-existing socio-political systems have survived at all than that they have come under strain. Perhaps also one should draw comfort not only from the fact that the changes wrought by technology in this century have been unprecedented, but also from the prognosis that, relatively, their cumulative impact must for all time remain unique.

From Roger Williams, 'The more effective political control of technical change', *Technology and Society*, Vol. 8, No. 2, July 1973.

This is not meant to imply that technical change is now about to 'stop on its own'. On the contrary, if one considers the availability of the basic inputs required to sustain it, that is, knowhow, material resources and energy, then there is every reason for assuming its perpetuation, though not necessarily its acceleration. Step changes, or 'breakthroughs', such as the discovery of nuclear energy, may well be fewer in the future than they have been in the recent past, but incremental advances in knowledge, which nevertheless can amount in total to major developments, appear capable of continuing indefinitely. Of the other two inputs, if one allows the eventual feasibility of fusion power, then this in effect removes both uncertainties, in that it makes accessible virtually unlimited stocks of energy, and thus also of natural resources.

Not everyone will accept, and none will accept unreservedly, the permanence of what Gabor[3] has called 'the whirling-dervish economy'. It needs, however, to be thoroughly appreciated that, in conditions of low or zero growth, economic redistribution, both within and to a lesser extent among societies, becomes a much more urgent political problem. As it is, neither this nor the education effort necessary to support such a levelling-off has as yet seriously begun. To state this is not to be anti 'anti-growth'. It is simply to point out that while the proponents of this, like other schools of the 'man must . . . or else' kind, may have a case which is logically sound and practically sensible, and while they may in the long run, as a leavening lobby, be politically very significant, it would be naive to expect them to precipitate any major short-run changes. The justification for scepticism lies in the depth of support given in modern industrial societies to material rewards. The correlation between aggregate political demands, by which one means any demands, including latent ones, which have a political dimension, and the outputs of political systems is at best imperfect and at worst a travesty. This is of course even more true of individual than of group demands. Furthermore, these demands are very unevenly expressed and all to a greater or lesser extent are subject to manipulation. But it remains true that it is through these demands that people expect to bridge the gap between their expectations and their achievements. Orthodox political brokerage then responds to the fact that economic and material demands generally are a good deal easier to interpret than non-material ones, and in conditions of economic growth, more straightforward to tackle as well. All this is really by way of defending an analytical concentration on societies accommodating themselves to a high rate of technical change, but certainly one must be prepared to see at least some of the graphs which plot current trends turn down under the pressure of social, economic, political, or even, despite what was said above, technical factors.

One is compelled at the outset to stress that whereas technological capability has grown over time, sometimes steadily, sometimes in a burst, there appears to be no equally reliable connection between political maturity and the passage of the years, the discipline brought to international relations by the advent of nuclear weapons perhaps alone excepted. Who shall say which societies are incapable of a collapse to barbarity? One is concerned here not with the social origins of discoveries and inventions but, because all of them eventually either become generally available or are rediscovered elsewhere, instead with the use to which they are put. A disturbingly wide range of possible conjunctions between technical capability and political maturity, with the latter always lagging the former, is evidently a circumstance which must be allowed for in examining the question of control. Indeed, the fact has even to be faced that this question could in the end turn out to be purely academic, in that the political nature of man may mean that ultimately he proves incapable of bringing his technology under sufficient control to ensure even his own survival under acceptable conditions: always one must remember the dinosaurs. On this point, this essay proceeds from the premise that the overall technological balance of advantage is still in the black: that is, on average things have got better, though remembering how many more of us there now are, the sum total of human misery may well now be greater than it has ever been. It is also assumed here that technical change can be brought under and/or maintained under sufficient political control at least to prevent any regression. Biases of this sort need to be declared openly. In this case they do at any rate make the problem of control slightly less a philosophical, slightly more a technical one.

In trying to understand this problem it seems advisable to deal separately with the cases of defence and non-defence-related technologies, on the grounds that the requirements of, and hence prospects for, control are very different in the two instances. And since the perils introduced by defence or military technology are so acute, it is as well to begin with them.

Military technology

Here the historical record shows that no confidence is placed in the efficacy of ethical barriers or even in international agreements, whatever their legal status, unless they are backed by provision for or the existence of inspection procedures and the force necessary to uphold them, or unless they cover only issues of minor significance. One might add further that the likelihood of an agreement between governments diminishes roughly in proportion to the gravity of the situation which would follow any unilateral breach of it. The only tenable hypothesis is then that all research possibilities which seem likely to have a military value will be studied, the only real constraints on development and deployment being the economic one concerning the availability of funds and manpower to pursue attractive options, and the calculative one relating to the balance of advantage between proceeding to develop and deploy and seeking to obtain a specific arms control agreement. It is the first of these constraints which so sharply separates the two super-powers from all the rest, and it is the two acting together which have made possible some measure of success in the SALT talks.

It will be recognised that the problem of controlling military tech-nology includes not only countries which are self-sufficient, but also those which engage in joint procurement and those which elect to purchase equipment or licences. Indeed, because secondary arms races have so often led to war, and because so many military technological developments eventually go on offer to the powers likely to become involved in these wars, failure to halt the dissemination of this category of technology is the most directly harmful of all. It is true that there are some restraints. By far the most important is the virtually unanimous acceptance of a qualitative difference between nuclear and non-nuclear weapons, but there are or can be others produced by the inter-play between the various influences, political, military, economic and organisational, which weigh with the supplier and the receiver. None-theless, all together they amount to no more than an accidental hotchpotch, and no significant improvement in this situation would appear to be on the horizon.

One's general conclusions at this time must therefore be first, that the further proliferation of nuclear weapons is a distinct possibility; second, that the steady technical improvement of existing nuclear weapon stocks and associated equipment will continue; and third, that similar im-provement in non-nuclear military technology will also persist, followed after a variable interval by the more general dissemination of this latter technology. Four further observations follow more or less directly. First, given that nuclear proliferation is almost certainly becoming easier, because of the growing familiarity for peaceful purposes with the fundamental technology, to maintain the existing balance between incentives and disincentives to acquire a nuclear capability, a progressive strengthening of political disincentives is called for. Second, since any use of nuclear weapons must, the consequences being incalculable, be irrational, nothing less than 100 per cent assurance against any accidental or improper discharge will suffice. This requires the constant monitoring, physical and psychological, by all nuclear weapons states of their whole command and control systems for these weapons, and it is consequently the more worrying a problem the more nuclear weapons powers there are. Third, for their own security, nuclear weapons states need to insulate their nuclear capability from any non-nuclear military en-tanglements in which they find themselves. Fourth, while the absence of modern technology does not prevent wars from being initiated, the unintended results of existing supply patterns may be gravely un-predictable, and therefore especially undesirable, and in any case it is certain that some risks are run which are avoidable.

It seems, therefore, that one can suggest that so far as the major powers are concerned military technology is under control in the sense that no critical unilateral breakthrough is likely; some definite economic constraints apply, though at a very high level of expenditure; and above all their international relations have come to be conducted in an unusually rational and realistic, if often very cynical, way. The situation is very different for those countries which must continue to fear potentially decisive military-technical instabilities, especially given that the perspective of their inter-actions is shaped by considerations little different from those which governed all international relations until recent years. They spend far less on military equipment than do the major powers, and yet it is for them that military technology is most seriously out of control, because in their case it is much more probable that the technology will actually at some stage be used.

Before turning to a discussion of non-military technology, it must be pointed out that certain technical developments of both the military and the non-military sort have already, and will no doubt increasingly, facilitate the task of the international terrorist and the urban guerilla, not to mention of the criminal fraternity. In this respect the complex nature of modern societies makes them perilously vulnerable, and to complicate the problem there seems certain to be at large a growing number of desperate individuals, most of them coming from the economically or politically depressed parts of the world. The threat of serious acts of violence or disruption perpetrated by such people, whatever the justice of their case, has now to be taken extremely seriously. Here technical developments seem likely both to provide new weapons for the defence, for example as regards aircraft security, and to create new targets, and therefore indirectly new weapons, for the offence, for example the rapidly growing number of civil nuclear power stations. There are clearly no controls on technical development which could eliminate this class of problem, though there are some which might minimise its significance.

Non-military technology

What, then, are the difficulties in the way of bringing non-military technology under control? And what in fact do those people mean who assert or imply that it is at present out of control? Now a process might reasonably be said to be 'under control' in proportion as it responds to action taken to alter it. Supplementary questions then concern the identity of the initiator of such action, and the criteria on which the action is taken. And particular difficulties are first that, save for certain rather exceptional cases there are no very scientific ways of assessing benefits against costs, and second that political systems, particularly the international one, reflect this, as well as having their own weaknesses as systems for making choices. Those who believe modern technology to be out of control then mean by this opinion that, while it may faithfully reflect the demands made upon it, these demands are mostly commercial, administrative or political ones, even many of the more

socially-orientated demands which persist being the product of manipulation. It is this, experienced intuitively, which reduces so many to confused passivity in the face of technical change. And those who do
attempt to discover for themselves a more active role naturally do so
for the most part only as regards specific issues, here seeking to prevent
a particular technical development, there trying to protect or restore
an endangered amenity.

Whatever one thinks of efforts of this sort, it is no disparagement of
tactics to address oneself to strategy, and at the strategic level it is
helpful in examining the control of technology to divide, not very
originally, national policy-making activities into three parts – the
formulation and analysis of alternative courses of action, the decision-
making process itself, and the means used to translate decisions into
action. The remarks which follow in relation to each of these three
stages should be viewed as very preliminary ones.

Taking them in order, it seems likely that the better and the more
widely technological developments are understood, the more probable
it is that technology itself will be felt to be amenable to control. (For
real control understanding must then lead to open debate, debate to
democratic decision, and decision to effective action, the second and
third stages referred to previously.) In its turn, full and wide understanding would seem to depend upon two things, institutionalised
arrangements for predicting and appraising techno-economic developments, and a widespread capacity for interpreting and evaluating them
in everyday terms. Both, obviously, are taxing requirements. Prediction
is beset with difficulties on several counts. Thus, even the best scientists,
engineers and technologists can be disastrously wrong in their projections, and although techniques of prediction have received substantial attention in recent years, they remain unsatisfactory. Plan we
do because plan we must, but only the future itself can reveal just who
is and who is not a skilled practitioner of the art of futurology. Then
again, it is important to distinguish between what have been called the
normative and the exploratory modes of prediction. Finally, above all
it is important to differentiate between technological prediction and
social and economic prediction, all three having their part to play.

The development of a widespread capacity for interpreting and
evaluating technical possibilities in practical terms is scarcely less
ambitious a goal. It calls for what might be described as the inculcation
of a technical-mindedness, a term to be construed for present purposes
as referring to the intermediate category between being 'expert' and
being wholly uninformed. The distinction can conveniently be illustrated
by reference to an editorial in *The Times* dealing with the American
commitment to deploy an ABM screen. In its words: 'Only experts can
have authoritative opinions whether such a system can work now or in
any set of eventualities, and the experts disagree. The difficulties boggle
the lay-mind – but Americans did visit the moon'.[4] With the first of
these two sentences it is difficult to quarrel, but the second neatly

evidences the lack of adequate technical-mindedness. It fails to take the vital point that whereas the lunar venture was a competition against the unchanging natural world, a static problem, the ABM amounts to a competition with an adversary scarcely less competent than oneself, a highly dynamic problem.

Very many other examples could be given and the creation, consolidation and elaboration of technical-mindedness deserves to be seen as one of the most challenging issues facing contemporary education. It is surely both unnecessary and undesirable that so many educated people should feel as unsure of themselves as they do in the face of the jargon of science and the mystique of numeracy.

The second stage of policy-making referred to above, the actual making of choices, clearly relates to the core distinguishing features of the political system concerned, that is, to the role within it of particular institutions, of parties, groups and individuals. The effect of technical change on these elements and the way in which they in turn react to and deal with problems precipitated by specific technical developments is evidently much too complex a subject to be treated here at any length. However, it may be helpful to observe that one way of examining the response of government is in terms of the participation and accountability it provides for, and in terms of the responsibilities and rights it confers on its citizens. By participation one means involvement in decision-making, and the significance of this index is unmistakable when it is remembered that a key characteristic of high-change societies is an increased decision-making load, not all of it naturally by official bodies. Inspection shows that the degree of participation varies from organisation to organisation, system to system, time to time, and decision to decision. Above all it is inescapable that equality in participation is virtually impossible. Among the difficulties are the substantive and procedural expertise needed for effective participation, the constraints of time and the need to protect the interests of those excluded for whatever reasons. Even in the most favourable circumstances and allowing that insufficient experiments have been made one is forced to acknowledge that participation as an aim is of restricted practical utility. The limitations of delegation and, by itself, of representation, are no less real. Hence the interest in accountability, which may for present purposes be regarded as the openness of programmes, institutions and systems to investigation by the public or its agents. Granted that there is no sharp distinction between politics and administration, there is some advantage in seeing participation as part of the political process, accountability as part of the administrative one. The principal reason for advocating as accountable a system as possible is then that the more accountable it is the more it may be expected to behave *as if* participation within it were perfect and equal. One is referring here primarily to the activities of governmental and of quasi-governmental bodies, and to those of private bodies where they are in part occupied with the conduct of public business, but the advantages of having an accountable society as well as an accountable state ought not to be neglected. It may be thought encouraging in this context that some private corporations already recognise a social responsibility.

Responsibilities and rights are in part the counterparts of participation and accountability. The more complex a society becomes the more it appears that certain minimum responsibilities need to be imposed on all its members and the more defences they need against the pressures exerted on them by their fellow citizens and by the state. The problems respectively of industrial action by key groups and of the misuse of computer-stored information belong here. The distribution and re-distribution of responsibility and the safeguarding of rights, including new rights, become critical when all is change.

It was suggested above that it might be held to be desirable to pro-mote technical-mindedness via the educational system to a greater extent than is the case at present. This is one means of minimising disaffection and alienation caused by incomprehension. However, there is also a quite real risk that one dysfunctional consequence of an ex-pansion in education will be a widening of what has become known as the credibility gap between government itself and those who have benefited from increased educational opportunity. In the more re-pressive societies this might be expected to lead to a resigned apathy or impotent bitterness on the part of the population at large. Even in less repressive ones, disillusion and cynicism regarding the role of government might become commonplace. In neither case need socio-political breakdown occur, but both are unhealthy situations. What is now being proposed is that developments of this sort may be short-circuited if on the one hand the policy mends its own fences with regard to participation and accountability, and if on the other the citizen is much better educated than he is at present to understand both his rights and his responsibilities.

Translation into action

A distinction having been drawn for the purposes of this essay between inputs to decisions, the decision-making process itself and the imple-mentation of decisions, in moving now to the third of these phases it becomes essential to point out not only that they overlap but that they form a closed cycle, and that there is therefore constant feedback. The objective in mind being the more effective use of technology, some of the questions which arise for the implementation structures of industrial societies can now be adduced. It will be realised that because 'effective-ness' has its own value connotations, not only are substantive issues the stuff of politics, but so also are procedural alterations of the sort outlined next. Among the issues which fall to be considered one might include:

1. The division between public and private economic activity, including the role of nationalisation, state-sponsored rationalisation, and the contracting out of public tasks to private bodies.
2. The formation of public policies bearing directly and indirectly on technical change in such a way as to further their execution by private individuals and companies acting in their own best economic interests.
3. Increased use of legal provisions, including administrative law, to encourage technical developments judged politically to be socially desirable.
4. Measures to mitigate the onset of inflexibility and ossification in public bodies charged with technical tasks, including arrangements for the balancing of institutional momentum and procedures for the winding up of projects, programmes, and organisations.
5. State financial support of appropriate groups and political parties, appropriateness and level of support possibly depending on legislatively determined criteria, including the size of the group, and the generality and public importance of its objectives.

There are certainly other procedural changes which might be considered, but this group of five will serve to show the essential familiarity of the ideas being advanced, and to stimulate reflection on what might be achieved through a suitable mix of approaches. Thus, under the first heading one has already had in Britain the various nationalised industries, the NRDC, the IRC, and so on, and in the United States the extraordinary exploitation of the contract device. Bodies and instruments such as these force the question as to where at any time it is publically most advantageous to draw the line between the public and private sectors, as well as what sort of line it is best to draw. Questions of this kind are not, to repeat, by any means entirely scientific questions, but they are a good deal more scientific than they have as yet been made to seem.

The second item listed has been discussed by, for instance, Professor Gabor. It will be appreciated that again here there is little that is fundamentally new. On the contrary, there has been much concern in Britain that public purchasing should be more efficiently employed to accelerate technological innovation. And, as it is, most government policies make possible private economic profits, either directly, e.g. regional policies, or indirectly, e.g. car safety and pollution legislation.

The possibility of invoking or extending legal mechanisms must obviously be evaluated against the general practices of the particular society. For example, more legal avenues have been open to the individual in the United States to combat pollution than seems to have been the case in Britain. But differences in the legal possibilities open in various societies do not necessarily derive wholly from basic political structures and traditions. Sometimes it is more inertia than anything else which inhibits imitation and adaptation.

In the fourth category come the problems of dealing in Britain with the UKAEA or Concorde, in the USA with NASA or the nuclear powered aeroplane. It is particularly interesting to note how in the USA, where in theory so much attention is paid to the concept of checks and balances, for much of the time no countervailing power has existed to the Joint Committee on Atomic Energy-Atomic Energy Commission combination. In Britain it has at times been embarrassing to observe ministers wringing their hands over Concorde. One encounters here really a very old administrative problem. It is simply that in the context of modern technology the costs of arriving at the wrong answer, or no answer at all, can be that much more severe. In this case, as in fact with each of the points being looked at here, the blame does not lie only with politicians: it lies also with academics, intellectuals, analysts and administrators. In this particular case one is merely regretting the fact that projects, programmes and organisations which are fuelled with enormous quantities of the most skilled research and engineering effort receive so little attention in the way of administrative research and design.

Turning to the final category, state financial support of groups is as a principle even in Britain not new, and elsewhere political parties too receive such aid. One is mainly, though not exclusively, concerned here with the weakness of the citizen as consumer. The private citizen is greatly disadvantaged financially by comparison with private companies, public corporations, trade unions and, as in planning questions, the state itself. One concedes that the rules governing financial support no less than the actual principle of support would be highly controversial, but so long as there are worthy voices that fail to obtain a hearing because they are too weak by contrast with the voices of other interests, so long there is some case for redressing the imbalance through financial assistance. The idea of a 'technical ombudsman' or institutionalised 'whistle-blower' is a natural extension of this proposal.

The objective in considering alterations in the structures through which policies are carried out and business conducted is very straightforward. It is, in the first place, to change the balance between the various pulls and pushes operating on technological innovation and change. Excluding the military pressures, which have been treated separately as not being amenable to the type of political and administrative adjustments reviewed here, the major factors stimulating technical change are economic and commercial in capitalist societies, economic and administrative in communist ones. Social pressures, while by no means always of negligible importance, are nonetheless frequently by comparison very weak. Offsetting one set of pressures by introducing or strengthening another set is obviously a fit subject for political debate. The difficulties in the way of action are compounded by the fact that nations do not live in economic isolation from each other. The adoption of policies or structural changes which lead to severe economic penalties domestically is very hard to defend, as for instance in the case of pollution controls introduced in the United States which Japanese manufacturers could meet much more easily than American ones. Even when the penalties fall mainly on foreign companies, international pressures may make it very difficult to hold to a domestically sound policy line. But while many questions bearing on the control of technology may be best tackled by common international action, this is not always the case, and there may even on occasion be important returns to independent national initiatives.

This has been only the briefest of reviews of ways by means of which technology might be brought under more effective control. Differences between political systems, in particular between communist and capitalist societies, are obviously of great importance, so that for instance, observations about accountability in many cases have a very hollow ring. On the other hand, administrative pressures for technical change may be substantially easier to offset than commercial ones. In any case, whether one welcomes or opposes technical change is of little moment. The important thing is to ensure that it operates to the maximum extent possible in the public interest: to this end there can be no relaxation.

References

1. S. J. Gould, 'The rational society', Auguste Compte Memorial Trust Lecture, 1970.
2. Jurgen Habermas, *Towards a Rational Society*, Heinemann, 1971, pp. 57–61.
3. Denis Gabor, *The Mature Society*, Secker and Warburg, 1972, p. 41.
4. *The Times*, 8.8.1969.

Contradictions of science and technology in the productive process

Mike Cooley

'Socially irresponsible' science not only pollutes our rivers, air and soil, provides CS gas for Northern Ireland, produces defoliants for Vietnam and stroboscopic torture devices for police states. It also degrades, both mentally and physically, those at the point of production, as the objectivisation of their labour reduces them to mere machine appendages. The financial anaesthetic of the 'high-wage (a lie in any case) high-productivity low-cost economy' has demonstrably failed to numb workers' minds to the human costs of the fragmented dehumanised tasks of the production line.

There are growing manifestations in the productive superstructure of the irreconcilable contradictions at the economic base. The sabotage of products on the robot-assisted line at General Motors Lordstown plant in the United States, the 8 per cent absentee rate at Fiat in Italy, the 'quality' strike at Chryslers in Britain and the protected workshops in Sweden reveal but the tip of a great international iceberg of seething industrial discontent. That discontent, if properly handled, can be elevated from its essentially defensive, negative stance into a positive political challenge to the system as a whole.

The objective circumstances for such a challenge are developing rapidly as the crushing reality is hammered home by the concrete experience of more and more workers in high capital, technologically based, automated or computerised plants. In consequence, there is a gradual realisation by both manual and staff workers that the more elaborate and scientific the equipment they design and build, the more they themselves become subordinated to it, that is to the objects of their own labour. This process can only be understood when seen in the historical and economic context of technological change as a whole.

Science and the changing mode of production

The use of fixed capital, that is, machinery and, latterly, computers, in the productive process marked a fundamental change in the mode of

Extracts from Chapter 5 of H. Rose and S. Rose (eds.), *The Political Economy of Science*, Macmillan, 1976.

production. It cannot be viewed merely as an increase in the rate at which tools are used to act on raw material. The hand tool was entirely animated by the workers, and the rate at which the commodity was produced – and the quality of it – depended (apart from the raw materials, market forces and supervision) on the strength, tenacity, dexterity and ingenuity of the worker. With fixed capital, that is the machine, it is quite the contrary in that the method of work is transformed as regards its use value (material existence) into that form most suitable for fixed capital. The scientific knowledge which predetermines the speeds and feeds of the machine, and the sequential movements of its inanimate parts, the mathematics used in compiling the numerical control programme, do not exist in the consciousness of the operator; they are external and act through the machine as an alien force. Thus science, as it manifests itself to the workers through fixed capital, although it is merely the accumulation of the knowledge and skill now appropriated, confronts them as an alien and hostile force, and further subordinates them to the machine. The nature of their activity, the movements of their limbs, the rate and sequence of those movements – all these are determined in quite minute detail by the 'scientific' requirements of fixed capital. Thus objectivised labour in the form of fixed capital emerges in the productive process as a dominating force opposed to living labour. We shall see subsequently when we examine concrete situations at the point of production that fixed capital represents not only the appropriation of *living* labour, but in its sophisticated forms (computer hardware and software) appropriates the scientific and intellectual output of the white-collar workers whose own intellects oppose them also as an alien force.

The more, therefore, that workers put into the object of their labour, the less there remains of themselves. The welder at General Motors who takes a robotic welding device and guides its probes through the welding procedures of a car body is on the one hand building skill into the machine, and deskilling himself on the other. The accumulation of years of welding experience is absorbed by the robot's self-programming systems and will never be forgotten. Similarly, mathematicians working as stressmen in an aircraft company may design a software package for the stress analysis of airframe structures and suffer the same consequences in their jobs. In each case they have given part of themselves to the machine and in doing so have conferred life on the object of their labour – but now this life no longer belongs to them but to the owner of the object.

Since the product of their labour does not belong to the workers, but to the owner of the means of production in whose service the work is done and for whose benefit the product of labour is produced, it necessarily follows that the object of the workers' labour confronts them as an alien and hostile force, since it is used in the interests of the owner of the means of production. Thus this 'loss of self' of the worker is but a manifestation of the fundamental contradictions at the economic base of our society. It is a reflection of the antagonistic contradiction between the interest of capital and labour, between the exploiter and the exploited. Fixed capital, therefore, at this historical stage, is the embodiment of a contradiction, namely that the means which could make possible the liberation of the workers from routine, soul-destroying, back-breaking tasks, is simultaneously the means of their own enslavement.

It is therefore obvious that the major contradiction can only be resolved when a change in the ownership of the means of production takes place. Much less obvious, however, is whether there exists a contradiction (non-antagonistic) between science and technology in their present form and the very essence of humanity. It is quite conceivable that our scientific methodology, and in particular our design methodology, has been distorted by the social forces that give rise to its development. The question therefore must arise whether the problems of scientific development and technological change, which are *primarily* due to the nature of our class-divided society, can be solved solely by changing the economic base of that society.

The question is not of merely theoretical interest. It must be a burning issue in the minds of those in Vietnam who are responsible for their country's programme of reconstruction. It must be of political concern to those in China, to establish if Western technology can be simply applied to a socialist society. Technology at this historical stage, in a class-divided society, such as Britain, is the embodiment of two opposites – the possibility of freeing the workers, yet the actuality of ensnaring them. The possibility can only become actuality when the workers own the object of their labour. Because the nature of this contradiction has not been understood, there have been the traditional polarised views: 'technology is good'; and 'technology is bad'. These polarised views are of long standing and not merely products of space-age technology. From the earliest times a view has persisted that the introduction of mechanisation and automated processes would automatically free people to engage in creative work. This view has persisted as consistently in the field of intellectual work as it has in that of manual labour. As far back as 1624, when Pascal introduced his first mechanical calculating device he said, 'I submit to the public a small machine of my own invention, by means of which you alone may without any effort perform all the operations of arithmetic and may be relieved of the work which has so often fatigued your spirit when you have worked with the counters and with the pen.' Only twenty-eight years earlier in 1596 an opposite view was dramatically demonstrated when the city council of Danzig hired an assassin to strangle the inventor of a labour-saving ribbon-loom, a defensive if understandable attempt, repeated time and again in various guises during the ensuing 500 years to resolve a contradiction at an industrial level when only a revolutionary political one would suffice. It is of course true that the contradiction manifests itself in industrial forms even to this day.

The obsolescence of fixed capital

There is first the ever shorter life of fixed capital (the increasing rate of obsolescence of machinery). Early wheeled transport existed in that form for thousands of years; steam-engines made by Boulton and Watt two hundred years ago were still operating about a hundred years later; a century ago, when an employer purchased a piece of machinery, he could rest assured that it would last his lifetime and would be an asset he could pass on to his son.

In the 1930s machinery was obsolete in about twenty-five years, during the 1950s in ten years, and at the moment computerised equipment is obsolete in about three to five years. Then there is the growing volume of fixed capital necessary to provide the total productive environment for a given commodity – the cost of the total means of production is ever-increasing. That is not to say that the cost of individual commodities will continue to increase. The most complicated lathe one could get a hundred years ago would have cost the equivalent of ten workers' wages per annum. Today, a lathe of comparable complexity, with its computer-tape control and the total environment necessary for the preparation of those tapes and the operation of the machine, will cost something in the order of a hundred workers' wages per annum. The industrial manifestations of the contradiction now begin to emerge very clearly indeed. Confronted with equipment which is getting obsolete literally by the minute, and has involved enormous capital investment, the employer will seek to recoup his investment by exploiting that equipment for twenty-four hours per day. In consequence of this, employers will seek to eliminate all so-called non-productive time, such as tea breaks, will seek to subordinate the employees more and more to the machine in order to get the maximum performance, and will insist that the equipment is either worked upon on three shifts to attain a twenty-four hour exploitation, or is used on a continuous overtime basis. This trend has long since been evident in the manual field on the workshop floor. It is now beginning to be a discernible pattern in a whole range of white-collar occupations.

The proletarianisation of intellectual workers

An analysis of this problem in British companies demonstrates that employers will wish to ensure that all their white-collar employees who use this kind of equipment accept the same kind of subordination to the machine that they have already established for manual workers on the shop floor. To say that this is so is not to make a prediction about the far-distant future. In 1971 my union (AUEW–TASS) was involved in a major dispute with Rolls-Royce, which cost the union £250,000. The company sought, amongst other things, to impose on the design staff at the Bristol plant the following conditions: 'The acceptance of shift work in order to exploit high capital equipment, the acceptance of work measurement techniques, the division of work into basic elements, and the setting of times for these elements, such time to be compared with actual performançe.' In this instance the union was able, by industrial action, to prevent the company from imposing these conditions. They are, however, the sort of conditions which employers will seek increasingly to impose upon the white-collar workers. When staff workers, whether they be technical, administrative or clerical, work in a highly synchronised, computerised environment, the employer will seek to ensure that each element of their work is ready to feed into the process at the precise time at which it is required. Mathematicians, for example, will find that they have to have their work ready in the same way as a Ford worker has to have the wheel ready for the car as it passes him on the production line. In consequence of this, many graduates, who in the past would never have recognised the need to belong to a real trade union, now find that they need the same kind of bargaining strength that manual workers have accepted on the shop floor for some considerable length of time. *In fact, one can generalise and say that the more technological change and computerisation enters white-collar area, the more workers in those areas will become pro-letarianised.* The consequence of this will not be limited to the work situation. They will spread right across the family, social and cultural life of the white-collar worker. Consider the consequences of shift working for example. In a survey carried out in West Germany it was demonstrated that the ulcer rate amongst those working a rotating shift was eight times higher than amongst other workers. Other surveys have shown that the divorce rate amongst shift workers is approximately 50 per cent higher than normal, whilst the juvenile delinquency rate of their children can often be 80 per cent higher. There are a whole series of examples in Britain of the manner in which the cultural and social life of AUEW–TASS members has been disrupted by the introduction of this kind of equipment.

Thus, whilst it is true that automated and computerised equipment *could* free people from routine, soul-destroying, back-breaking tasks, and free them to engage in more creative work, the reality in our profit-orientated society is that in many instances it actually lowers 'the quality of life'.

There are also good grounds for assuming that automated and computerised systems will in many instances diminish rather than enhance the creativity of scientific and technological workers. Computer Aided Design (CAD) is a useful occupational aperture through which to view a scenario that will become commonplace to many in the next few years.

In selling the idea of computers to the design community, it is suggested that the computer will merely deal with the quantitative factors and the designer will deal with value judgements and the creative elements of the design process. It is of course true that the design process is, amongst other things, an interaction of the quantitative and the qualitative. It is not, however, true that design methodology is such that these can be separated into two disconnected elements which can then be applied almost as chemical compound. The process by which these two opposites are united by the designer to produce a new whole is a complex and as yet ill-defined and ill-researched area.

The sequential basis on which the elements interact is of extreme importance. The nature of that sequential interaction, and indeed the ratio of the quantitative to the qualitative, depends on the commodity under design consideration. Even where an attempt is made to define the proportion of the work that is creative, and the proportion that is non-creative, what cannot be readily stated is the stage at which the creative element has to be introduced when a certain stage of the non-creative work has been completed. The very subtle process by which designers review the quantitative information they have assembled, and then make the qualitative judgement, is extremely complex. Those who seek to introduce computerised equipment into this interaction attempt to suggest that the quantitative and the qualitative can arbitrarily be divided, so that the computer handles the quantitative. (This is in reality a devious introduction of 'Taylorism' into advanced technological work – an attempt to further subdivide an 'intellectual activity' into its 'manual' and 'intellectual' components.)

Since CAD dramatically increases the rate at which the quantitative is handled, a serious distortion of this dialectical interaction takes place, frequently to the detriment of the qualitative. There are therefore good grounds for assuming that the crude introduction of the computer into the design process, in keeping with the Western ethic of 'the faster the better', may well result in a deterioration of the design quality. It is typical of the narrow, fragmented and short-term view which capitalism takes of all productive processes, that these important philosophical considerations are ignored. Much design research is limited to considerations of design techniques and associated hardware and software with precious little regard for the objective requirements of the design staff or, more importantly, the public. Such research accurately reflects our economic base: equipment and hence capital first; people last.

[. . .] The emergence of fixed capital as a dominant feature in the productive process means that the organic composition of capital is increased and industry becomes capital intensive rather than labour intensive. Human beings are increasingly replaced by machines. This in itself increases the instability of capitalism; on the one hand, capitalism uses the quantity of working time as the sole determining element, yet at the same time continuously reduces the amount of direct labour involved in the production of commodities. At an industrial level, literally millions of workers lose their jobs and millions more suffer the nagging insecurity of the threat of redundancy. An important new political element in this is the class composition of those being made redundant. Just as the use of high-capital equipment has spread out into white-collar and professional fields so also the consequences of high-capital equipment do likewise. Scientists, technologists, professional workers, clerical workers, all now experience unemployment in a manner that only manual workers did in the past. Verbal niceties are used to disguise their common plight. A large West London engineering organisation declared its scientists and technologists 'technologically displaced', its clerical and administrative workers 'surplus to requirements', and its manual workers 'redundant'. In fact they had all got the good old-fashioned sack! In spite of different social, cultural and educational background, they all had a common interest in fighting the closure of that plant, and they did. Scientists and technologists paraded around the factories carrying banners demanding 'the right to work' in a struggle that would have been inconceivable a mere ten years ago. Technological change was indeed proletarianising them. In consequence of the massive and synchronised scale of production which modern technology requires, redundancies can affect whole communities. During a recession in the American aircraft industry in the early 1970s a union banner read: 'Last out of Seattle please put the lights out.' Because of this change in the organic composition of capital, society is gradually being conditioned to accept the idea of a permanent pool of unemployed people. Thus we find in the United States, in spite of the artificial stimulus of the Vietnam War, over the past ten years about five million people have been permanently out of work.

We have witnessed in this country the large-scale unemployment of recent years. Unemployment is considerable in Italy, and even in the West German miracle there are sections of workers – particularly over the age of fifty – who are now experiencing long terms of unemployment. This unemployment itself creates contradictions for the ruling class. It does so because people have a dual role in society, that of producers and consumers. When you deny them the right to produce, you also limit their consumption power. In an attempt to achieve a balance, efforts are now being made to restructure the social services to maintain that balance between unemployment and the purchasing power of the community. In the United States, President Kennedy spoke of a 'tolerable level of unemployment'. In Britain in the 1960s Harold Wilson, stoking the fires of industry with the taxpayer's money through the Industrial Reorganisation Corporation to create the 'white heat of technological change' spoke in a typical double negative of a 'not unacceptable level of unemployment.'

A remarkable statement for a so-called socialist Prime Minister! The net result is that there is on the one hand an increased work tempo for those in industry, whilst on the other hand there is a growing dole queue, with all the degradation that that implies; nor is there any indication that the actual working week has been reduced during this period. Indeed, in spite of all the technological change since the war, the actual working week in Britain for those who have jobs is longer now than it was in 1946. Yet the relentless drive goes on to design machines and equipment which will replace workers. Those involved in such work seldom question the nature of the process in which they are engaged. Why, for example, the frantic efforts to design robots with pattern recognition intelligence when we have a million and a half people in the dole queue in Britain whose pattern recognition intelligence is vastly greater than anything yet conceived even at a theoretical level?

The system seeks in every way to break down the workers' resistance to being sacked. One of the sophisticated devices was the Redundancy Payments Act under the 1964–70 Labour Government. Practical experience of trade unions in Britain demonstrates that the lump sums involved broke up the solidarity at a number of plants where struggle was taking place against a closure.

A much more insidious device is to condition workers into believing that it is their own fault that they are out of work, and that they are in fact unemployable. This technique is already widespread in the United States, where it is asserted that certain workers do not have the intelligence and the training to be employed in modern technological society. This argument is particularly used against coloured workers, Puerto Ricans and poor whites. There is perhaps here fertile ground for some of the 'objective research' of Jensen and Eysenck.

The concept of a permanent pool of unemployed persons as a result of technological change also brings with it the danger that those unemployed would be used as a disciplining force against those still in work. It indoubtedly provides a useful pool from which the army and police force can draw, and during the recent redundancies in Britain, a considerable number of redundant workers from the North-east were recruited into the army and then used against workers in Northern Ireland. Coupled with the introduction of this high-capital equipment is usually a restructuring known as 'rationalisation'. The epitome of this in Britain is the GEC complex with Arnold Weinstock at its head. In 1968, this organisation employed 260,000 workers and made a profit of £75 million. In consequence of quite brutal redundancies, the company's work force was reduced to 200,000, yet profits went up to £105 million. These are the kind of people who are introducing high-capital equipment, and they make their attitude to human beings absolutely clear. It is certainly profits first and people last! One quotes Arnold Weinstock not because he is particularly hideous (he is in fact extremely honest, direct and frank) but because he is prepared to say what others think. He said on one occasion that 'People are like elastic, the more work you give them, the more they stretch.' We know, however, that when people are stretched beyond a limit, they break. My union has identified a department in a West London engineering company where the design staff were reduced from thirty-five to seventeen and there were six nervous breakdowns in eighteen months. Yet people like Weinstock are held up as a glowing example to all aspiring managers. One of his own senior managers once boasted that 'he takes people and squeezes them till the pips squeak'. I think it is a pretty sick and decaying society that will boast of this kind of behaviour.

Most industrial processes, however capital intensive they might be, still require human beings in the total system. Since highly mechanised or automated plant frequently is capable of operating at very high speeds, employers view the comparative slowness of human beings in their interaction with the machinery as a bottleneck in the over-all system. In consequence of this, pay structures and productivity deals are arranged to ensure that the workers operate at an ever faster tempo.

In many instances the work tempo is literally frantic. In one auto-mobile factory in the Midlands in Britain they reckon that they 'burn a man up' on the main production line in ten years. They recently tried to get our union to agree that nobody would be recruited for this type of work over the age of thirty. For the employer it is like having a horse or dog. If you must have one at all, then you have a young one so that it is energetic and frisky enough to do your bidding all the time. So totally does the employer seek to subordinate the worker to produc-tion, that he asserts that the worker's every minute and every move-ment 'belong' to the employer. Indeed, so insatiable is the thirst of capital for surplus values, that it thinks no longer in terms of minutes of workers' time, but fractions of minutes. The grotesque precision with which this is done to workers can be seen from a report which appeared in the *Daily Mirror* of 7 June 1973. It gave particulars of the elements which make up the 32.4 minute rest-allowance deal for body press workers on the Allegro car: trips to the lavatory 1.62 minutes (note; not 1.6, not 1.7, but 1.62!): recovery from fatigue 1.30 minutes, sitting down after standing too long sixty-five seconds, for monotony thirty-two seconds. The report went on to point out that, in a recent dispute, the workers sought to increase the monotony allowance by another sixty-five seconds!

[. . .] Although this is the position on the workshop floor, it would be naive indeed to believe that the use of high-capital equipment will be any more liberating in the fields of clerical, administrative, technical, scientific and intellectual work.

Age limits are now gradually being introduced in the white-collar areas. In 1971 the *Sunday Times* gave a list of the peak-performance ages for mathematicians, engineers, physicists and others. For some of these the peak-performance age was twenty-nine and thirty. It has been suggested that in order to utilise this high-capital equipment as effec-tively as possible, a careers profile should be worked out for those who have to interface with it.

When workers reach their peak-performance age, it is suggested that this should be followed by a careers plateau for three or four years and thereafter, unless the empoyee has moved into management, that they be subjected to a 'careers de-escalation'. The obvious extension of the careers de-escalation is redundancy. Practical experience demonstrates, particularly during periods of redundancy, that older people are being eliminated in this way. They are being eliminated or down-graded to lower-paid work simply because they have committed the hideous crime of beginning to grow old. We are, as Samuel Beckett once said, 'all born of the gravedigger's forceps'. Growing old is the most natural human process. It is a biological process, but, in the contradictory nature of our profit-orientated society, it is treated almost as a crime. It is true that the kind of equipment we have been discussing imposes very stringent demands upon those who have to interface with it. Seen in terms of the total man/machine systems, people are slow, inconsistent, unreliable, but still highly creative. The machine is the dialectical opposite, in that it is fast, reliable, consistent, but totally non-creative. As people attempt to respond to the machine, enormous stress is placed upon them. My union has identified areas within the design activity where by using interactive graphic systems the decision-making rate of the designer is increased by 1,900 per cent.

Needs

Ken Coates

The two related crises which have received a great deal of attention in the ecological debate raise the whole problem of popular participation in social planning to a new level of urgency. Both the acute depletion of certain non-renewable resources, and the aggravated difficulties of pollution and waste, have combined to cause men and women to question, ever more insistently, two things: the wisdom of allowing market forces to determine, unfettered, the rate of use of scarce natural resources; and the implications of permitting entrepreneurs to cite the market as their alibi in order to avoid accusations of systematic mis-application of materials, to say nothing of people. However, even before the recent growth of concern about the human environment, the demand for large extensions of democratic power was already becoming urgent.

During the postwar years, the growth of State intervention in the administration of privately-controlled economies, with the concomitant increase in both publicly-controlled enterprise and welfare provision of public services, has created large sectors of the advanced economies which are not necessarily crudely subordinate to market pressures, and which can indeed, exert certain modest counter-influences within society, from time to time adversely affecting the free operation of the market. The result of this encroachment, however tentative and hesitant it may have been, has been a notable revival of concern with the concept of need, as distinct from the conventional economic notion of demand, which had dominated social thinking while ever the rationality of the market remained virtually unchallenged.[1]

The imagined sovereignty of 'demand' is obviously linked with the hegemony, or desired hegemony, of the market over all socio-economic decisions. The conventional distinction between 'effective' demand and its implied ghost, 'non-effective' demand, which would be sheer nonsense within any strict interpretation of market-based economic models, reflects an uneasy, if usually partial recognition of the human or social inadequacy of such models. It has long been generally recognised, for

Extracts from Chapter 11 of M. Barratt Brown, A. Emerson and C. Stoneman (eds.), *Resources and the Environment: a Socialist Perspective*, Spokesman Books, 1976.

instance, that market forces alone will never meet the housing needs, or the health needs, of large sectors of the populations working in even the most successful market economies.[2] Since the market must necessarily produce an unequal distribution of income and wealth, there are always within its sway larger or lesser groups of people who lack the resources to translate some of their basic needs in these and other fields into 'effective demand'. Hence the growth of public provision, and of watchful underdog pressure groups in all the major economies. Orthodox economists were not always blind to these difficulties, and Marshall, for instance, troubled himself with the distinction not only between 'necessities' and other commodities, but also between the 'necessities of efficiency' and the necessities of existence.[3] But whilst all necessities were either provided in the market place or not at all, this remained an abstract preoccupation, and 'need' was condemned to seem a phantom idea outside the writings of utopians and socialists.

What is need?

Today, in the self-styled welfare states, the existence of a large infrastructure of local authority housing at more or less subsidised rents, of a free or poll-tax contributory health service, of extended facilities for public education, has revitalised the awareness of 'need' in distinction from, and often as opposed to, 'demand'. The Seebohm Report in Britain, for instance, gave semi-official status to the idea that 'the personal social services are large-scale experiments in ways of helping those in need'.[4]

Yet what *is* need? In the arguments of the current poverty lobby, and above all of the writers associated with the Child Poverty Action Group, there has been a consistent tendency to stress the learned nature of individual needs, and to erode not only Marshall's distinction between necessities of different kinds, but also that between necessities and what other conventional economists call 'comforts' or even 'luxuries'. Undoubtedly the material basis for such a sustained intellectual offensive has been the non-market area of publicly provided social security.

A French study has made an effort to quantify the growth of this public sector of need-provision. CREDOC, the Centre for Research and Documentation on Consumer Affairs, identified three kinds of need: *elementary needs*, such as food, clothing, toiletries, etc; *environmental needs*, such as housing, leisure, transport; and '*needs related to the person*', such as education, sports, health, cultural provision. They then attempted to aggregate the expenditures in each category which were made in the open market, the costs of freely provided public services, and those other costs which were refunded by social security services.[5] Their findings offer an interesting perspective on the subject:

	1959		1970	
	Collective share	Private share	C/S	P/S
Elementary	0	100	0	100
Environmental	10	90	12.5	87.5
Person	54	46	68	32
All Services	12	88	19	81

Of course, many questions remain to be asked within this framework. We cannot assume that these expenditures are uniform for all social groups, and the variations between one group and another can tell us extremely significant things about the social structure concerned.

What remains very plain is that public provision, taken at its own valuation, has different motors from market-oriented production. Commonly the social services 'create' or 'discover' needs which hitherto had never been imagined by the governors of society, and possibly not even by some of the beneficiaries of the process. In the field of adult education, poor as it is in endowments, this is a truism. But it can also be held to be relevant in many other areas. In the newly formed British National Health Service, the original heavy demands for false teeth and spectacles triggered off a celebrated public controversy, once these items became freely available. It was argued at the time that this rush for aid reflected the privation previously imposed by the system of market provision on those too poor (or too mean) to exercise 'effective demand'. But in a similar way, the elaboration of medical technology constantly creates new and newer needs, some of them involving far more investment than teeth and glasses. No-one could 'demand' a kidney machine until there was one.

The democratic determination of needs

[. . .] Gunnar Myrdal, in his interesting study *Beyond the Welfare State*,[6] points out that the institutions of welfare in the West have grown up in a democratic environment in distinction from the mechanisms of planning in the USSR and other 'communist' countries, which came into existence in the context of an authoritarian political framework. Unfortunately, the soil in which welfare has grown does not mean that it necessarily retains democratic properties itself. We have hardly succeeded in rendering the public social services democratic in themselves, either in the sense of asserting direct popular participation in, and control of them; or in the more fundamental and indispensable sense of subjecting them to effective and satisfying detailed public accountability.

Part of the problem can be seen in one of the most interesting studies of the taxonomy of need, published in *New Society* by Jonathan Bradshaw.[7] Bradshaw is rightly concerned about the amorphousness

of the concepts of need, and in an effort towards clarity separates four
distinct definitions:

First, he identifies the idea of normative *need, which may be sum-*
marised as the bureaucratic determination, by an administration or social
scientists, of minimum levels of adequacy. These norms may be matched
by remedial provision, or they may not. Examples he offers include the
British Medical Association's nutritional standard, or Peter Townsend's
'incapacity scale'. Much progress has been made in defining such norms
in the fields of housing and education during recent years.

Secondly, he recognises felt *need, as the stated wants of those for whom*
services are offered.

Thirdly, he lists expressed *need, or demand (not in the economic sense)*
in which lacks will provoke actions, demanding a service. Examples he
offers include hospital waiting lists, or possibly, housing waiting lists.

Finally, he accepts the idea of comparative *need, in which either*
persons or areas are compared with others, and found to lack amenities
which are generally accepted as necessary elsewhere.

Bradshaw then goes on to offer a model connecting these different
concepts which can interrelate those more or less precise measures of
need which may be elaborated on the basis of each taken individually.
The important thing about this whole valuable exercise is that it is
oriented at planners and policy-makers exclusively, to enable them to
refine and evaluate their judgements. And it is exactly this 'need' of
the planners which demonstrates how far our services are from being
able to live up to Gunnar Myrdal's expectations about their 'democratic' content, since effective participation and consultation would by
themselves produce notable refinement in most public plans, as well as
allowing planners to educate themselves in the process.

The relevance of this problem to the wider ecological issues, demanding as they do significant extensions of planning, both in order to eke
out scarce materials, to research and develop substitutes, and to clear
up and prevent mess, should be evident. Democratic forms of society
will be increasingly difficult to maintain unless we can effectively extend
the principles of social accountability and direct popular participation
in decision-taking into what are, at present, either authoritarian or
technocratic preserves. Naturally, this is not to argue against the development of technology, now more urgent than ever, but to argue
for its application under genuinely democratic controls, in response
to democratic initiatives.

At this point, one must obviously consider the tools which are
available for such controls. The growth of governmental and local
administrative organs, voluntary organizations, trade unions, and pressure groups certainly provides us with a confusion of institutions. What
is required is not simply a refinement of organizational forms, still
less a proliferation of offices, but an enrichment of the simple

traditional constitutional doctrine of separation of powers, such as might prove possible once we began to take the notion of accountability seriously. Any genuine separation of powers exists to prevent the concentration of authority in a manner harmful to civil liberties. Bitter experience, in a succession of countries, reveals the peril of minimising the importance of the continuous extension of such checks and controls, to render them relevant and effective to cope with the enormous (and up to now, largely necessary) growth of bureaucratic administrative forms.

In its pure form, this problem poses itself most clearly in the 'socialist' societies, in which planning is unimpeded by the institutions of private property, yet in which democratic initiatives are as yet markedly limited and, indeed, restricted. This has been perceptively understood by Mihailo Markovic (the Yugoslav scholar who was dismissed, with his colleagues in the Belgrade School of Philosophy, after an unprecedented Governmental campaign which culminated in an arbitrary decision by the State authorities of Serbia to over-rule the University's statutes. At the beginning of 1975, against the will of their colleagues, the Belgrade philosophers were suspended from teaching duties).

Markovic argues[8] that the doctrine of separation of powers needs now to be consciously applied to information and communication services, so that not only raw data, but also access to competent, and if necessary, adversary, technical advice, should become available to groups of citizens as of right, for whatever social purposes might seem relevant to them.

In capitalist economies, the resistance to such doctrines has a dual root, in contrast to the single, bureaucratic-political source of limitations on information flows which control the communist states. Capitalist societies encourage a certain dissociated pluralism in the communications media, and in the fields of intellectual organization: although they have given rise to a modified bureaucracy in both local and national Government and their out-stations, which is not without its East European parallel. But the major obstacle to freedom of information is still, in such societies, undoubtedly located in the institutions of private property, which require that not only material producer goods, but certain kinds of knowledge, be restricted to more or less exclusive proprietorship. To establish truly universal access to knowledge would be to negate the domination of resources by particular interests: and it is this salient fact which has encouraged the industrial demand for accountability, commonly pursued under the slogan 'open the books'.[9]

Needless to say, this is not to argue that universal access to knowledge *can* be achieved without other prior material changes: George Orwell pin-pointed this question with characteristic clarity when he wrote that: 'Until they become conscious they will never rebel, and until after they have rebelled they cannot become conscious.'[10] While the problem is confined solely to human consciousness, it is insoluble.

Grass roots demands for a 'social audit' and needs budget

In industry, the grass roots urge for access to information has been reflected in official programmes adopted by both the British Labour Party[11] and the Trades Union Congress.[12] The whole strategy of 'planning agreements', as devised in the Party's industrial policy statements, was originally conceived as a two-way squeeze on private monopolies of information, from trade union and Governmental sides respectively.[13] Companies would be compelled to disclose certain whole categories of information, both to the state and their own employees (through the unions), thus facilitating both collective bargaining and tripartite planning decisions. In the event, the Wilson administration discreetly withdrew from the honouring of this commitment, but, instead, adopted parts of the institutional framework which had been proposed by the Labour Party in opposition, carefully filleting this of the real powers which had been intended for it.

But whilst the Government has chosen caution, the grass-roots organizations of the trade unions have shown increasing belligerence on this question. One of the main by-products of the movement of factory occupations, which began at Upper Clyde Shipbuilders, was the development of the notion of the 'social audit'.[14] Originally canvassed as a response to pit closures during the 1960s, this idea came to life in a most spectacular way, when the Scottish TUC convened an extended public enquiry into the overall socio-economic effects of the proposed closure of the shipyards. Naturally, the balance sheets of UCS provided many arguments for closure. But, taken in conjunction with the social costs of unemployment, rehousing and renovation of industrial potential, these arguments became much less convincing. A wider accounting framework posed questions which could never even be asked within a straightforward calculation of profit and loss within the shipbuilding industry itself. Even excluding the moral costs of closure, which is itself a moral choice which may or may not be justified, the simple cash costs of social security benefits and redevelopment could, when carefully computed, provide powerful evidence for maintaining an otherwise 'unprofitable' concern in being. The example of the Scottish TUC was subsequently emulated in a number of other threatened enterprises. At the River Don Steelworks in Sheffield, white-collar and production workers combined to produce a blueprint of the effects of closure proposals, which aroused widespread concern amongst industrialists who were British Steel Corporation customers, and resulted in effective pressure for a stay of execution. By the time that the 1974 Wilson administration took office, this kind of reasoning had taken root very widely, and the new industry minister, Mr Tony Benn, found it perfectly possible to encourage its more general application.

Confronted by a widespread liquidity crisis, British industry was facing a particularly difficult time. Not only were there bankruptcies and closures of plants on a wide scale, but a number of transnational companies were brought to the point at which they decided to close all or part of their British production potential, and to opt for attempts to hold their previous market shares by importing products from their overseas plants. Tony Benn greeted the workers' representatives who beseiged him for Governmental help in these situations with a novel proposal: he commissioned independent consultants to prepare feasibility studies under the control and guidance of the relevant trade union bodies. This innovation was applied in cases such as the closure of Imperial Typewriters' factories in Leicester and Hull:[15] it stimulated the unions into complex efforts at alternative planning. Not only did they have to argue with qualified professionals about the possibilities of continued or modified production in the plants concerned: they were also powerfully motivated to examine the overall performance of their former employers, to document the investment and marketing programmes which had produced their present adversity, and to seek to arouse public discussion on the social priorities involved.

The demotion of Mr Benn after the result of the EEC referendum was not sufficient to prevent the continuance of this type of approach. When Chrysler Motors announced their closure plans towards the end of 1975,[16] the instant response of the shop stewards was to replicate this example, in a most careful and imaginative way. Perhaps the most dramatic example of the social audit at work is to be found in the extraordinary initiative of Lucas Aerospace workers,[17] who, encouraged by Mr Benn, prepared a detailed blueprint for the transfer of their industry to 'socially useful and necessary projects'.

Naturally, the social audit has, until now, remained mainly a labour of self-education and, in a sense, propaganda. But it is not difficult to see the potential which it contains as an instrument for democratic planning. By putting experts to work for oppositional groups, it calls in question the prerogatives of managers and professional planners, and ends the monopoly of initiative.

If the welfare sectors of our economy were to learn from these experiments, they could rapidly extend their innovative capacity in a very real way. If the social audit is relevant to productive effort, then its correlative in the field of social consumption would be the 'needs budget', or inventory of social demands.[18] There is nothing to stop local authorities, or welfare agencies, from initiating an open and continuous discussion upon the question of which needs should have priority, and how scales of priority would be determined. This could enfranchise all the welfare pressure groups, and bring them into an organized effort to evaluate the relative importance of their own particular claims on public resources. As things are, most bureaucracies calculate their future development in terms of x per cent expansion across the board in favourable times, and y per cent cuts during the lean years. A rudimentary jockeying can take place between departments, but it is no secret that the outcome of this is frequently determined as much by the personal capacities of the jockeys as by the comparative urgency of the needs upon which they ride. If needs budgets became as general a feature of the work of such agencies as their normal revenue and expenditure accounts, then the process of popular consultation and discussion which would be involved would itself constitute a real resource, which could itself help to expand the material means which were available to solve specific problems.

In the middle run, such democratic advances as the social audit and the needs budget will prove themselves necessary if there is to be any future for democratic political forms in general. The capitalist industrial powers have advanced half-way to democracy, but if there is not a continued forward movement there will be a retreat. Half-and-half autocracy and self-government is no permanent mixture: it is, in our situation, an impasse, in which government of any kind, leave alone self-government, becomes increasingly impossible.

If we are to consider that the debate on the environment has warned us of real hazards, we must anticipate attempts to discover authoritarian solutions for them. The alternative, which perhaps begins with the kind of tentative reforms outlined here, will see needs as growing in an increasingly self-aware social process, and will seek to meet them by recognising their combined personal and social identity. This task could never be begun outside an ever-expanding democracy.

References

1. Cf. notably Peter Townsend, 'The meaning of poverty', reprinted in his collection *The Social Minority*, Allen Lane, 1973, pp. 35 et seq. Also two essays by the same author in *The Concept of Poverty*, Heinemann, 1970.
2. Recently this recognition has been extended, as city governments themselves have met mounting financial pressures. Cf. Theodore W. Kheel, 'The quality of regional development – the case of New York', in *Qualitat des Lebens*, Vol. 6, Europaische Verlagsanstalt, 1972.
3. Alfred Marshall, *Principles of Economics*, Vol. 1, p. 122. See also Charles S. Wyand, *The Economics of Consumption*, Macmillan, 1937, Chapter 5.
4. Even so, the Seebohm Report provided no satisfactory definition of 'need'.
5. Bernard Cazes, 'Planning for the quality of life in mixed economies', in *Qualitat des Lebens*, Vol. 7, Europaische Verlagsanstalt, 1972.
6. G. Myrdal, *Beyond the Welfare State*, Duckworth, 1960, Cf. Chapters 7 and 8 especially.
7. J. Bradford, *New Society*, 3.3.1972, No. 496, pp. 640–3.
8. M. Markovic, *On the Legal Institutions of Socialist Democracy*, Spokesman Pamphlet No. 55.
9. Cf. Michael Barratt Brown, *Opening the Books*, IWC Pamphlet No. 4, 1968.
10. G. Orwell, *1984*, Penguin Edition, p. 60.
11. The Labour Party, *Report on Industrial Democracy*, June 1967 and *Labour's Programme*, 1973.
12. TUC, *Interim Report on Industrial Democracy*, 1973, and *Report on Industrial Democracy*, 1974.
13. See Stuart Holland, *Strategy for Socialism*, Spokesman Books 1975, pp. 62–76, and the same author's *The Socialist Challenge*, Quartet Books, 1975, Chapters 7, 8, 10 and 11.

14. Michael Barratt Brown, *UCS. The Social Audit*, IWC Pamphlet, No. 26, 1971.
15. *Why Imperial Typewriters Must Not Close*, IWC Pamphlet, No. 46, 1975.
16. Joint Union Declaration of Chrysler Shop Stewards and Staff Representatives, *Chrysler's Crisis: The Workers' Answer*, 8.12.1975.
17. Lucas Aerospace Combine Shop Stewards Committee, *Corporate Plan*, E. F. Scarbrow, 1976.
18. Cf. my paper 'The social audit and the inventory of social needs', in *Community Development Journal*, Vol. 8, No. 3, OUP, Oct. 1973.

Social aspects of the environmental crisis

Barry Commoner

[. . .] We can trace the origin of the environmental crisis through the following sequence. Environmental degradation largely results from the introduction of new industrial and agricultural production technologies. These technologies are ecologically faulty because they are designed to solve singular, separate problems and fail to take into account the inevitable 'side-effects' that arise because, in nature, no part is isolated from the whole ecological fabric. In turn, the fragmented design of technology reflects its scientific foundation, for science is divided into disciplines that are largely governed by the notion that complex systems can be understood only if they are first broken into their separate component parts. This reductionist bias has also tended to shield basic science from a concern for real-life problems, such as environmental degradation.

The isolation of science from such practical problems has another unfortunate consequence. Most people are less interested in the discipline of science than they are in its practical effects on their daily lives. And the separation between science and the problems that concern people has tended to limit what most people know about the scientific background of environmental issues. Yet such *public* knowledge is essential to the solution of every environmental problem. For these depend not only on scientific data, but ultimately on a public judgment which balances the benefits to be gained from a particular technology against the associated environmental hazards.

In effect, the citizen faces an important question about modern technology: does it pay? Whether we ask this in the direct language of profit and loss or in the more abstract language of social welfare, the question is crucial. Sooner or later, every human endeavour – if it is to continue – must pass this simple test: is it worth what it costs?

It might appear that for most environmental issues this question has already been answered. After all, power companies seem eager to build plants for nuclear fuels rather than fossil ones and farmers rapidly adopt new insecticides and fertilizers. Apparently their cost accounting tells them that the new technologies yield the best available margin between

Extracts from Chapter 9 of Barry Commoner, *The Closing Circle: Confronting the Environmental Crisis*, Jonathan Cape, 1972.

income and costs. The environmental crisis tells us, however, that these calculations are not complete – that certain costs have not yet been taken into account.

For example, what are the true costs of operating a coal-fired power plant in an urban area? The obvious costs – capital outlay, maintenance, operating costs, taxes – are of course well known. But we have recently discovered that there are other costs and have even begun to put a dollar value upon them.

We now know that a coal-burning power plant produces not only electricity, but also a number of less desirable things: smoke and soot, oxides of sulfur and nitrogen, carbon dioxide, a variety of organic compounds, and heat. Each of these is a *non*good and costs someone something. Smoke and soot increase the householder's laundry and cleaning bills; oxides of sulfur increase the cost of building maintenance; for organic pollutants we pay the price – not only in dollars, but in human anguish – of some number of cases of lung cancer.

Some of these costs can be converted to dollar values. The United States Public Health Service estimates the over-all cost of air pollution at about $60 per person per year.[1] About one-third of urban air pollution is due to power production from fossil fuels, representing about $20 per person per year. This means that we must add to the cost of power production, for each urban family of four, about $80 per year – an appreciable sum relative to the annual bill for electricity.

The point of this calculation is obvious. The *hidden* costs of power production, such as air pollution, are *social* costs; they are met, not by a single producer, but by the *public*. To discover the true cost of the many benefits of modern technology, we need to look for, and evaluate, all the hidden social costs represented by environmental pollution.

Every environmental decision therefore involves a balance between benefits and hazards. This is expressed in the official United States policy regarding allowable public exposure to radiation from atomic operations which states:

> *The establishment of radiation protection standards involves a balancing of the benefits to be derived from the controlled use of radiation and atomic energy against the risk of radiation pressure. This principle is based on the position adopted by the Federal Radiation Council that any radiation exposure involves some risk, the magnitude of which increases with the exposure ... the various benefits to be expected as a result of the exposure, as evaluated by the appropriate responsible group, must outweigh the potential hazard or risk.*[2]

On this basis, the government has adopted as a guideline that a particular radiation exposure – for example, 10 rads to the thyroid gland – is 'acceptable' for the general public. But since every increase in radiation exposure thereby increases the risk to health, there is a definite risk associated with a 10-rad dose to the thyroid. One calculation suggests that it might increase the national incidence of thyroid cancer about tenfold; another estimate suggests only a 50 per cent increase. In any case, if we accept as the price of nuclear power, for example, that citizens shall endure 10 rads of exposure to their thyroids, then some people, at some time, will pay that price with their health.[3]

The same is true of other environmental issues. For any effort to reduce an environmental hazard will compete with the benefits available from the technological process that produces it. If radiation emission standards are made more rigorous, the health hazard from nuclear power operations could be reduced, but the added expense of achieving them would increase the cost of power and might render the nuclear industry incapable of competing with fossil-fuel power plants. This would severely curtail a major federally financed technological program and raise serious political issues. Similarly, it would be possible to reduce nitrate pollution from feedlots by returning the wastes to the land, where in nature they belong. But this would reduce the economy of the feedlot operation. Organic fertilizers could be reintroduced in place of inorganic nitrogen fertilizer in order to reduce the environmental hazard of excess nitrate in surface waters; but since inorganic fertilizers are cheaper to buy and to spread, crop production costs would rise. Urban pollution involves many cost/benefit decisions. For example, smog levels cannot be reduced without supplanting urban automotive traffic with electric-powered mass transit systems, or possibly by introducing new types of vehicles. The first of these actions would impose a massive economic burden on cities that are already unable to meet their social obligations; the second course would mean a serious disruption of one of the mainstays of our economy, the automobile industry. In the same way, the government's decision in 1970 to close the biological warfare arsenal at Pine Bluff, Arkansas, was protested by the local chamber of commerce, which expressed a readiness to accept the possible environmental hazard – and to enjoy the benefits of the 200 jobs associated with the arsenal – for the sake of 'deterring' an enemy with the threat of bacterial attack.[4]

We come then to a crucial question: who is to be the Solomon of modern technology and weigh in the balance all the good that comes of it against the ecological, social costs? Or, who will strike the balance between the concern of the prudent manager of a nuclear power plant for economy and the concern of a mother over the health of her child?

Confronted by decisions on nuclear power, radiation, nitrate levels, photochemical smog, bacterial warfare, and all the other technicalities of environmental problems, it is tempting to call in the scientific expert. Scientists can, of course, evaluate the relevant benefits: how many kilowatt hours of electricity a nuclear power plant can deliver and at what price, or the yield of corn to be expected from nitrogen fertilizer. They can also evaluate the related risks: the radiation dose to people in the vicinity of the power plant and the hazard to infants from nitrate levels exacerbated by fertilizers. These evaluations can be derived from appropriate scientific theories, principles, and data.

However, no scientific principle can guide the choice between some number of kilowatt hours of electric power and some number of cases of thyroid cancer, or between some number of bushels of corn and some number of cases of infant methemoglobinemia. These are *value* judgments; they are determined not by scientific principle, but by the value that we place on economic advantage and on human life or by our belief in the wisdom of committing the nation to mass transportation or to biological warfare. These are matters of morality, of social and political judgment. In a democracy they belong not in the hands of 'experts', but in the hands of the people and their elected representatives.

The environmental crisis is the legacy of our unwitting assault on the natural systems that support us. It represents hidden costs that are mounting toward catastrophe. If it is to be resolved, these costs must be made explicit and balanced against the benefits of technology in open, public debate. But this debate will not come easily. For the public has little access to the necessary scientific data. Much of the needed information has been, and remains, wrapped in government and industrial secrecy. Unearthing the needed information and disseminating it to the public is, I believe, the unique responsibility of the scientific community. For to exercise its right of conscience, the public must have the relevant scientific facts in understandable terms. As the custodians of this knowledge, we in the scientific community owe it to our fellow citizens to help inform them about the crisis in the environment.

This partnership between scientist and citizen is, I believe, the clue to the remarkable upsurge of public action on environmental issues that we have witnessed in the United States in recent years. Here are some examples:

1. The Limited Nuclear Test Ban Treaty of 1963, a major reversal of United States foreign policy, is perhaps the first of the great ecological victories achieved by the partnership between the American public and the scientific community. For nearly a decade after Hiroshima, while the United States, the USSR, and Great Britain rapidly developed and tested nuclear weapons, the American public was kept in ignorance of the crucial environmental facts. No one knew that every explosion produced massive amounts of strontium 90 and other radioisotopes; that strontium 90 would be carried through the food chain and lodge in the developing bones of children; that *any* increase in radioactive exposure increases the risk of cancer and other radiation hazards. Rigid secrecy kept these facts from the public; the American people were paying the biological price of nuclear tests not even knowing that it had been asked of them.

However, beginning in about 1953, the independent scientific community began to agitate for the release of government-held data on fallout. By 1956 sufficient information had been released to provide scientists with an effective understanding of what was happening. At this point, led by Linus Pauling, scientists, first in the United States and later throughout the world, appealed through a petition for action to halt nuclear tests and the spread of fallout. This appeal brought no immediate action, but for the first time broad sections of the public began to understand the nuclear peril.

There then developed in the United States the scientists' information movement – the effort of independent scientists organized in local committees under the aegis of the Scientists' Institute for Public Information to inform the public about the basic scientific facts on fallout. This campaign restored the missing element in the political process – the grist of data was supplied to the public conscience.[5]

We have a fairly good historical record of the consequences. Previously unconcerned senators were moved to support the Nuclear Test Ban Treaty by a flood of passionate letters from parents who objected to raising their children on milk contaminated with strontium 90. The senators were not so much impressed that their constituents were irate (they are accustomed to that), but that they knew how to spell strontium 90! Presumably the prospect of facing not merely an irate voter but an informed one stirred them to action. Of course, there was also purely political pressure for the treaty; but that pressure succeeded, I am convinced, because it was armed – with the facts.

When the Test Ban Treaty was achieved, some observers expected scientists to lose interest in fallout. Instead, many of them saw that fallout was only part of a larger problem – the untoward environmental effects of modern technology – in which public education was also vital. It was at this point that the St. Louis Committee for Nuclear Information substituted 'Environmental' for 'Nuclear' in its name and converted its bulletin into the magazine now known as *Environment*.

2. A more recent example is the public victory over the Pentagon on the matter of disposal of nerve gas. For years a huge deadly supply of nerve gas was stored in tanks lying directly in the path of planes using the Denver airport. This menace went unnoticed until scientists of the Colorado Committee for Environmental Information issued to the public a factual statement which pointed out that an unlucky plane crash might wipe out most of the Denver population. This, and other explanations by independent scientists in *Environment*, of how nerve gas had killed 6,000 sheep in Utah (a fact long denied by the Army) and the resultant public outcry, finally persuaded the government to remove the gas. On the advice of its experts, the Army began to haul the gas by rail across the country in order to dump it in the Atlantic. At once scientists of the St Louis Committee for Environmental Information pointed out the enormous risks involved in this procedure and showed that the material could be inactivated on the spot. Once more, the Army's position was reversed. Curiously, the new decision to detoxify the material, like the earlier one to ship it, was also validated by the government's committees of experts. They corrected their initial mistake, and the government's policy was changed, but only after the relevant

facts were unearthed by the scientific community – and brought to public attention.

3. For years the government spent billions of dollars and precious human resources on the development and production of biological weapons, only to abandon them not long ago when, despite the constraints of military secrecy, a few crucial facts about their uncontrollable dangers – if they were ever used – were brought home to the public by independent scientists: Matthew Meselson of Harvard, E. G. Pfeiffer of the University of Montana, Arthur Galston of Yale, and Victor Sidel of the Einstein Medical College, among others.

4. And what led to the recent government decision to halt the spread of DDT in the environment? Surely not the advice of industrial experts, who, along with many government advisers, for many years spoke only of the advantages of this insecticide. No, it was Rachel Carson who calmly and courageously unearthed the ecological facts and brought them eloquently to the public attention. Following her lead, other scientists spoke up. Armed with the facts, citizens sued for action. Tragically late, action was taken. Nor is this task complete; as the US markets for DDT are blocked, manufacturers increasingly ship the pesticide abroad.

5. The defeat of the SST over the massive, persistent opposition of the Nixon administration, the aircraft industry, and a number of labor unions is recognized as a crucial turning point in environmental politics. In 1969 Senator Gaylord Nelson of Wisconsin and his colleagues could muster only nineteen votes against the SST in the Senate; in 1970 they defeated it by fifty-two votes. What happened in the intervening year is clear enough: the public became acquainted with the facts about the SST – its sonic boom, its possible effects on the ozone blanket that shields the earth from solar ultraviolet radiation, and its economic futility – and voiced their opposition. Their representatives listened. As one senator put it when asked to explain why he switched from support to opposition to the SST: 'I read my mail.'

6. And let us also pay tribute to Mr Norvald Fimreite, a graduate student of zoology at the University of Western Ontario, for he holds the world record, I believe, for the fastest, one-man, large-scale ecological action. On 19 March, 1970, he wrote to the Canadian Department of Fisheries and Forestry to report that he had found 7.09 ppm of mercury – a value thirty-five times greater than the allowable limit – in pickerel from waters that feed Lake Erie. The Canadian government responded at once. Within a month chloralkali plants were pinpointed as a source of the mercury; they have been forced to change their operations. Meanwhile the Canadian government has banned the taking of fish in the area; sport and commercial fishing have been halted and the polluters are threatened with legal action.[6]

There are many other examples: the nuclear reactor planned for Bodega Bay, California, and abandoned when a local citizen's committee, aided by the St Louis Committee for Environmental Information, helped publicize a report that showed that, since it sat on the great San Andreas fault, the reactor might rupture in an earthquake; the Minnesota Committee for Environmental Information which made a study that led the state of Minnesota to adopt new reactor emission standards – much more stringent than AEC standards; the Northern California Committee for Environmental Information, which was instrumental in making Berkeley the first city to commit itself to natural, biological control of insects in its parks and streets; the scientists of the Rochester Committee for Environmental Information, who collected water samples that revealed the inadequacy of the city's sewage treatment – a new bond issue resulted; the New York Scientists' Committee for Public Information which unearthed an official report that showed that a new cross-town expressway, about to be adopted, would probably generate enough carbon monoxide to cause pedestrians to stagger in the streets – despite well-advanced plans, the project was dropped.

Add to all this the valiant efforts of Ralph Nader and the devoted students who have worked with him to uncover and make public the facts about air and water pollution and the inadequacies of protective regulations. And add, also, the legal actions taken by conservation organizations, by community groups, or simply by single, determined citizens to halt environmental hazards. All these efforts have been based not only on public morality, but on facts – unearthed by scientists and brought into public view through the newspapers, radio, television.

There is one grim reason for all these successes: the country has been vastly ignorant of the extent and depth of the environmental crisis because crucial facts remained buried in inaccessible reports or shielded by official and industrial secrecy. When the facts were revealed, citizens were ready to weigh the benefits against the risks and make the moral judgment which is the spark to political action.

All this has taken some people by surprise. For there is a myth in some political circles that public policy is determined more by narrow self-interest than by concerns for values as nebulous as the integrity of the environment. They would argue as well that there is no way to establish the general public attitude toward the moral acceptability of a given balance between benefit and risk and that, realistically, this judgment can only be made by some appropriate governmental agency. The answer to this argument is that public opinion has, in fact, already established rather well-defined limits to the risks that are acceptable for the benefits to be derived from a wide range of activities.

The benefit/risk issue is associated with many aspects of personal life: driving a car, traveling in a train or an aircraft, skiing, working in an industrial plant or living near it, the use of X-rays for medical diagnosis, watching a color television set, using a microwave oven or a synthetic insecticide. These are personal, voluntary acts. Other benefit/risk issues relate to large-scale social enterprises in which the risks are taken involuntarily. These include the widespread use of pesticides and fertilizers in agriculture, all forms of power production, air pollution due to urban traffic, and indeed all of the massive sources of environmental pollution.

Recently efforts have been made to evaluate, from the available statistics, the quantitative balance between the benefits and risks associated with such activities that has been accepted by the general public. For a number of such activities, Chauncey Starr has evaluated the risk (which he defines as 'the statistical probability of fatalities per hour of exposure of the individual to the activity considered') and the benefit, calculated from the dollar equivalent value derived by the individual from the activity. The ratio of benefit to risk that is acceptable to the public can be seen from a plot of the risk against the benefit, calculated in these terms.[7]

The results of such a plot are quite striking. When the value of the benefit is small, the acceptable risk is also relatively low; as the value increases, the acceptable risk also rises – but at a rate that is very large relative to the increase in value (the acceptable risk rises, approximately, in proportion to the cube of the benefit). Also, as the beneficial value of various activities increases, the acceptable risk reaches an upper limit. Since a wide variety of activities fit this general formula, we must conclude that there has been, deeply inherent in our society, some general standard of public judgment regarding the acceptable balance between benefit and risk. Moreover, the influence of a purely moral factor such as the distinction between an involuntary and voluntary activity is measurable in the results. Involuntary and voluntary activities fall on *separate* curves of the same general shape, but for the same benefit the acceptable level for involuntary risks is 10,000 times less than that acceptable for voluntary ones. These calculations show that the acceptable benefit/risk ratio is determined by a general public consensus; where regulatory agencies are involved, their actions appear to reflect rather than create the common public view. In effect, they place a numerical value on a matter of public morality – that, in Starr's words, 'we are loath to let others do unto us what we happily do to ourselves'.

Now, however, it has become apparent that we are in the midst of a revolution in public attitude toward the acceptability of levels of environmental deterioration which have for a long time been tolerated without general complaint. The explanation for this change is suggested by the clear 10,000-fold difference between the acceptable benefit/risk ratios of voluntary and involuntary activities. This reflects a more stringent public morality when actions of some members of society impose risks on others who are given no choice in the matter. The new assaults on the environment considerably intensify this moral factor. The public has now become aware, I believe, that the new environmental pollutants represent an assault by the present generation not merely on involuntary *living* victims – who have some recourse, however difficult – but on generations not yet born and therefore utterly defenseless. In response, the public is in the process of establishing a new set of acceptable benefit/risk ratios. For a given benefit, the new ratio will accept only a risk that is far below even that acceptable for involuntary risks imposed on the present population. This, then, is the moral response to the assaults on the integrity of the environment which threaten the well-being and even the survival of succeeding generations.

In politics, environmental protection is sometimes regarded as a 'motherhood' issue; no one can really oppose it. In fact, it is often suggested that environmental issues are so innocuous that they serve to divert people from more serious, controversial issues – a kind of ecological 'cop-out' from the problems of poverty, racial discrimination, and war. In practice, it hasn't quite turned out that way; as a political issue, environmental protection is neither innocuous nor unrelated to basic questions of social justice.

For example, in the ghetto, environmental protection is sometimes regarded as an irrelevant diversion from the plight of the blacks. Some approaches to environmental action give substance to this view. This was dramatized during Earth Week 1970 at San Jose State College in California, where a student environmental program was climaxed by the burial of a brand new car, as a symbol of environmental rebellion. The event was picketed by black students who believed that the $2,500 paid for the car could have been better spent in the ghetto. The San Jose burial reflects a kind of personalized approach to the environmental crisis which is sometimes adopted by ecological crusaders. They reason – erroneously, as we have seen – that pollution is caused by the excessive consumption of goods and resources by the United States population. Since the wastes generated by this intense consumption pollute our environment, the eco-activist is advised to 'consume less'. In the absence of the added statistic that in the United States the per capita consumption by blacks is much less than that of the white population, such observations are not likely to make much sense to blacks or to anyone who is concerned with social justice.

Disaffiliation of blacks from the environmental movement would be particularly unfortunate, because in many ways blacks are the special victims of pollution. A white suburbanite can escape from the city's dirt, smog, carbon monoxide, lead, and noise when he goes home; the ghetto dweller not only works in a polluted environment, he lives in it. And in the ghetto he confronts his own, added environmental problems: rats and other vermin, the danger of lead poisoning when children eat bits of ancient, peeling paint. And, through its history, the black community can be a powerful ally in the fight against environmental degradation. The environmental crisis is a crisis of survival, an issue that is not familiar to middle-class Americans. They have not yet learned how to face such a soul-shaking threat; witness our continued failure to appreciate that the existence of ready-armed nuclear weapons means that doomsday may be tomorrow. For blacks, the issue of survival is several hundred years old. If they too have not yet mastered it, they have at least had a good deal of experience that may be enormously valuable to a society that, now as a whole, must face the threat of extinction. Blacks need the environmental movement, and the movement needs the blacks.

There is also a close relationship between environmental issues and poverty. A classic illustration is provided by the recent events at Hilton Head, South Carolina.[8] There, on a beautiful shoreline site, adjacent to large, well-kept estates, a chemical company proposed to build a large plant which, in the absence of unprecedented, expensive environmental controls, would certainly degrade the local environment. Opposed to the plant were the estate owners, conservationists, and shrimp fishermen who feared the aesthetic and ecological effects of the plant's effluents. In support of the plant were the chemical company and many of the poor people in the area, who saw the opportunity to relieve their long-standing unemployment. Where lies justice in this matter? It might be possible to compute the economic benefits of the plant and compare them with the economic cost of the effects of pollutants on shrimp fishing and on the local natural ambiance. Would it then be sufficient to compare the benefits with the costs and decide in favour of the more economical action? Clearly the matter cannot end there, for the environmental problem, even if 'solved' in this way, raises other, more fundamental issues which are not solved by environmental action. For example, if the plant is blocked (which is in fact what happened), this action, in effect, says to the unemployed that their right to a job is less important then the integrity of the environment. The appropriate response may well be that a society that can find the means to save a marsh ought to be equally capable of finding the means to employ its citizens.

A similar situation arose in connection with the SST; unions strongly supported the project because its abandonment would throw some thousands of workers out of jobs. To a person thus unemployed, the immediate response may well be anger directed against the 'eco-freaks' who opposed the SST. On further reflection, such a person might wonder about the rationality of an economic system that forces a person to fight for a job with the knowledge that the product would wake babies in the night and increase the incidence of ultraviolet-induced skin cancers.

There is an equally close link between environmental problems and the issues of war and peace. Like detergents and DDT, nuclear armament is a huge technological blunder. When in the 1950s the Pentagon generals and their scientific advisers decided to rely on nuclear weapons for the nation's defense, they were apparently unaware of what the scientific community, its voice strongly amplified by public response, has since told them: that it will not work, that no nation would survive a nuclear war.

In the same way, the Pentagon replied to an inquiry from the AAAS that it would not use herbicides in Vietnam if it believed that these agents would have 'long-term ecological effects' on that tortured land.[9] Now we know from the efforts of the AAAS and other independent scientists that the United States has indeed conducted ecological warfare in Vietnam. In response, the government has, at last, greatly restricted the military use of herbicides in Vietnam. There is equal force in the fact that the United States government has now abandoned the manufacture of biological warfare agents, after long defending them – against opposition from the scientific community – as effective and necessary for the nation's 'defense'.

It seems to me that these ecological insights raise very profound questions about the competence of our military to defend the nation, as they are charged to do. It adds force to the mounting evidence of purely military blunders in the United States war in Southeast Asia. It raises the momentous issue of at last freeing mankind from the threat of annihilation, from the intolerable burden of living, every day, within minutes of catastrophe.

The environmental crisis is hardly a 'motherhood' issue. Nor is it a diversion from other social questions. For as we begin to act on the environmental crisis, deeper issues emerge which reach to the core of our system of social justice and challenge basic political goals.

The force of this challenge is revealed by the implications of two alternative routes of environmental action: action *of* the public and action *by* the public. Those who favor the first route, march under Pogo's banner: 'We have met the enemy and he is us.' They are committed to personal acts that lessen environmental impact: they walk or bicycle rather than drive a car; they use returnable bottles and phosphate-free detergents; they produce no more than two children. These are the rudiments of a new, ecology-minded personal life-style. It is designed to minimize the two factors that intensify pollution that are under personal control: consumption and population size.

In contrast, action directed toward the third source of environmental impact – the counterecological design of production technology – is necessarily social, rather than personal. As indicated earlier, this factor has a far more powerful effect on pollution levels than the other two. It will be recalled that, in the United States, population rise accounts for 12 to 20 per cent of the increases in postwar environmental impact, while the technological factor accounts for 40 to 95 per cent of these increases. If, to take a conservative illustration, the technological factor has had five times the effect of rising population, then there would have been the following alternative means by which we could have *prevented* the rise in pollution level since the Second World War. If we chose to allow population to grow, as it did, by about 43 per cent, then *a 30 per cent reduction* in environmental impact would have been required of productive technology. If, on the other hand, we chose to allow the environmental impact of technology to increase, as it did, by about 600 per cent (in this example), then *an 86 per cent reduction* in population size would have been required. (See note for the relevant computation.)[10]

It seems rather clear that of the two factors, technology is by far the more effective one. On the other hand it is not subject to direct personal control.

Which route should we take? Should people be urged to consume less and produce fewer children in order to reduce pollution levels? Or should we, rather, concentrate on the ecological reform of technology? Or both?

Since powerful resistance is likely to delay technological reforms, and reduction in consumption is hardly sensible in the face of continued poverty and need, it is often proposed that the primary effort should be made to slow the growth of the United States population. Apart from the fact that a large *reduction* in population would be needed to achieve a noticeable effect on pollution levels, this is, of course, a perfectly logical argument. So long as we continue to use it, ecologically faulty production technology will certainly do less damage to the environment if fewer people demand its products. Clearly, there are logical grounds for supporting *both* ecological reform of production technology and the reduction of population growth as a basis of environmental improvement.

References

1. For current estimates, see First Annual Report of the Council on Environmental Quality, *Environmental Quality*, 1970, p. 72.
2. Federal Radiation Council, Staff Report, No. 2, 1961, p. 2.
3. C. W. Mays: 'Thyroid irradiation in Utah infants exposed to iodine 131', *Scientist and Citizen*, Vol. 8, No. 8, Aug. 1966, p. 3.
4. See *New York Times*, 10.6.1971.
5. For description of these and similar activities and the addresses of SIPI activities (for readers interested in participating in them) see *SIPI Report*, Vol. 1, No. 1, SIPI, 1970.
6. *Chemical and Engineering News*, 13.4.1970, p. 9.
7. See his article in *Science*, Vol. 165, 1969, p. 1232.
8. St Louis *Post-Dispatch*, 17.1.1971.
9. The statement given here is from a letter to the AAAS Board of Directors, from John S. Foster, Jr., Director of Defense Research and Engineering, Department of Defense, dated 29.9.1967. See statement of AAAS Board of Directors in *Science*, Vol. 161, 1967, p. 253, which describes one of the early skirmishes in the struggle between scientists and the military over herbicide spraying in Vietnam. The outcome was a Presidential order, in 1971, to halt spraying.
10. The computation of the reduction in environmental impacts due to technology and population size that would have been needed to prevent the postwar rise in pollution levels is achieved as follows. First, recall that pollution level = population size × production/capita × pollution-emission/production. In this computation, it is assumed that the second ('affluence') factor remains unchanged, which is approximately the case for most pollutants (excepting those arising from automobiles). Then, suppose that in 1946 the pollution level = 1, population size = 1, and pollution-emission/production = 1, while in 1968, pollution = 10, population size = 1.4, and pollution-emission/production = 7. The foregoing approximates the actual

changes for a number of pollutants. Now, if we were to set out in 1946 to keep the pollution level from rising (i.e. maintaining it at a value of 1), then, if the population size were allowed to increase to 1.4, the 'technology' factor (pollution-emission/production) would need to be reduced to 0.7 if the pollution level were to remain at 1 (since $1.4 \times 0.7 =$ approximately 1). This represents a 30 per cent improvement in technology with respect to pollution emission. On the other hand, if the technology factor were allowed to increase to 7, then in order to maintain the pollution level at a value of 1, the population would need to be *reduced* (between 1946 and 1968) from 1 to 0.14 (since $0.14 \times 7 =$ approximately 1). This represents an *86 per cent reduction* in population size.

The entropy state

Hazel Henderson

Many models exist of the unfolding shape of advanced industrial societies. Proposed here is yet another: that of the 'entropy society'.

Daniel Bell gave us the notion of a 'post-industrial society' transcending via technology the ideologies of left and right, and one in which most of the labor force would be employed in service and knowledge-based industries. John Kenneth Galbraith sees a 'new industrial state' of detente between business and government: a 'technostructure' with power falling to cadres of bureaucrats, technicians, and managers, and with only the vestiges of a market economy.

Gunnar Myrdal describes the future evolving from the mixed market and planned economies of which Sweden is typical.[1] And Roger Garaudy foresees the shape of advancing bureaucratized communism in the USSR, as well as the more decentralized worker-managed models of communism such as that now developing in Yugoslavia.[2] And while Karl Marx's prediction of the decline of capitalism did not count on the labor force becoming bourgeois, as it has in today's highly industrialized societies, the crystal-ball-gazing of capitalism's school of market-oriented economics has proved equally cloudy.

Another model of the unfolding pattern of industrial societies might well be that of the 'entropy state'. Simply put, the entropy state is a society at the stage when complexity and interdependence have reached the point where the transaction costs that are generated equal or exceed the society's productive capabilities. In a manner analogous to the phenomenon that occurs in physical systems, the society slowly winds down of its own weight and complexity, with all its forces and counter-forces checked and balanced in a state of equilibrium.

We seem unwilling to come to terms with the fact that each increase in the order of magnitude of technological mastery and managerial control requires and inevitably leads to a concomitant order of magnitude of government coordination and control. Thus we see the irony of those corporate technological innovators who decry the government bureaucracies that all technological innovations call forth.

From Hazel Henderson, 'The entropy state', *Planning Review*, Vol. 2, No. 3, April/May 1974.

Worse, as the industrial system grows more complex, specialized, and differentiated, it becomes increasingly difficult to model the labyrinth of variables in such a web of social and physical systems. Any system that cannot be modelled cannot be managed. Indeed, systems analyst Jay Forrester has noted that such complex systems tend to behave counter-intuitively and are stubbornly resistant to human manipulation.

Because advanced industrial societies develop such unmanageable complexity, they naturally generate a bewildering increase in unanticipated social costs: in human maladjustment, community disruption, and environmental depletion. All these effects of uncoordinated, unplanned activities and suboptimization are called by economists, in almost a Freudian slip, 'externalities'. The cost of cleaning up the mess and caring for the human casualties of unplanned technology – the dropouts, the unskilled, the addicts, or those who just cannot cope with the maze of urban life or deal with Big Brother bureaucracies – mounts ever higher. The proportion of GNP that must be spent in mediating conflicts, controlling crime, protecting consumers and the environment, providing ever-more comprehensive bureaucratic coordination, and generally trying to maintain 'social homeostasis' begins to grow exponentially. New levels of expenditure to maintain this social homeostasis are augured daily, as in the recent calls for new legislation to provide government compensation for crime victims and for new agencies to counsel and assist those who succumb to chronic debt.

Another emerging facet of complex societies is the newly perceived vulnerability of their massive, centralized technologies and institutions, whether manifested in the loss of corporate flexibility, urban decline, power blackouts, skyjacking, or the many frightening scenarios of sabotage and violence now occurring daily.

Meanwhile expectations are continually inflated by business and government leaders, and it becomes more difficult to satisfy demands of private mass consumption while trying to meet demands for more and better public consumption, whether for housing, mass transit, health, education, welfare benefits, parks and beaches, or merely to keep the water potable and the air breathable. The enormous burdens of military expenditures add to this allocation problem in most industrial countries. But even without such huge arms commitments, the ever-inflating bubble of expectations is cause for concern. The recent elections in Denmark are a case in point. Paradoxically, a taxpayer's revolt unseated a liberal government in irritation over the costs of a highly popular social welfare program – an apparent inability of voters to understand the inevitable trade-offs between high levels of public goods and services and private consumption.

The symptoms of the entropy state are also visible in Japan. Notwithstanding military expenditures held to less than 2 per cent of the GNP, the ruling Liberal Democratic Party is strained by labor unrest, soaring wage settlements, growing social dissatisfaction as inflation reaches annual levels of 16 per cent, and the rising public investment costs of pollution control, sewage treatment, housing, and social security benefits. Britain too is exhibiting signs of industrialism's next stage, the entropy state. Social conflict increases as the resource base shrinks, and more equitable sharing has become the inevitable demand. Rampant inflation, soaring public investment costs and social welfare services, and the ineluctable bureaucratization follow a pattern that grows more familiar each day. There seems now to be a dawning realization on the part of the stoic British that belt-tightening is a way of life and that achievement of even a modicum of satisfaction will now require nothing less than a new frame of mind and lowered expectations.

Inflation is now so ubiquitous in advanced industrial economies that it has become one of their structural features, rather than a temporary affliction. It can no longer be described by economists as a trade-off for unemployment, since in many countries, including our own, we have both. Traditional Keynesian remedies of pumping up the whole economy in order to ameliorate areas of structural unemployment and mask the true conflict over the distribution of wealth are now beginning to be felt as too costly in that they raise rates of inflation and deplete resources. Economist Irving Freidman suggests that vastly inflated expectations for both public and private consumption are now a key factor.[3]

Another explanation for inflation comes from thermodynamicists, who insist that economists do not yet understand the drastic multiplier effects of developing energy and resource scarcities. Simply stated, such energy researchers as the brothers Eugene and Howard Odum say that economists and Federal Energy Office officials have not yet grasped the crucial difference between *gross* energy and *net* energy.[4,5] Gross energy is typified by all those theoretical barrels of oil locked in such less accessible forms as shale and tar sands. But it will take millions of barrels of oil to crush the rocks, heat and retort the shale and sands, not to mention the refining and transporting, as well as the millions of gallons of scarce water that would have to be diverted from farm use in the process. What is left over at the end of all this investment of energy and resources is net energy, only a fraction of the quantity theoretically available (gross energy). Indeed the Odums claim that so far the nation's entire nuclear power enterprise has only yielded a few percentage points of net energy, because the process is so heavily subsidized with coal and oil – for uranium extraction and enrichment and scores of other energy and capital-intensive steps that precede the final output of electricity from a nuclear plant. Inflation, in this explanation, is driven by the increasing amount of money and energy a society must keep diverting to the job of extracting and refining lower and lower grade energy and materials. Therefore, there are fewer real goods and services produced and prices soar, as the multiplier effect of additional energy-intensive processing of these resources into finished goods is felt.

But the energy situation has merely revealed and lent impetus to what may be the unfolding 'end game' of industrial societies. First there will be the frantic efforts to invest more and more capital in energy exploitation and resource extraction, despite the already visibly diminishing marginal returns to much of our capital-intensive production. Consider, for example, the case of agriculture where, according to agricultural researchers David Pimental,[6] Michael Perlman, and others, by a key measure – how much energy is used for a given output of calories – our US-type highly mechanized, fossil-fuel subsidized farming is now the most inefficient in the world. In other overautomated processes as dissimilar as fishing and operating mass transit systems, the marginal returns to capital investment are falling: fish catches are now destructively overefficient, while on such transit systems as San Francisco's BART, workers are displaced by costly and erratic automated train controls.

The current stage of hurling massive quantities of capital at the increasingly fruitless endeavor of trying to produce greater supplies of energy and resources, will, in time, be played out. The learning experience will be horrendously costly because it will foreclose many other more realistic options. Capital, amassed from our previously bountiful sources of energy and materials, now represents our society's last diminishing store of low entropy (i.e. concentrated potential for useful work). As evolutionist Gregory Bateson illustrates,[7] capital is our precious stock of stored flexibility for performing an orderly social transition to adapt to new conditions, just as a chrysalis uses its stored energy to turn itself into a butterfly. Instead we see a tragic situation developing, as oil companies, electric utilities, and basic manufacturing industries all attempt to borrow larger and larger quantities of capital to squeeze new supplies from degenerating and depleted deposits of fossil fuels, materials, and minerals.

Banks, in turn, oblige their corporate borrowers, if necessary, by borrowing expensive funds themselves and issuing their own debt instruments, thus adding to the mirage. Sometimes the wasteful, disastrous capital-spending plans of corporations and utilities can be halted only by massive pressures from consumers and environmentalists. By fighting rate increases and higher prices and by forcing companies to more fully internalize social and environmental costs, such groups may deflect company plans by 'upping the ante' and making their own capital spending and borrowing plans less viable. We can see this occurring now in many energy companies and electric utilities.

As the emerging capital shortage becomes more acute and interest rates and inflation continue to soar, we may find that debt service will become the biggest item in corporate and municipal budgets. It will then become more evident that inflation is the manifestation of a massive, futile economic wheel-spinning, where money flows faster and faster, economic activity becomes more feverish, people work harder, and the GNP appears to be climbing reassuringly. The only problem will be that fewer and fewer products, goods, and services will result from this hyperactivity, and money will simply become less and less related to real value. At some point we will recognize that investing capital to call forth diminishing supplies is a tragic misdirected effort. At that point, presumably, interest rates will fall, in spite of the increasing scarcity and value of capital, since most of the precious remaining supply will be needed to maintain existing plants, equipment, housing stocks, public buildings, and amenities, and will not be available for whatever high-yield uses may still remain. At this point, we will have drifted to a 'soft landing' in the steady-state economy, while symptomatic inflation will have masked our declining condition.

The entropy state may be the future of advanced industrial societies unless as yet unimagined advances in computer science enable us to manage and control the complexity of these societies, and unless we improve our ability to devise accurate social indicators. Even then, the attempt to control such impenetrable systems will inevitably mean greater government control, further loss of freedom and individuality, and will lead us closer to the computerized state of which George Orwell warned in his book *1984*. Another path may lie in deliberately trying to reduce the interdependencies by simplifying some of the overly developed systems that have now reached such obvious diseconomies of scale. We might take, not the Luddite's axe, but the surgeon's scalpel, and with a delicacy borne of desperation, begin to isolate and sever some of the interdependencies in our social and technical systems, so that the variables might once more be reduced to a manageable number.

Some systems seem to work best on a very large scale. For example, the telephone system must be widely standardized and is, by definition, composed of interlocking elements. But other systems and institutions can be more efficiently operated on a smaller scale. Perhaps cities and many corporations fit into this category. Some have even suggested that if we convert individual homes and apartment buildings to solar, wind, and methane power generation, then the only reason that homeowners would need to be connected to central power stations would be to sell power back to utilities for resale to their own industrial customers! Certainly we are now seeing the trade-offs in building larger and costlier central power plants with longer, more expensive, energy-wasting transmission lines. But to expect existing utilities and energy corporations to develop such radically different systems would be as naive as it would have been to give the buggy whip makers the responsibility of developing the automobile.

Similarly, we might change the mix of human and machine energy that our production methods currently employ. Many of our farm families were driven off their land because of the now energy-wasteful automation and the large-scale investments that corporate farming requires. A return to smaller farms might yield benefits in human satisfaction and would save enormously on energy and transportation. This capital-to-labor equation has changed for hundreds of other production processes in our society, as the cheap energy trip comes to an end. We can communicate instead of commuting, fill in the wasted spaces in the suburban sprawl, use our existing buildings more efficiently and renovate old ones. Then we can bicycle more: perhaps one day walk the shortened distances more safely; grow our own vegetable gardens; and spend more time in family and community activities. As the Ford Foundation energy study shows, such changes in our life styles could achieve tremendous savings of energy and capital and could stretch all our resources. The entropy state might be held at bay for many generations by such new values and symbols of success.

In the last analysis, Bell's 'post-industrial society', the technostructure of Galbraith's 'new industrial state', the various models of socialism, communism, and welfare capitalism mentioned earlier are all too heavily dependent on increasing economic growth and technological mastery. Even service economies are wholly dependent on their primary agricultural, manufacturing, and resource bases. The Bucky Fulfilling dreams of technologically based abundance of the 1960s now seem adolescent and remote. Perhaps the crumbling faith in the gods of technology will be restored and justified, and premonitions such as this, of the entropy state, can be happily banished from our minds. But at least running scared may buy us some time and retain some of our precious store of flexibility, so that we may yet transform ourselves into a new culture in harmony with the earth.

References

1. Gunnar Myrdal, *Beyond the Welfare State*, Yale University Press, 1960.
2. Roger Garaudy, *Crisis in Communism: Turning-Point in Socialism*, Grove Press, 1972.
3. Irving S. Friedman, *Inflation: A World Wide Disaster*, Houghton Mifflin, 1973.
4. Eugene Odum, *Georgia Conservancy Magazine*, Fourth Quarter, 1973.
5. Howard Oduml, *AMBIO* (Journal of the Royal Swedish Academy of Sciences), Vol. 2, No. 6, 1973.
6. David Pimental, *Science*, Vol. 182. No. 4111, 2.11.1973.
7. Gregory Bateson, *Steps to an Ecology of Mind*, Ballantine, 1973.

Government and technology

Aspects of public policy for innovation

Christopher Freeman

Changing values and changing priorities

[. . .] The tremendous success of the Manhattan Project (the development of the atomic bomb), the radar programme and military aircraft during the Second World War had convinced governments that an enormous investment in science and technology could produce an astonishing payoff in purely military terms. The effectiveness of weapons had been increased, not by a small percentage, but by orders of magnitude. Consequently, as the tensions of the Cold War increased, there was a readiness to invest even vaster sums in the development of the H-bomb and appropriate delivery systems. It should be noted, as Hitch[1] has pointed out, that the military establishment was by no means always so research-minded and was once a by-word for hidebound opposition to science. As he has suggested, this may have major implications for other civil professional groups who have not yet come to accept the revolutionary potentiality of a big investment in modern science and technology. The thought is often expressed that if human beings can use science and technology to get to the moon, it should not be beyond the wit of man to solve some of our more urgent terrestrial problems, such as urban transport. Although naively formulated, this thought nevertheless contains an important truth. What science and technology can achieve *is* partly a question of the social priorities and goals set for research.

One of the consequences of the successful development of the A-bomb was to give immense prestige and weight to the nuclear and aircraft lobbies[2] in national decision-making for R and D. The fashion set in the 1940s dominated world R and D expenditures in the next decade. In the early 1950s at the height of the Cold War the powers which then led the nuclear weapons race were devoting more than half their national R and D resources and more than 90 per cent of their public expenditure to these objectives. It should be remembered that the R and D programmes were effective in the narrow sense in which they were conceived. Although attended by fantastic cost overruns, they never-

Extracts from Chapter 9 of Christopher Freeman, *The Economics of Industrial Innovation*, Penguin, 1974.

theless produced successive generations of ever more sophisticated weaponry. Moreover, those who queried the extraordinarily high priority given to these programmes were often met with the 'spin-off' argument according to which they benefited technology and economic progress in general. The demonstration effect of the Manhattan Project not only served to justify a succession of 'big technology' projects in the countries which originated it, but also led to a wave of competitive and imitative efforts. Its repercussions were not confined to the military field, but set the tone in national priorities in fundamental research and civil technology (see, for example, Greenberg[3]). The primacy of nuclear physics in civil research, and of nuclear energy programmes in national fuel research, cannot be entirely dissociated from the socio-political consequences of the awesome achievements of nuclear weapons. The first *de facto* science policy institutions in many countries were government nuclear-research organizations.[4]

The launching of Sputnik in 1957 had perhaps even greater repercussions. Although it probably owed its successful development to the overall priority given to rocket-type delivery systems for nuclear weapons, its importance obviously transcended these objectives. It led immediately to a further massive competitive increase in American public expenditures on R and D, and to major changes in policy for science and technology in many other countries. It impelled the American President to set as the major national priority for US technology the prestige objective of putting a man on the moon by 1970. This objective was triumphantly achieved, and few would question the magnitude of the technical achievement.

Yet already before the moon landing, expenditure on NASA was being cut back and American priorities were changing. From a \$5.5 billion peak in 1965, expenditure fell to an estimated \$3.4 billion in 1971; that is, from 35 per cent of public R and D expenditure to less than 20 per cent.[5] Paradoxically, the greatest triumph of 'big technology' led not, as in the 1950s, to even bigger projects, but to the first major cutback in R and D expenditures since 1946. For the first time in a generation, unemployment of Ph.D.s became a temporary problem in the United States. It is obviously extremely important for those concerned with science policy to understand fully the reasons for this transformation and its implications.

One way of looking at the change is simply to regard it as 'missions accomplished'. According to this view, the rundown of the space programme was the perfectly logical consequence of the successful achievements of the Apollo missions. In the same way, the reduction of expenditures on nuclear R and D in the United States and other countries may also be regarded as the necessary sequel to the successful development of several types of viable nuclear reactors, and an adequate stockpile of nuclear weapons. Obviously, there is an important element of truth in this interpretation, but it is not by any means the whole story. Whereas in the 1950s a succession of 'big' projects sustained a continuous rapid expansion of the whole R and D system, this is no longer the case. The appetite of the military – space complex for new projects is voracious but there is no longer the same disposition to satisfy it. New factors are at work, especially in the United States, but also in other countries. The most obvious new factor in the world situation was the reduction in tensions between the super-powers.

But along with this reduction in tension, and reciprocally interacting with it, has gone a subtle change in public opinion and social values, and the emergence of new problems. The extent of this change may be gauged by three events in the USA which would have been almost inconceivable in the 1950s. The first of these was the majority vote in the United States Senate against continuing a major programme of support for the civil SST. The second was the Mansfield Amendment debarring the military and space agencies from promoting scientific research that was not directly relevant to the attainment of their declared objectives. The third was the introduction of a Bill to set up an Office of Technology Assessment, which would be empowered to commission major surveys of the potential consequences of possible innovations whether in the private or public sector. All of these moves could be justified in their own terms and, indeed, in terms of the long-run interests of science and technology. But they were nevertheless indicative of a new mood in Congress and a substantial weakening of the aerospace lobby. Nor was this new mood confined to America. The succession of crises in European Launcher and Development Organization (ELDO) and the British withdrawal, the mounting opposition to the continuance of a European SST, and the cut-backs in both British and French military and space appropriations, were all symptoms of the same mood. The extent of this change in the 1960s should not be exaggerated. There were disquieting signs in the early 1970s of a renewed growth of military R and D both in the super-powers and also in some smaller countries and some developing countries.

The main question raised in these debates was not so much the *competence* of science and technology to achieve social goals, but the priorities and the values which determine those goals. These values and goals change over time and are necessarily the subject of continuing debate. The much more critical approach to the SST in the United States and in Europe may be seen as only one instance, although a spectacular one, of this general change in public priorities and values. To measure the change is difficult, although attempts have been made to do so in some countries. In the German Federal Republic, where the most systematic attempt was made, the priorities both of the public and of the civil servants responsible for science policy were found to be the almost exact reverse of those implied by the actual pattern of expenditure.[6] That is to say that military, nuclear and space objectives were rated very low and a much higher priority accorded to 'welfare' objectives – research on the environment, medical research and education. Clearly energy research would now have a very high priority.

The science and technology system has shown its capacity to respond fairly rapidly to a great variety of new demands. This applies both to private industry and to the public sector, as well as to the universities. Certainly there are problems of mobility, adaptability and substitution of various categories of scientific and technical manpower. But the 'big science' and 'big technology' programmes of the 1950s and 1960s have at least demonstrated unequivocally that there is far more flexibility and capacity for swift response to changing demands than had often been assumed. Science and technology are already contributing to the solution of many environmental, development and welfare problems, and they are certainly capable of meeting much greater demands. The problem for policy is to articulate these demands in such a way that the system can respond effectively. This leads to a discussion of the general problem of 'consumer sovereignty' in relation to innovation, and the ability of both the political system and the economy to assess the needs and desires of the population.

Innovation in consumer goods and services

The achievements of the military innovation system are undoubted. There has also been the very great technical achievements of innovators in capital goods, components and materials in the twentieth century. The *buyers* of capital goods and intermediate products, as of weapon systems, are often scientifically and technically sophisticated customers. They are their own 'customers' for many process innovations, and when they are purchasing outside they often have greater technical sophistication than their suppliers (for example the chemical firm selecting a pump or a filter). They may often use their purchasing power to commission technical innovations. Buyers in these markets are concerned with genuine technical characteristics and may lay down stringent technical performance specifications. They are less likely to be impressed by product differentiation, and advertising plays a less important part than with consumer goods while technical services to customers play a much more important part.

Most innovation case studies agree that those innovators who take considerable trouble to ascertain the future requirements of their customers are on the whole more successful. The SAPPHO comparisons of success and failure in innovation showed that most failures were associated with either neglect of market requirements or relatively poor understanding of the customer's needs. To this extent the argument here is at variance with Galbraith's assumption of 'producer sovereignty' in imposing innovation on the market.

These results are superficially encouraging in so far as they indicate that at least in capital goods the market has been effective in stimulating the types of innovation which match real customer needs and – potentially, if not always in practice – social welfare. There are certainly also examples of *consumer* goods which confirm the SAPPHO conclusions on user needs. Take, for example, the Danish plastic toy, 'Leg-o'. This firm took an enormous amount of trouble to ascertain the needs and preferences of the users (in this case, mainly children). It has been rewarded by the most successful sales and export performance of any toy in the world. On the only occasion when the firm introduced a new product without its usual exhaustive prototype tests with users, the innovation was a failure. There are many other examples of great consumer benefits from household products and from drugs. Moreover, most consumers have benefited from the rise in living standards made possible by the productivity advances due to technical innovation in capital goods, materials and communication systems.

Nevertheless, generalizations about the benefits of technical innovation do need to be heavily qualified outside the area of capital goods. Empirical research in this field is still very inadequate and such initiatives as the Gothenburg programme relating the quality of consumer products to R and D are particularly welcome. Most innovation studies have been concerned with the more spectacular 'break-through' innovations and have hardly considered the type of 'annual model' changes which are more characteristic of many consumer products. There are reasons for believing that buyers in these areas are far less capable of making sound technical judgements than in the capital goods area. They may typically have rather poor sources of information and lack the capacity to make any serious technical assessment.

A glance at the distribution of industrial R and D expenditures in any country shows a heavy concentration in capital goods and materials. Consumer industries have very little and much of these limited R and D and other scientific inputs are used for product differentiation in oligopolistic markets, and in the closely related activity of planned obsolescence. The growth and welfare implications of this kind of industrial R and D are very dubious. Fisher, Griliches and Kaysen[7] have shown the very high costs of annual model changes in the US car industry and the 'planned obsolescence' in car exhaust pipes was strongly criticized in a recent UK government report.[8] Obviously it was this aspect of technical innovation which Galbraith had in mind in developing his critique of 'producer sovereignty'. This critique is much more relevant to consumer goods than to capital goods.

This raises the more general problem of the economic theory of the market and the direction of innovation. Theoretically, the ideal consumer market is supposed to provide consumers with the power to choose between an array of alternatives. Possessing 'perfect' information they are free to choose the 'best buy' for price and quality, thus compelling suppliers to adapt their output to consumer needs through the competitive mechanism. This was the ideal of 'consumer sovereignty'. Of course, no economist ever imagined that reality would ever quite correspond to the ideal. Consumers would never really be 'perfectly' informed and very frequently there would be some form of collusion between suppliers or other elements of monopoly. But in some primary commodity markets, fruit and vegetable markets, and some markets for capital goods the reality has probably often approximated quite closely to the ideal abstract model.

Economists have devoted a great deal of attention to the problems of maintaining consumer sovereignty (see, for example, Knox[9]). Much of the theory of monopoly and the critique of advertising has been concerned with the erosion of consumer choice. In many countries anti-monopoly and consumer protection legislation attempts to restrict or reverse the powerful tendencies towards concentration of producers and greater 'producer sovereignty'.[10] We are not concerned here so much with this *general* problem but with the *specific* consequences of *technical* innovation on consumer markets.

There are three main ways in which technical innovation may diminish 'consumer-sovereignty' and which the normal type of anti-monopoly legislation does little to affect:

1. The theory of consumer choice is essentially *static*. The consumer supposedly chooses from the *existing* array of goods and services. But in areas where technical change is important this array has been determined by choices of R and D project or innovation decisions many years before. The critical element lacking in 'consumer sovereignty' is therefore the power to influence the *future* array of goods and services. Apologists for the present state of affairs maintain that consumers do in fact exert this influence *indirectly* because producers are concerned to anticipate their wishes in order to make a profit. Up to a point this is true, as we have seen in the case of many products, but the possibility exists that the innovation decision-makers will impose *their* preferences and *their* choices, rather than those of the consumer. The example of the Ford Edsel shows that this producer power is far from unlimited and Edsel is not quite so exceptional as Galbraith suggests, so that this point is far from being a purely academic one.

2. The theory of consumer choice implies perfect information about the available array of products or services. If we are thinking of a house-wife looking at the prices and quality of vegetables on a dozen different stalls in a street market this model may not be too far from the truth. But it breaks down where any degree of technical sophistication or product differentiation come into the picture, as with cars, television and other consumer durables, and increasingly with a great variety of processed food and chemical products. This market situation is essentially one of completely unequal access to technical information, as all the consumer associations are well aware. The extremely unsatisfactory nature of the repair and maintenance services for consumer durables in all industrial countries is one illustration of this problem. Despite the fact that there are thousands

of garages competing for the motorist's custom, consumer dissatisfaction is chronic and well founded.

3. Consumers cannot possibly be aware of the various long-term side-
effects of a multitude of individual choices about many products.
The individual who buys a car did not and could not work out the
long-term consequences for the urban environment of millions of
similar decisions. Nor indeed did the suppliers. Yet the social costs
may well be so great that they negate the private benefit to most
consumers, as Mishan has so persuasively argued.[11] The problems
of waste disposal in relation to plastics and nuclear power are other
examples of long-term social costs inadequately considered.

Policy for consumer innovation

The relative effectiveness of the social mechanism in the capital-goods
and materials sector, by contrast with the consumer-goods sector,
suggests a number of important policy conclusions, which might help
towards stimulating real as opposed to superficial improvements in performance of consumer goods. In the first place, consumer buying power
may be strengthened by the provision of objective scientific and technical
assessment services. These are already established in several countries
either by consumer associations or public authorities. As the technical
sophistication of products increases, the need for them is obviously
growing. They are an important source of counteracting power to the
otherwise strong trend towards 'producer sovereignty'. But they will
not be wholly effective unless the information which they provide is
disseminated through the mass media and unless they have really good
laboratory test facilities. Their power might then be sufficient to oblige
innovators in consumer goods, as in capital goods, to be more concerned with genuine technical and design improvement rather than
with product differentiation through advertising and 'brand image'
techniques.

Second, legislative standards and regulations may be used to protect
consumers and to reinforce the work of consumer associations. These
have, of course, always been very important in food and chemical
products, but the importance of the 'technological' content of legislation is likely to grow substantially, as the food industry increasingly
becomes a branch of the chemical industry and the 'science base' of
other consumer products becomes more and more important. However, while technological change is fast, legislative change is often slow.
Major questions are therefore raised about the relationship between
statutory law and administrative law and regulations. Institutional
innovations have already been made to cope with the need to safeguard
citizens against the dangers of unregulated innovation, for example,
in the pharmaceutical field. Such procedures may increasingly be
necessary in other industries too. The need to avoid bureaucracy and to

combine speed, flexibility and economy with adequate standards of protection represents a challenge to the 'social' innovation system more complex than that facing purely technical innovators.

The need is also commonly recognized for the limits of advertising to be more rigorously circumscribed, both in the interests of good taste and for reasons of consumer protection. An obvious example is the continued large-scale advertising of tobacco. Economists are generally agreed that, so far from constituting any threat to *consumer* sovereignty, such measures represent a reassertion of this principle and a limitation of *producer* sovereignty.

Finally, however, legal regulation and consumer assessment are limited in their effects on innovation by their essential nature as a screening or filtering process. Indirectly, they may also stimulate producers to seek different types of innovation, but they will not act directly on the source of innovations. Yet in the capital goods market this direct intervention is one of the most potent sources of beneficial advance. Not only do many producers design and develop their own process innovations, tailored specifically to meet their requirements, but they also specify to other suppliers the type of innovation which they need. This *direct* stimulus is often lacking in the consumer goods area, although of course imaginative entrepreneurs do sometimes take a great deal of trouble to try and find out what housewives and other consumers really do want. Groups of consumers may also take such initiatives. The problem is often one of adequate articulation of a felt need. But the problem may often also be that producers are almost exclusively oriented to product differentiation and brand image, rather than to imaginative technical innovation or to social needs. For example, efforts to design safer cars and a relatively pollution-free car are very obvious social needs, but the R and D effort which went into improving safety or preventing pollution was negligible until recently. Interestingly enough, the stimulus came not from the R and D of producers but from outside critics and public regulation. The same is even more true of designing a generally more satisfactory land transport system, particularly in congested urban areas.

Several other examples may be cited to illustrate the extent to which innovators and designers may neglect the interests of users and simply pursue their own fashions and enthusiasms. The example of housing is particularly striking in Britain. In the 1960s, there was a fashion among architects and town-planners for high-rise flats, ('high' blocks of flats may be defined for this purpose as blocks with six or more stories). The extraordinary feature of this particular technological fashion was that such flats were much more expensive than conventional housing or low-rise flats throughout this period.[12] (Estimates vary between 1.3 and 1.8 times the cost per square foot.) Moreover, this was a period of very great financial stringency when local authorities were under constant pressure from central government (and from electors) to prune their expenditures and cut back on their services. Yet in spite of this almost all major cities put up thousands of high flats throughout the 1960s.

This might have been justifiable if there had been overwhelming evidence of consumer preference for high-rise living, from sociological surveys and/or a clear readiness to pay the much higher rents on an economic basis. No such evidence was ever produced. The sociological surveys were inconclusive but most of them showed, if anything, a dislike of high flats among council tenants, particularly those with children and old people.

Another example is in medical services. Heart transplants are an extremely important scientific/technical advance in surgery. But there is little or no attempt to relate the cost of such developments to the cost of other more urgent socio-medical needs. Both in medicine and in architecture there is a strong flavour of the 'Concorde' mentality in the profession – what is expensive, but technologically 'sweet', is good for the consumer.

These examples demonstrate the extent to which the values and preferences of designers and innovators may be *imposed* on the consumer, whether through private firms or public authorities. This does not imply malevolence or contempt for the consumer. On the contrary, in every case, the innovators believed that they were acting in the best interests of the consumer. It is only a special illustration of a problem which has long been familiar to political scientists. The separation of research, development and design into specialized functions with their own ethos, fashions, interests and enthusiasms, inevitably carried with it this danger of lack of social accountability. In theory again the competitive market mechanism ought to be able to perform this function automatically. But it has been argued that the market place mechanism, which theoretically was supposed to ensure correspondence between consumer wishes and supply, no longer performs this function adequately, if it ever did so in some sectors. This means that increasingly the *political* mechanism must restore the lost consumer sovereignty which the autonomous market mechanism can no longer assure.

It might have been expected that socialist societies would have been able to make social innovations, which would link the public R and D system more closely to consumer needs. But the evidence available does not justify this conclusion, possibly because they have been poor countries attempting to industralize rapidly, and in the case of the Soviet Union and China, to compete militarily with other great powers.

There seems no reason in principle why the more enterprising consumer associations should not go into the business of specifying desired technical performance parameters in the same way as capital-goods buyers. They might do this either in association with public authorities or on their own, depending upon circumstances. Ultimately this could even lead to the award of R and D contracts and procurement contracts. Some chain stores and department stores already act in this way on behalf of their customers and, in closing this loop, the civil sector would only be learning the social technique which was learnt by the military sector a generation ago, and by capital goods innovators long ago.

Just as in the military field, the effective performance of this function requires the use of publicly owned R and D facilities. From this stand-point the network of government laboratories is extremely important, but the problem of their project and programme selection is a complex one. The extension of the 'Sunday Soviet' concept so successfully used in the war-time radar programme is the type of thing which is required. It would probably also be sensible to place a part of the scientific and technical resources of public government laboratories directly at the disposal of the consumer associations for testing and research. In one form or another the government laboratories must be brought into far more direct and continuous contact with the potential users of their innovations. This also implies that their missions should be defined not in terms of a particular product group, which inevitably leads to obsolescence, but in terms of broad social needs or branches of tech-nology, such as transport or communications.

The feasibility of this type of development has already been clearly demonstrated by the experience of the AEA laboratory at Harwell. Since its mission was redefined in the 1960s, Harwell has been rather successful in developing its links with industry, so that it now acts as a centre of scientific advice and technological excellence for many firms. In chemical engineering, for example, Harwell has outstanding ex-pertise in high-temperature technology, cryogenics, heat transfer, fluid dynamics, two-phase flow, control instrumentation, materials tech-nology, especially ceramics, corrosion and hazardous waste disposal.[13,14] By good management and imaginative entrepreneurship, Harwell has succeeded increasingly in transferring this technology to industry, using such devices as 'user clubs' ('Sunday Soviets'). Contracts can also play an important part in strengthening this coupling and the new 'Require-ments Boards' set up under the Rothschild reorganization in 1973 may also prove a useful device. So far, however, the reorientation of govern-ment and RA laboratories has affected mainly capital goods, materials, instruments and components, rather than consumer goods as such. Perhaps the Consumer Protection Unit may ultimately acquire such a role, linking the Consumer Associations with the scientific and tech-nological facilities and expertise available in the public and university sector.

The 'customer-contractor' principle of the Rothschild Report[15] can be of great value if it is interpreted in this sense – as an assertion of the need for all R and D organizations to operate with a sense of social responsibility, and a way of improving the 'coupling mechanism' be-tween the scientific community and the public. However, the Report tended to assume a one-to-one correspondence between the interests and preferences of Government departments and the interests and preferences of the public on whose behalf they are acting. This is of course very far from being the case. Departments may often share the technological fashions and preferences of designers without checking back to the actual wishes of consumers. (This was in fact the situation both in the case of aircraft development and of high-rise flats.)

One must certainly hope that the executive branch will be responsive to the known wishes and needs of the population, and will be active in trying to ascertain these preferences where they are not known. But the experience of politics over several thousand years has shown conclusively that this cannot be relied upon (Armytage,[16] and Lenin,[17]). Methods are therefore essential which can ensure that the executive branch is subjected to a continuous process of critical review and control. Local and spontaneous initiatives are important but so too is Parliament, and the strengthening of the Parliamentary process in relation to science and technology is a matter of urgency. The increasingly active role of the Select Committee on Science and Technology in Britain (see *Reports*[18] and Poole and Andrews[19]) is highly encouraging, but it needs far stronger research and information services. To some extent the problems of critical review and control can be approached directly by forms of public representation on all kinds of Government committees, boards, commissions and review panels, and by open access to a great deal of information about the work of Government departments and laboratories, both centrally and locally. Official reports on government R and D of all kinds leave a great deal to be desired. Probably Sweden and Yugoslavia have gone further than most countries to develop the kind of political machinery that is needed. There is little sign yet of 'open government' in the UK in these areas.

References

1. C. J. Hitch, 'Comment' in National Bureau of Economic Research, *The Rate and Direction of Inventive Activity*, Princeton UP, 1962.
2. The expression 'lobby' is used here not in a pejorative sense, but in the normal sense of political science, to describe an interest group with a distinctive set of attitudes.
3. D. S. Greenberg, *The Politics of American Science*, Penguin, 1969.
4. S. Dedijer, 'International comparisons of science', *New Scientist*, Vol. 21. No. 379, 1964, pp. 461–4.
5. OECD, *R and D in OECD Member Countries: Trends and Objectives*, OECD, Paris, 1971.
6. H. Krauch, *Prioritaten fur die Forschungsploitik*, Carl Hanser Verlag, 1970.
7. F. M. Fisher, Z. Griliches, and C. Kaysen, 'The costs of automobile model changes since 1949', *Journal of Political Economy*, Vol. 70. No. 5, 1962, pp. 433–51.
8. Department of Trade and Industry, *Report of the Committee on Corrosion and Protection*, HMSO, 1971, p. 128.
9. F. Knox, *Consumers and the Economy*, Harrap, 1969.
10. J. B. Heath, *International Conference on Monopolies, Mergers and Restrictive Practices*, HMSO, 1971.
11. E. J. Mishan, *The Costs of Economic Growth*, Penguin, 1969.
12. R. McCutcheon, 'High flats in Britain, 1945–1971', M.Sc. dissertation, University of Sussex, 1972.

13. C. M. Nicholls, 'The role of government research establishments', *Chemistry and Industry*, Aug. 1973, pp. 778–82.
14. W. Marshall, *Harwell and Industrial Research*, OUP, 1969.
15. Rothschild Report, *A Framework for Government Research and Development*, Cmnd 4814, HMSO, 1971.
16. W. H. G. Armytage, *The Rise of the Technocrats*, Routledge and Kegan Paul, 1965.
17. V. I. Lenin, *State and Revolution*, Martin Lawrence, 1917.
18. Select Committee on Science and Technology, 1st, 2nd, 3rd and 4th *Reports* HMSO, 1972.
19. J. B. Poole and K. Andrews, *The Government of Science in Britain*, Weidenfeld and Nicolson, 1972.

Government and high technology

John Jewkes

1. A question of motives

[. . .] My question is this: why have successive British governments spent such large sums on the encouragement of high technology – which for practical purposes means nuclear energy, aircraft – especially the Concorde and the Rolls-Royce RB-211 engine – and computers?

The sums involved have been considerable even for these days of casual public prodigality. The cost of the development of the several reactor systems by the Atomic Energy Authority comes to well over £800 million. The development costs of the Concorde, shared between British and French governments, have risen to about £1,000 million. The cost to government of the RB-211 has amounted to about £150 million. Government has already made available for research and development on computers some £28 million, and the final bill is expected to be four or five times larger. So far the returns on these sums have been very disappointing, some would say derisory. We have built up no export market in nuclear reactors. It is doubtful whether the price of electricity is lower than it would have been without these reactors. We could have purchased reactors from other countries more cheaply than those we have built ourselves. Again it is generally accepted that the research and development costs of the Concorde will not be recouped by sales. The RB-211 engine still has to justify itself commercially. Our computer industry is not self-supporting.

Of course what the future holds, either in the increase of costs or the emergence of some return upon costs, is anybody's guess. But clearly it would be unwise to delay too long in striking a balance as to whether, on the basis of experience and in the nature of things, this kind of activity on the part of the Government justifies itself. And, in the striking of such a balance, the recently published Sixth Report from the House of Commons Expenditure Committee,[1] Session 1971–72, on *Public Money in the Private Sector*, together with the Minutes of Evidence, offers a unique collection of documentary evidence upon which I intend to draw heavily in what I have to say.

Extracts from John Jewkes, 'Government and High Technology', Occasional Paper No. 37 of *The Institute of Economic Affairs*, 1972.

Definition
It is important to recognise what is meant by the word 'high' in the term high technology. 'High' does not mean poised above sordid commercial considerations. Indeed successive British governments have always defended the money spent on the ground that it is likely to produce profits. Again 'high' does not mean that such branches of technology involve especially advanced levels of scientific study or technical achievement. The main centres of scientific excitement and progress in these days are surely to be found in biology, genetics and chemistry generally. And it is by no means obvious that what is called for in technical ingenuity is any less advanced in chemicals, pharmaceuticals or electronics than in any other field. 'High' does not mean those technical achievements which are comparatively free of the social irritations comprehensively described as pollution. On the contrary, the generation of nuclear energy carries with it quite terrifying problems for the disposal of lethal wastes and the booms of the supersonic aircraft everywhere endanger the chances of selling it. 'High' does not even imply the need for uniquely large capital expenditure. The sums I have quoted are, indeed, substantial. But they are no larger than, often not so large as, those which are devoted to exploration by the great oil companies and the great mining companies of the world.

High risk and high purpose?
No, high technology means exceptionally high-*risk* technology – projects to which companies, in close contact with realities, will not give their support because the chances of profit seem too small, problematical or remote, but where the Government, for one reason or another, feels that it knows better. Private enterprise will not jeopardise the requisite shareholders' capital but governments feel justified in risking the taxpayers' money.

It is here that the questions to the answers begin to pile up thick and fast. What has been the fundamental purpose of governments in taking this line? Why do they feel that their judgement should override those of others who might, on the surface, seem to be better qualified to judge? Why do they choose nuclear energy, supersonic aircraft or computers for this special treatment rather than any of the other numerous industries? And, perhaps most important of all, how have governments assessed their success or failure and reacted to it?

Fear as the spur
Now, although the explanations and defence of this government strategy can be set down in more specific terms, some of which I will turn to in a moment, I suspect they all run back to one common central cause. That cause is *fear* – the fear on the part of an industrial country with a high standard of living that, with the steady spread of industrial expertise throughout the world, its own comfortable ways of living will be endangered by the competition of poorer countries. The fear

is certainly not confined to Britain. America watches with alarm the encroachment of Japan and even of the European Community; Europe trembles at the evidence of the Japanese economic invasion; all the richer industrial countries shudder at the recent remarkable achievements of some smaller Far Eastern countries in the making of electrical goods and shipbuilding. Who is to say that, twenty years from now, many or most of the motor-cars or colour television sets will not be made in China or Taiwan or Korea, or that Birmingham or Detroit or Tokyo or Dusseldorf will not suffer the fate that fell upon the Lancashire cotton towns between the two world wars? What will be left, it is asked, for the at-present rich countries to make and to sell to keep themselves going?

Such fears are understandable, highly contagious and largely without foundation. They become dangerous only if they are wrongly conceived of to be real and thereby produce panic reactions. It is indeed discouraging to have to record that such panic reactions are already evident. America, although still one of the freest trading areas in the world, seems to be moving towards protection for its most cherished industries. Europe is adding to its dislike of cheap imported food an equal distrust of cheap imported industrial products. Every country which makes ships or aircraft is busy subsidising so that inevitably the world is likely to have more aircraft and ships than it wants or is anxious to buy. Many countries that wish to expand and need capital which they cannot provide for themselves look askance at capital from abroad – the only place from which it can come – or insist upon accepting it only upon terms which render it unlikely that it will be offered.

It would take me too far afield to explain why, in my opinion, these fears are dangerous in proportion as they are without basis. But briefly I would remind you that the economic theory of comparative advantage implies, except in some unlikely sets of circumstances, not only that richer and poorer countries can always continue to trade to their mutual advantage but also that, among the richer countries themselves, specialisation of production is so highly developed that the very richest and the not quite so rich will always be in a position to raise each other's standard of living. If you are suspicious of the truisms of economic science I can put it in this way: in the last quarter of a century the best customers of every industrial country have been the other industrial countries.

2. Government sponsorship or market decisions?

I have digressed here because fundamentally I think the preoccupation of British governments with high technology is due to an almost neurotic reaction to the fear that other countries and governments are treading on our heels or have indeed actually surpassed us and that our only answer is to belt on even more rapidly with high technology to catch up with those in front or to escape from those who pursue.

Now, of course, any country will be better off if it becomes more lively and energetic in technical matters that have profitable commercial uses. But that is an answer to a question which is not relevant. The relevant questions here are two. Is it true that success in high technology industries is the widest and most open gateway to economic success – especially where it comes to ability to export? And even if it were, are governments, and government agencies, the bodies best fitted to pick their way to success among the infinite uncertainties and complexities in the world of high technology. Which is the best way of picking the winners, leaving it to governments or leaving it to private effort and the market?

Which horses to flog?

Some extremely interesting statistical investigations bearing upon the first of these questions have been carried out recently, some of the best by the National Economic Development Office.[2] Thus it can be asked, which products are growing most quickly in world trade? The answer is that they are not products found wholly or even mainly among the high-technology commodities. The front runners in fact are furs and fur clothing; watches and clocks; footwear; musical instruments and sound recorders; office machines; organic chemicals; scientific instruments and furniture. Similarly, the tentative efforts made to identify those products in which the UK has revealed its highest comparative advantages in world trading do not suggest that the high-technology goods have been the leaders. Of course these statistical exercises cannot be conclusive although they may well expose palpable mis-statements of fact. In trying to interpret them it must always be remembered that what has happened in the past may not happen in the future. And also, that when a government sets out to tone up an industrial system it never really knows where to start. Should it try to stimulate the already progressive industries – which might turn out to be a policy of flogging to death horses already putting their best foot forward. Or should it set out to help the industries which are lagging behind – which might prove to be a policy of flogging horses virtually already dead. But the figures suggest that economic prosperity at least for Britain is more likely to come from producing the mundane rather than too much of the airy-fairy stuff.

Public policy, for better or worse, must be based on qualitative judgements. I do not think we are ever likely to find immutable laws here. It is easy enough to suggest that since governments tend to stand for control and uniformity and lack imagination they will suffer from a blind dread of innovation. Instances can be provided in support of this idea. It would be just as easy to spin the opposite theory that, possessed of the taxpayer's money and seeking for political kudos wherever it was to be found, governments will strike out recklessly along unknown paths. We must try to determine which is the more likely in our times and our surroundings.

Sources of innovation

It is worthwhile pointing out that the idea that governments have an increasingly important and effective part to play in stimulating the highly innovating industries is somewhat paradoxical. For in the last fifteen years a good deal of academic research has been carried out into innovation in private industry. Two conclusions, as a result, are by now I think widely accepted. One is that innovation does not flow wholly, or even mainly, from the largest corporations. The very size of a corporation may make it in some ways a centre of resistance to change. The other is that some of the largest corporations are themselves recognising that to force the pace too rapidly in the search for new things can be a business mistake, leading to losses and a lack of balance of effort among the many activities of a company. But if all this is established for private effort, why should it be taken for granted that governments, the largest of all institutions, should not suffer from the same inherent disabilities of size?

The obvious fears of statesmen in these days that technical advance in civil industries will not be fast enough without massive government intervention have many sources. Politicians personally often appear to be fascinated by the more dazzling technical devices which make the headlines in the newspapers. Lord Beeching has commented that: 'I think [the British Government] has wasted an enormous amount of money on things justified by the pursuit of advanced technology – an almost childlike desire to play with toys'.[3]

National prestige

Beyond that it is often claimed that national independence and prestige depend upon spectacular successes in technology. This, of course, is not a new story. Lenin once said that communism equals the political preponderance of the proletariat plus electricity. This same kind of argument has carried force in the western world. President de Gaulle, who could always express in the noblest language even the dottiest of economic ideas, spoke of the need 'to push relentlessly our technical and scientific research in order to avoid sinking into a bitter mediocrity or being colonised by the activities, inventions and capacities of other countries'. British statesmen have not been altogether immune. A former Prime Minister once spoke of the 'white heat' of a scientific revolution. One Minister of Technology became almost incandescent at the thought of the technical miracles to come. It all adds substance to the unkind comment that high technology is 'the last refuge of the enthusiastic nationalist'. This approach is really not good for sober commercial calculations.

One result of all this is the ready way in which British governments in recent years have fallen victim to what can be described as the hocus-pocus of discussion on technology. Ministers, in the face of the evidence, have clung to the ideas that innovation comes mainly from large organisations; or that there is a correlation between expenditure on research and development and national economic growth; or that the country is confronted with a disastrous brain-drain. And it is still being claimed that we live in a period of exceptionally rapid technical progress and one in which the time elapsing between invention and application tends to get shorter whereas it seems to be true that ours is really an epoch of comparative technological sluggishness when there are not very many authentically new things about and even these, for many different reasons, are being developed rather slowly. (How much longer, for example, will we have to wait for efficient battery-operated motor-cars which will enable the pounding, smelly reciprocating engine to be thrown on the scrap-heap; or the typewriter which will type as one dictates, which will release hundreds of thousands of young women for other more interesting tasks; or audio-visual cassettes which will enable us to break away from the tyranny and the interminable boredom of modern television; or a cure for the common cold; or much cheaper and efficient ways of digging tunnels so that the surface of the earth could be reoccupied by the people instead of being over-run by machines; or really substantial cuts in costs of de-salinisation rendering it possible to turn deserts into gardens. This list could easily be extended.)

So we find major decisions being made by statesmen because they feel in their bones, or if you will pardon the vulgarity, they have a 'gut feeling' that this or that course is correct. I do not wish to press this point too hard. After all, innovation mainly comes from discarding preconceived ideas. As Sir Denning Pearson has said, 'Anyone who undertakes the development of an engine like the RB-211 must be an optimist.'[4] But there is or should be this difference between private and public effort. With private effort the glitter of all things bright and beautiful is toned down by the shadow of the balance sheet and the possibility of bankruptcy. But with governments the sky gleams brighter longer.

Independent advice?
As main agents in innovation governments will always have difficulty in obtaining sound, independent advice. If the British Government, for example, is interested in the potentialities of a new British aero-engine, whom can it consult? Only Rolls-Royce, which can be expected to look upon the sunny side of doubt, or one of its active competitors in other countries which can be expected to be biased in the other direction. If the Government is interested in a new British aircraft, there are now only two British companies; is the one to be consulted about the soundness of the views of the other? With nuclear energy, of course, the Government has been its own agent for research and development. The Atomic Energy Authority has been virtually the sole judge of progress and possibilities on matters where its own standing and

existence have been at stake. It is, therefore, not surprising that so many mistakes in prognostication have been made, nearly all on the same side. The Atomic Energy Authority has provided for governments a series of predictions always over-optimistic, regarding the speed with which technical problems will be overcome, the costs of development programmes, the price at which electricity will be available and the extent to which nuclear energy would replace other forms of energy.[5] Its current calculations and predictions seem no less sanguine. As for the Concorde, the British Government entered into a binding agreement with the French Government with imprecise knowledge of the probable cost – which has in fact increased from £150 million to £1,000 million.

Government, of course, may take the advice of outside consultants, but these can rarely if ever possess anything more than a limited knowledge of all the commercial and technical circumstances of the case. Or it may set up, in its own Departments, groups of technical experts. But this doubling up of staff must add to costs and sometimes leads, as I will try to show in a moment, to officials defending government schemes in which they can have very little confidence.

But what of the Treasury? Cannot these highly trained and experienced officials be regarded as a solid long-stop on these occasions? Fortunately we have, in the Report from the Expenditure Committee, a most illuminating, although perhaps not surprising, account of the manner in which the Treasury operates in such cases, evidence indeed which deserves to be more widely and carefully read than has apparently been so up to now. As I interpret it, it amounts to a statement that Treasury controls can operate only within very wide margins. Officials can inject into deliberations and decisions what they regard as 'an appropriate degree of scepticism'. They know that in these affairs of high technology estimates always suffer from the same complaint – they are always too optimistic. But the limitation of Treasury control was well put in the evidence:

> . . . *over the years we have come to apply a discount factor, . . . to all technical advice we are given. When any scientist tells us that such and such a thing can be done within x years, we probably say 2x; and if the technicians say the cost will be y millions, we probably say 5y millions. This is a sort of rule of thumb, pure experience.* . . .[6]

This is all highly reminiscent of my own experience in war-time when I was concerned with the planning of the aircraft programme and when, in the exigencies of those times, we were forced to engage in wild guessing and often to rely upon our own judgements of the value of the estimates being set before us by aircraft manufacturers. But I cannot believe that in peace-time a viable economic system can be operated on the basis of this kind of guesswork, with margins of error of this magnitude.

Good money after bad

Another disability of government is this. With innovation at the high level we are discussing, skill and judgement in withdrawing from untenable situations are just as important as imagination and courage in pushing on under apparently unpromising circumstances. I always think that private industry, and especially the biggest companies within it, has in the past lost a great opportunity of teaching the world what is meant by business enterprise by not telling more openly and fully the stories of their big and costly failures in innovation. There is nothing to be ashamed of here. On the contrary, some of these losses constitute some of the most vivid illustrations of what is meant by risk-taking. But there are good reasons for supposing that governments which embark on high technology will always be in greater danger than private industry of being drawn further and further into fruitless expenditure and under less compulsion to cry off at the right time.

This is not merely because a government by a reversal of policy, and thereby a confession of failure, loses political face; or that it can put its hand into the deepest pocket of all – that of the taxpayers; or that it can often muzzle its critics with the charge that they are smirching the great achievements of their own country. Perhaps more important is the danger of the Government building up implied or expressed obligations difficult or impossible to discard or dishonour. Thus, although it is quite clear that the Government did *not* give an open-ended commitment to Rolls-Royce over the RB-211, yet there can be little doubt from the evidence that both Rolls-Royce and the Lockheed Aircraft Company were disagreeably surprised when, as it was put, the Government 'pulled the carpet from under their feet'. In the case of the Concorde, the fact that a British government had an agreement to collaborate with the French made any reversal of policy even more difficult and complicated. Sometimes the built-in obligations are inescapable. As the case for nuclear energy well illustrates, when Civil Service permanent establishments become too large for their tasks the line of least resistance will naturally be that of trying to make work for redundant staffs.

Problem of continuity

There are other secondary, although by no means minor, reasons why governments are perhaps not very effective agents for high technology enterprises. One is that such projects, by their very nature, can produce results only over a long period, whereas the life of a government is normally short. Continuity may thus be endangered. Another is that when a government does finally reach a point at which a reversal of policy is decided upon, it often moves precipitately, as if to make up for lost time. Some day, I suppose, we will have the results of a full-scale inquest into the Rolls-Royce affair. But, on the basis of the evidence now extant, it is possible to wonder whether Rolls-Royce would not have re-negotiated its contracts more favourably than did the

Government subsequently and whether, indeed, there was any real need to nationalise the company at all.[7]

3. Dangers in government projects

I turn now to two disagreeable dangers, disagreeable in the political and constitutional sense, which may become associated with the kind of government projects I am discussing. The first is the possibility of secrecy in the handling of public funds; the second is that of thrusting upon the shoulders of public servants tasks which may change for the worse the character of the public service itself.

Secrecy
As for secrecy, a revealing case is that of the refusal of officials, of course under instructions from above, to provide a breakdown of the estimated cost of the Concorde which finally led the chairman of the Trade and Industry Sub-Committee of the Expenditure Committee to the sharp comment that: 'I realise the policy is not yours . . . but I think it is the most outrageous example of Parliament being denied information about public expenditure since John Hampden refused to pay ship money. . . .' The curious must turn for details of this case to the Expenditure Report itself.[8] But the outline was this. The Government was in fact regularly informing parliament of its own estimated *total* cost of the Concorde. But it refused to disclose its own estimated costs of the main sections of the work – the airframes, the engines, etc. – carried out by the main contractors. The reason was that in reaching its own estimated total cost it had included estimated costs for the main sections of the work higher than those which had been submitted by the main contractors – that is to say the Government, doubtless embittered by past experiences, had allowed something for contingencies. But why this stratagem? The officials explained that if they had provided the breakdown of their own costings this 'would have weakened the discipline and incentive imposed upon main contractors of trying to complete the programme within their estimates of costs'.

Even so the practice, as the Expenditure Committee pointed out, was questionable in that it involved concealment on the part of the Government. The Committee might have added that the practice was also probably unavailing. It could only have succeeded if the main contractors, already engaged in a highly co-operative task involving day-to-day contacts, could have been prevented from talking to each other about these costs. And as soon as the stratagem was suspected by the main contractors they would, of course, become quite happy to work to the Government's higher cost figures – and the so-called discipline effect would disappear.

Defending the indefensible

The second danger is, I think, more important. If Ministers are to reach important decisions in high technology by 'gut feelings' and if their civil servants are increasingly called upon to defend these policies by rational argument (which we all know they will do because of their strong traditions of loyalty and will do well because of the accumulation of experience and the high competence of the Service), is there not the danger that the whole character of the Service will be adversely affected by having thrust upon it the embarrassing task of defending what is rationally indefensible and known to be such.

References

1. Hereafter referred to as 'The Expenditure Committee'.
2. M. Pavic and A. H. Rajan, *Product Changes in Industrial Countries' Trade: 1955–1968*, NEDO Monograph 2, 1971.
3. The Expenditure Committee, Vol. III, p. 457.
4. The Expenditure Committee, Vol. III, p. 493.
5. Duncan Burn, *The Political Economy of Nuclear Energy*, Research Monograph 9, IEA, 1967.
6. The Expenditure Committee, Vol. II, p. 66.
7. The Expenditure Committee, Vol. III, pp. 483–502: evidence of Sir Denning Pearson and Sir David Huddie.
8. The Expenditure Committee, Vol. III, pp. 588–91.

Monitoring technical projects

The Council for Science and Society

Monitoring

1. The three stages

[. . .] Monitoring is not a simple or uniform operation. Each project
has its own pattern of development, passing through a succession of
stages which demand different modes of monitoring. At the risk of
schematizing and oversimplifying a variety of immensely complicated
cases, we may think of three characteristic stages in the history of
a particular project: (*a*) *Conception;* (*b*) *Decision;* (*c*) *Operation.* The
duties, powers and responsibilities of the monitors must be adapted to
these stages of technological development on which they are designed
to act.

2. The stage of conception

At its beginning a new superstar project is merely an idea. As time
passes, under the influence of events and of people, it becomes a practical
goal for the activities of various organizations and individuals, and the
subject of research, design studies, feasibility report, etc. These processes can cost quite a lot of effort and money; but up to the crucial
moment of deciding to *invest* in the new project (e.g. to build the new
bridge, set up production facilities for the new aircraft, manufacture
and market the new drug), it is all hypothetical, a figment of a corporate
imagination, without substance to do good, or ill.

In this initial stage, the creative innovator must have faith in the
value of his project, and finds it very difficult to be objective in assessing
its practical effects. He starts with an assumption that his conception
will achieve what he claims for it, and also that it will not have any
deleterious consequences that will make its development undesirable.
His assessment is thus inevitably prejudiced.

To counteract such tendencies, the monitors must employ their
creative powers to the full. They should imagine the great variety of
ways in which the proposed innovation can go wrong, technically,
environmentally or socially, both in its original version and its later

Extracts from *Superstar Technologies*, the report of a working party of the Council
for Science and Society, Barry Rose (Publishers) Ltd, 1976.

modifications. This process can go far beyond the limits of the 'reasonable foreseeability' required by law in the assessment of responsibility for damages. Of course, the more unlikely and remote consequences must be recognized as such, and distinguished from those capable of more precise estimation. The latter may usually be the principal points of contention. But a free-ranging inquiry, perhaps even up to the point of science fiction, is necessary for the monitoring at the stage of conception to be fully effective.

This is not to suggest that any reliable forecasting technique is available for forecasting all dangers and difficulties. Our impression *is*, however, that even the crudest prognostications of the social impact of innovations have frequently been neglected. Historical examples may be misleading, but with the benefit of hindsight it seems likely that if this type of forecasting had been a normal procedure during the early development of the motor car, the use of leaded petrol would not have been taken up so freely, and research into electric and other non-polluting motors for cars would have been undertaken much earlier. Nobody could have predicted the actual rate at which motor cars would multiply, but the risks incident on their large-scale might have been identified in time to initiate the research and development of alternative means of transport before the need became desperate.

Imaginative projections and counter-projections by innovators and monitors provide the makings of a creative public controversy. The major goal of technological assessment is not to ensure certainty, but to inspire a conflict of views that will maintain a spirit of healthy self-criticism amongst the innovators. To be effective this process must be as open as possible, with identifiable partisan groups, goaded into serious and rigorous research to defend their position or attack their opponents in a principled debate. In other words, the monitoring operation initiates an *advocacy process*, modelled on the familiar methods by which ordinary scientific knowledge is acquired and consolidated. It is interesting to observe precisely such a process, spilling over into the normal realm of pure, academic science, developing around such questions as the effects of traces of fluorocarbons (used as aerosol propellants) on the ozone layer in the upper atmosphere, or the likelihood of catastophic results from the failure of the pressure vessel surrounding a nuclear reactor. Hypotheses of this kind are just as amenable to scientific discussion and clarification as those that arise, for example, in astrophysics and cosmology.

[. . .] Lest we be misunderstood, we should state explicitly that by 'monitoring' we do not mean 'prevention'. It is always easier to predict simple costs and hazards than to depict complex and uncertain benefits. For some major facilities, as roads, airfields and hazardous factories, there is the danger that residents of *every* possible location will say 'put it somewhere else'. The prospect of lengthy and costly tests and public debates may well discourage innovation in high-technology fields. Of course, some will welcome a deceleration of technological progress; but a tendency to discouragement and stagnation could be very difficult to reverse.[1] If the problem of achieving a right balance of progress and control in technology seems insoluble, we can at least say that it is thereby placed among the genuinely political questions by which society continuously re-defines its goals and values.

3. The stage of decision

Eventually, the design of a project must harden, in preparation for the decision to invest large sums of money. The innovation thus moves into the market place, into the realms of commercial exploitation. But even supposing that it is well established that there are no serious snags that could reasonably be foreseen, the need for monitoring is not finished.

The investment decision is crucial, and involves the balancing of many imponderables – the state of the market, financial resources available, potential gains, risks, and contrary forces. This decision is not normally in the hands of those who have developed the innovation or designed the product, but lies with people such as ministers or company directors who have little or no technical knowledge.

It is essential, therefore, that reliable expert advice is available to the decision-makers – advice that they can ignore only at their peril. At this stage, more than at any other in a technical development, the opinions of experts must be capable of effective and independent expression. All too often, however, the experts with relevant competence are committed to the project, having spent their time hammering out the very design that is now under consideration. This is partly the case in a superstar technological project, such as Concorde, whose conception and development for a long time pre-empted the services of a high proportion of the experts in a major industry in several countries.

The task of providing effective monitoring power at this stage is thus more urgent and more difficult. A deliberate effort must be made to maintain a corps of experts who are not committed to the project, and they must be given sufficient incentive to subject the whole scheme to critical appraisal for its wider, non-commercial, costs and benefits. To counter the interests supporting the project, the monitors are bound to attach themselves to alternative power groups – perhaps the Treasury opposing wasteful government expenditure, or 'public interest' organizations fearful of dangerous side-effects, or those whose personal interests are actively threatened by the innovation as proposed.

At this stage the monitoring process no longer lies in the realm of hypothesis and intellectual debate: it has moved into the political arena. It therefore partly takes the form of a trial of strength between power groups. The experts are caught up in an *adversary process*, which has no counterpart in the gentlemanly world of pure science; even when they do not have long-term personal interests in the outcome of the contest, they often find themselves in an unfamiliar role as *mercenaries* hired to support one or the other party.[2]

Technical adversary processes of this kind are quite novel to the

British governmental system. But in the United States there is already valuable experience of public controversy on technological issues, usually before the 'jury' of a Congressional Committee debating legislation authorizing government funding. Of such controversies, the most constructive example was the historic debate on whether to deploy anti-ballistic missile systems to defend cities. Several highly significant points arise from this case.

The most important point [. . .] is the absolute necessity of assuming an independent power base, entirely outside the government machine, for monitors of technical projects arising within the executive branches of the government. Technological monitoring demands as many safeguards from the pressure of other interested parties as does the administration of justice. It is equally important that the price of these safeguards be recognized, namely that this monitoring be concentrated on wider, non-commerical costs of a project. Without such a restriction, the standing and credibility of any such external monitoring agency could quickly be destroyed.

4. The stage of operation

[. . .] The need for technological monitoring certainly does not cease when the innovatory project has come into operation. Indeed it is misleading to imagine that the earlier stages of the innovatory process come to an end: technological change is highly dynamic, with new and larger models, new design concepts, wider applications, etc. following hard on each other's heels. The history of the development of the jet engine, for example, shows a succession of new concepts and increases of scale within rapidly changing economic and social contexts. Social and environmental problems such as airport noise may increase in scale even more dramatically, so that by the time they are recognized they are fated to be intense and insoluble for years to come.

But the monitoring of ongoing operations, such as industrial factory production, puts somewhat different demands on the organization. The conjectural elements in the situation have resolved themselves into the material reality. The need for imaginative projection into an unknown future is largely replaced by the apparently safe routine of methodical and meticulous performance of such mundane tasks as inspecting factory premises, checking air and water for pollution, testing food and drugs for dangers to health, etc. But the questions that arise in this practice may not always be simple and factual. Genuinely acceptable limits of concentration of toxic chemicals, cannot be automatically decided from test data. Animal studies are of dubious relevance, and epidemiological data may be scanty or absent until irreparable harm has been done. The criteria of 'acceptability' to which monitors must work may be frequently based on uncertain scientific results, and influenced by institutional and political factors. Even some great victories of monitoring, such as the nearly complete exclusion of thalidomide from the USA, may on close inspection be revealed as due more to luck and muddle than to sharp-eyed vigilance in the agency.[3]

Even when a monitoring agency has discovered a serious risk being imposed on society, its real work has only begun. The costs of change to a firm are no longer hypothetical losses of profit on a projected innovation; there are enormous hard-cash expenditures involved in, say, recalling 100,000 motor vehicles with dangerously defective brakes, or building a complete new plant to separate trace chemicals from effluents, or closing down a hydro-electric generating station and draining a lake because of cracks in the dam. Although a clear public statement of the existence of these dangers has some power to get them put right, experience has shown that an offending organization is not always blessed with a strong conscience, and may delay voluntary action far beyond the point where serious damage is already being caused. The abolition of private industry does not eliminate such problems, as we see from the pollution of Lake Baikal and the Caspian Sea;[4] and the Chinese mount propaganda campaigns for environmental responsibility among possibly polluting industries, basing their argument mainly on thrift.

It is clear that monitoring at the stage of operation must be carried out by organizations with legal authority to ensure compliance with their edicts. Advocacy and adversary processes must now give way to *coercive processes*. The monitoring organization must be strong and single-minded, able to resist a variety of sources of corruption. In practice, only the authority of the state in the form of Acts of Parliament, defining and prescribing the powers of inspectorates and other administrative organs, are adequate to the task. But as in any other state agency, legal powers are not enough to ensure good work; public accountability, individually and collectively, for monitors and their organizations should be as firm a principle here as elsewhere in the public service.

These needs have long been recognized, and monitors in the form of public health authorities, quarantine authorities, factory inspectorates, etc. are part of the ordinary administrative machinery of modern government in all civilized countries. The main problem is to recognize quickly the potential dangers of innovatory techniques (e.g. the use of X-ray machines for fitting footwear) and to bring regulatory machinery into action before the damage occurs. Independent initiatives are essential here. Only those very close to a process can see when it is just starting to go wrong; the workman or maintenance man may be the only one with a sufficiently early warning to avert disaster. Monitoring agencies must therefore earn the confidence of operatives in their effectiveness and integrity [. . .]. Achieving this may well conflict with the other interests and pressures affecting the agency. The weakness of governmental action, both in the civil service and the legislature, is the lack of sensitive devices for detecting the symptoms of damage before they become grave and scandalous. This is where other monitoring institutions, including enlightened individuals, can play a most important part, by drawing public attention to signs of danger.

Monitoring agencies

1. Agencies and fora
[. . .] We have seen how every technical project passes through distinct stages of development, affecting different groups of people, and requiring different modes of monitoring. Each mode in turn involves its own sorts of agencies for the monitoring operations, and also an appropriate forum for airing disagreements. Here we review these agencies and fora, to ascertain how they may be most usefully improved and made accountable to the public at large or to a superior decision-making body.

2. Countervailing agencies
[. . .] The unforeseen costs and dangers arising from a technical innovation fall mainly upon persons outside the innovating organization. It is in the interests of such persons to monitor the innovation, and to minimize these dangers. The rapid growth of countervailing monitoring agencies, such as consumer and amenity defence groups, is a recent phenomenon of great significance in the social control of advanced technology.

The insurers of technical projects and products have a high stake in the prevention of expensive failures or disasters. The growth of a very effective monitoring operation out of this financial incentive is exemplified by the history of Lloyd's Shipping Register, which has had a decisive influence, over a very long time, on the safe design and operation of most ships. Industries threatened by an innovation have their own stake.

Some organizations with a scientific concern, rather than a purely local interest, do make important technical contributions to debates on policy questions. In this country there have been Friends of the Earth and the International Institute for Environment and Development on energy questions, as well as the groups specially concerned with transport, such as the Independent Commission on Transport[5] and the doughty Anti-Concorde Project. In America there are more local groups of scientists, affiliated with the Scientists' Institute for Public Information, that provide information and testimony on public-interest problems.[6]

A broader, much more diffuse interest group is the general public, as consumers of new products, or as residents of a neighbourhood whose amenities are likely to be damaged by a large new project. In theory, all such interests are protected by a benevolent local or national government; in practice, the Lord helps those who help themselves by associating in voluntary organizations to fight for their interests. Local and general associations for environmental protection now play an important, sometimes decisive, part in monitoring technical change.

In conflict with a voluntary public interest group, the protagonists of a technical innovation usually have great advantages of coherence, single-mindedness, professional and commercial incentives, and very large resources of expertise, advocacy and, above all, money. Public interest groups are often weak in organization, short of money, inexperienced, and amateurish in technical skills. But where such groups represent the only consistent open opposition to a major project (for example, where governmental agencies have already been persuaded by the projectors) they can be decisive in initiating a public adversary process that brings to light significant defects in the plan. The history of the opposition to the plans for a third London airport perfectly illustrates this point. It is thus a wise general policy to give such groups an opportunity to be heard early and to provide them with the means to employ technical experts and legal representatives of the highest calibre.

If countervailing monitoring by public interest groups is to be effective, it must rest upon sound foundations of knowledge about technical issues among a broad segment of the population. 'Participatory technology' may not yet be very effective as a monitoring force, but the term hints at the importance of disseminating information and education about technology beyond the elite of professional experts. The recent Swedish consultations on nuclear power were an interesting exercise in this direction. Unfortunately the British Trades Unions locally and nationally have been far behind those of many other countries in initiating studies of technological matters, even where the interests of their members are directly involved. However, the opportunities created by the Health and Safety at Work, etc. Act 1974 have been appreciated by some unions here, so we may see a change for the better.

3. In what forum?

If a countervailing agency is to be effective as a monitor, it must have a forum in which to act. In some instances – for example, where dangerous defects in consumer goods are brought to light – the publicity of an adverse comment in the mass media is enough to ensure compliance. There was a time, in Britain, when publication of honest reports on consumer goods was gravely inhibited by the fear of legal proceedings from aggrieved manufacturers. That fear would now seem to have receded in the private sector, but something like a Public Information Act to unveil the activities of officials in the public sector is still needed to ensure effective monitoring there.

In Britain the courts of law do not provide any convenient means for the challenging of technical innovations and projects. Experience in the United States has shown that while the courts are still far from ideal, American traditions and practices permit them to be used effectively (by organizations such as the Environmental Defence Fund) in the monitoring of both the stages of decision and of operation. Voluntary groups there can use the device of a class action suit on behalf of a population defined only by its being injured; and their lawyers can hope to recoup expenses from the sometimes considerable damages that are awarded. Here we have neither class action suits, awards-sharing between client and lawyers, nor the prospect of large damages. Even our statutory monitoring agencies have been effectively deterred from taking flagrant cases to court by the derisory penalties available (though this is now changing). Voluntary groups have only a few isolated bases for legal action, and a very thin tradition of work in this field. Further studies of possibilities in the legal system might reveal many unsuspected methods. For example, the prerogative order of *mandamus*, now increasingly used to require social service agencies to fulfil their statutory obligations, might be tested in a case against a lax inspectorate.

The most usual open forum for an investment decision is a special tribunal or statutory inquiry established to deal with particular types of controversial development, such as a motorway project. It must be admitted that amenity issues that have to be decided in such fora are not normally technological, and the procedures are seldom well adapted to an adversary process involving technical experts. Indeed, for the long-term purposes of monitoring – i.e. eventually arriving at the optimal balance between safety, social benefit and social cost – these procedures are very defective since they must concentrate on the decision to go ahead with the particular scheme proposed by the developers, rather than opening public discussion on the aims of the scheme as a whole, and the potentialities of alternative designs. Here again, there is much scope for further study on needs and procedures.

Traditionally the final arbiter in all such controversies has been Parliament, though here, more than in many areas, sovereignty will be shared with the European Economic Commission. But there will still be a role for Parliament as a watchdog, where questions must be answered by the executive, and evasions or prevarications are on the record, liable to be eventually exposed. The seething controversy over the nuclear power programme, with particular reference to the safety and economy of alternative reactor systems, was not brought out into the open until the matter was taken up by the Commons Select Committee on Science and Technology. US experience with Congressional Committees favours a considerable extension of this practice as a forum for major controversies about technological projects. Although the procedures of such committees may often appear cumbersome, the fact that the members of the committee are laymen, and that they have the power to call for expert evidence from a diversity of sources, is appropriate to the needs of the occasion. It is well worth noting, incidentally, that the US Office of Technological Assessment (OTA) is conceived as an arm of Congress, providing it with the expertise to face up to the immense resources of executive agencies in conflicts over monitoring.[7]

4. Government monitors

[. . .] As the guardian of the national interest, and the protector of the people, the governmental apparatus is deeply involved in all aspects of technological monitoring. Through its research institutions, public services and nationalized industries, the state machine is in at the conception of most superstar projects. The investment decision usually involves a high proportion of public money and is subject to political considerations such as national prestige, foreign earnings, and employment prospects (*vide* Concorde). Monitoring of on-going production is almost entirely in the hands of the government inspectorates. [. . .] In principle a government monitoring agency should have no difficulty in providing itself with adequate resources and expertise. In practice, a career as a full-time civil servant does not always attract the most brilliant and resourceful engineers and applied scientists. The qualities of critical imagination and of multi-disciplinary experience that are particularly important in monitoring at the stage of conception are often seriously lacking in a bureaucratic agency with routine tasks. Recruitment of the best people is not helped by the continuing impression that the highest positions, even in monitoring agencies, go to 'generalists' rather than to technically qualified men. We should beware of a situation developing here, in which the firms being monitored can simply buy superior technical talent for frustrating the intentions of the state monitoring agencies in every dialogue or confrontation.

A government monitoring agency certainly has the power to demand all the information it wants – although such demands are often resisted in the name of commercial secrecy. The constraints of internal confidentiality imposed by the Official Secrets Acts hamper the workings of the official monitors themselves; they cannot act against abuse simply by publishing it, and even where they have a strong case for positive action, they are unable to enhance their credibility by publishing all the evidence. Although the legal situation is now changing rapidly for the better, it will still require strong pressures from countervailing agencies to change ingrained habits and attitudes.

Any bureaucracy easily becomes self-contained and self-sufficient. It is seldom in close touch with the needs and opinions of the man in the street. A research sociologist in the Department of the Environment does not necessarily know as much about what people want from their vehicles as an experienced second-hand car salesman or traffic warden. In the words of Harold P. Green, 'Technological assessment is therefore likely to boil down to what the experts think should be exacted from the public in that the public will have the benefits that the experts think it should have.'[8]

The most serious weakness of government monitoring agencies is their possible lack of institutional independence and public accountability. As we have said, the government is itself a party to many large-scale projects and technical innovations. The dangers and defects of internal monitoring are inherent in the situation. One test of the quality of a government's commitment to the ideals of a monitoring system is the strength and protection it builds into the constitution of an agency. As an elementary step, the functions of promoting an industry must be kept quite separate from those of regulating it. This principle should be used as a basic criterion in the assessment of every monitoring agency.

The government machine is, of course, so enormous and disjointed that it must contain within itself fierce clashes of opinion and interest. To some extent, the views of, say, the Departments of the Environment and Energy counteract the enthusiasms of the Department of Trade and Industry for the development of a supersonic aircraft. The controversies that rage through Whitehall, the ebb and flow of inter-departmental battle, the famous victories, the successful generals – all this is well known to the reader of quality newspapers, political memoirs or semi-fictional novels. A high-level committee meeting may be the setting for a genuine adversary process, where advocates of conflicting policies contend for the support of a less-expert majority. But the conflicts go on behind closed doors, and the final decision, by a minister, or by the Cabinet itself, need not be justified publicly by reference to all the available evidence. Indeed the convention is that there should be no indication of the fact of the conflict.[9] Once the decision has been made, every effort is made to supress contrary views (e.g. of independent consultants in confidential reports) in the name of political coherence, party unity, the independence and integrity of the civil service, and other such shibboleths. The monitoring process – which certainly should not stop with each 'irrevocable' investment decision – is thus gravely hampered by a blanket of silence imposed on all potential critics. This is very evident in the story of Concorde.

In America, traditionally a society with fewer long-lived official secrets than our own, the principle of advisers' confidentiality has been effectively breached. The crucial incident was the anti-ballistic missile debate between 1967 and 1969.[10] In September 1967, the US Secretary of Defence announced that the US would employ an anti-ballistic missile system. In August 1969, responding to extensive lobbying in opposition to this proposal, half the Senate voted against it, agreeing instead only to the protection of a few American missile sites, rather than whole cities. In the period 1945–66 Congress had never challenged the executive on any military expenditure. Not only was the success of the opposition unprecedented, so also was the role of scientists, both inside government and outside. For, perhaps stung by such taunts as 'Inside advisers are prostitutes', the opposition group of insiders carried their debate out to Congress and to the public. One very senior leader expressed the principle 'To support whatever the administration does, right or wrong, violates the code of conduct for government employees.' He felt responsible to Congress as well as to the executive, whose professional adviser he was. The dilemma was not new, but its resolution was. By distinguishing between his personal views and the specific opinions he had been asked to tender to the executive, he had felt able to inform Senators and Congressmen of his own views, without revealing what had been his confidential advice to the administration. This became a firmly established distinction. Could such a distinction and the behaviour which follows from it become accepted in the United Kingdom? Certainly pressures for this kind of attitude are bound to increase even here; the question is whether the relaxation of restrictions in an orderly manner will be prevented by civil service secretiveness, by Parliament's reluctance to give its select committees real teeth. We may need to wait for a major scandal or disaster to give the integrity of 'inside' experts a chance to operate.

References

1. J. Freeman Dyson, 'The hidden cost of saying no', *Bulletin of the Atomic Scientists*, June 1975, Vol. 31. No. 6, p. 23.
2. S. A. Lakoff, *Scientists and the Adversary Process*, Draft presented at the Annual Meeting of the American Political Science Association, Chicago, Illinois.
3. James Turner, *The Chemical Feast*, Grossman, 1970, pp. 220 ff.
4. Jon Tinkler, 'What's happening to Lake Baikal?' *New Scientist*, Vol. 14, June 1973, pp. 694–5; M. I. Golman, *Spoils of Progress*, MIT Press, 1972.
5. *Changing Directions—A Report from the Independent Commission on Transport*, Coronet Books, London, 1974.
6. 'Science information groups', *Environment*, Vol. 17, No. 5, July/Aug. 1975, p. 16.
7. *Technology: Process of Assessment and Choice*, (Report of the National Academy of Sciences), US Government Printing Office, 1969.
8. Harold P. Green, 'Taking to the courts' (A review of *Defending the Environment*, by Joseph L. Sax), *Science*, Vol. 172, 1971, p. 48.
9. *Attorney-General* v. *Jonathan Cape & Others*, The Times, 2.10.1975.
10. Anne H. Cahn, 'American Scientists and the ABM: a case study in controversy', in A. M. Teich (ed.), *Scientists and Public Affairs*, MIT Press, 1974, pp. 39–120.

Legal frameworks for the assessment and control of technology

Laurence H. Tribe

Too often scientists and students of science policy have reviewed the law as a rather trivial affair, embodying little more than a glorified system of traffic regulations designed to avert intolerable congestion and collision. Any such view is, of course, a vast oversimplification, for legal processes and institutions have always offered a far richer and subtler set of choices than the 'traffic control' model suggests. It is the law, after all, that furnishes much of the architecture for such complex and varied social edifices as those of marriage, economic partnership, personal privacy and representative government. As such examples illustrate, law may operate not only negatively, by promulgating and enforcing the various constraints which serve as the 'ground rules' of social interaction, but also positively, by facilitating or expressing human relationships and aspirations, or by defining powers and establishing offices. Indeed law, broadly conceived, spans the full range of deliberate arrangements by which men may seek to implement or to embody the many values that matter to them.

Two cultures: science and law

Perhaps because few scientists or technologists have had much occasion to view law in this broader perspective, they have been largely unaware of the central role it must play in any effort to influence the development of science and of science-based technology in humane directions – an ironic failing, inasmuch as this is an enterprise for which increasingly influential segments of the scientific community have come to feel a special responsibility.

At the same time, otherwise sensitive lawyers and legal scholars have typically perceived their professional roles in terms likely to exclude much concern for the social direction of scientific and technical development, treating such subjects as mysterious specialities outside their central competence. Yet it is the law in its commonest manifestations which, however inadvertently, supplies much of the context within which

Extracts from Laurence H. Tribe, 'Legal frameworks for the assessment and control of technology', *Minerva*, Oct. 1971, pp. 243–55.

research and development are encouraged, permitted, or inhibited. And it is the law which forms a large part of the framework through which the fruits of such scientific and technical endeavours are disseminated or suppressed, and in terms of which the costs and benefits of their effects are distributed. Legal structures of rights and responsibilities designed with wholly different ends in mind will thus influence the evolution and shape the consequences of science and technology – unless those who contribute to the design of such legal structures direct their attention to these issues in a timely way.

What emerges is a new sort of gap between the 'two cultures' – between scientists and technologists unaware of the great significance of law to their most humane aspirations, and lawyers unaware of the profound impact on science and technology of their most familiar tools. At their best, those tools might be used to mould the role of science in society in creative human directions, but no such achievement is likely unless efforts are made to bridge the gap described here. This article represents one tentative effort in that direction. My aim, more precisely, is to explore in a preliminary way the question of how an enlightened society should use the legal process to influence the development and application of science-based technology.

As my starting point, I take the recent report to the United States Congress by the National Academy of Sciences' Technology Assessment Panel,[1] on which I served as executive director. Beginning with an awareness of the mounting concern over society's inability to direct technological developments along paths sufficiently responsive to the broad range of human needs, our panel undertook to identify the most critical deficiencies in the many processes of assessment and decision-making, both private and public, that influence the evolution of technology in our society. We asked ourselves how society might best begin a task we recognised to be extremely difficult – that of modifying those processes so that they reflect a greater sensitivity to the widely ramified effects of technological choices on the human environment. To that end, we looked for ways to increase the likelihood that such choices would be informed by a more complete understanding of their second- and third-order consequences, and would be guided by criteria which reflect such consequences in a more timely and systematic way. And we asked how society might accomplish those objectives without denying itself the benefits that continuing technological progress has to offer, especially to the less-favoured portions of society and mankind in general.

Within this framework, we found that existing mechanisms, whether they involve public agencies or private groups, possess intrinsic limitations, some structural in origin but others psychologically determined, which leave serious gaps in the range of processes assessing and directing the development of technology in society. In formulating issues for assessment and in defining the costs and benefits of alternative outcomes, those assessments too often overlook or undervalue the broader contexts in which their indirect effects are felt. In calculating gains and losses, they give too little weight to the preservation of future options and the avoidance of irreversible consequences. They pay insufficient attention and give inadequate support to research and monitoring programmes designed to minimise technological surprise and calculated to deal more rationally with the burdens of uncertainty. And they frequently reflect the interests of unduly narrow constituencies, creating insufficient opportunities for beneficial public participation in choices generating major public consequences.

Realising that difficulties so pervasive could not be overcome at a single stroke, we were nonetheless persuaded that they could gradually be reduced by a programme of technology assessment broader in scope and conception than any currently in existence. We concluded that such a programme would have to include a constellation of new institutions within the United States Government, charged with the responsibility of reviewing, integrating and improving the government's own procedures of technological assessment and choice, but we neither contemplated nor foresaw a highly centralised process of technological evaluation, much less of technological regulation, even for those areas of technology largely dependent upon federal programmes and policies. On the contrary, we concluded that it will remain both necessary and desirable to rely primarily on a pluralistic distribution of responsibilities for technological assessment and decision-making, and that the major problem is to enhance the quality of such assessment and decision-making wherever it occurs.

The nature of the legal challenge

[. . .] The task of designing a suitable system of technological decision-making is critical even for those who seek solutions in centralisation rather than in pluralism, because in no society can the currently fragmented processes of technological assessment and choice be integrated in the foreseeable future into anything resembling a unitary decision-making system. At least for a substantial period, it will therefore be essential to improve the effectiveness of those fragmented processes at each point in the system where they occur – and that task will invariably entail re-examining and perhaps redesigning the legal structures by which those processes are shaped.

Because of the remote systemic effects and synergistic interactions that characterise much of contemporary technology and its effects, there is lacking here the neat, one-to-one correspondence between acts and consequences which might otherwise make it possible for us to achieve our purposes simply by attaching sanctions to clearly definable conduct demonstrably responsible for specifically designated categories of unwanted results. Furthermore, the conduct to be dealt with here is intimately bound up with socially useful activity; the undesirable effects of technological development are ordinarily the indirect consequences of activities which benefit, and are desired by, large numbers of individuals. They are not commonly the direct effects of intentionally antisocial actions. The objective of any policy of control over technological development will typically be not the complete termination of an activity but its modification or quantitative reduction.

Little consensus is possible as to the specific objectives to be sought or the concrete consequences to be avoided with respect to technological change and its effects. For this reason, and for the further reason that much of what is required entails increased levels of basic scientific research and monitoring, law must operate here not merely to impose precise constraints but to elicit a rich pattern of affirmative responses. The most traditional of all legal techniques to induce modified behavior, that of the criminal prohibition, will therefore be of little use here. For criminal sanctions are workable only when we can define in advance and in highly specific terms the precise conduct we wish to prohibit, and when that conduct creates a clear and present threat of tangible harm to some victim who will be in a position to complain. Neither of these conditions is likely to be met in technology assessment.

Three models of legal control

The various legal methods which are appropriate to the task of influencing technological development can usefully be divided into three partially overlapping categories:

1. Issuing specific directives
I have in mind the governmental determination of one or more of the precise steps to be taken in the course of research, development, and/or final application of a technological process – ranging from complete government ownership of the process to ordinary administrative regulation of private activity.

2. Modifying market incentives
Included here are all deliberate modifications of the market within which decisions about the development or utilisation of a particular technological process are taken – by techniques ranging from the creation of prior rights to enjoin a particular development, to the enforcement of subsequent rights to be compensated for the damages it has caused and to the imposition of taxes measured by the marginal amount of such damages, to the disbursement of public subsidies.

3. Changing decision-making structures
This category includes all alterations in the composition, powers, or obligations of those organisations which make the basic decisions with respect to an area of technological development or application, be they

private corporations, professional associations, public agencies or other institutions.

Each of these three basic ways in which law can be employed to influence the decision-making environment of technological processes possesses its own characteristic capacities and limitations – as does each sub-type within any of the three categories. Such work as has been undertaken on each of these forms of legal control has tended to ask simply how that particular form might be exploited – without seriously investigating what general principles, if any, might characterise the fields of technology, or the social purposes, for which the form in question is best (or least) suited. Without some attempt to identify such principles, there can be little hope of developing workable criteria for matching specific classes of problems and/or particular sets of objectives with the most appropriate legal strategies, and of arriving at relevant and consistent standards by which the suitability of various strategies might be tested and compared. My immediate purpose, therefore, is to begin this needed exploration.

Comparing the three models when the objective is optimal resource allocation

I should like to organise my analysis around the kinds of objectives at which legal control of technological development might aim. The most traditional of those objectives, certainly, is the encouragement of technological choices (and social choices related to technology) which do not interfere with optimal resource allocation, in its broadest possible sense. A central aim of pollution control, for example, must always be the deployment of physical, environmental and other resources – manpower, minerals, clean air, quiet – so as to yield the largest aggregate quantity of human satisfaction over time. When one says that a given technological process creates 'too much pollution', one means in these economic terms that some change in the process making for less pollution, some altered deployment of resources, could yield a net increase in human satisfaction. Ideally, the technological process should be 'cleansed' just to the point at which any further antipollution effort would cost more in other satisfactions foregone than it would be worth. To alter the technology beyond that point would result in a net loss.

The classic legal approach in this sort of situation, when law has intervened at all, has been the first model – that of issuing specific directives, usually in the form of administrative orders, to abate pollution in a designated way. For several reasons, however, this approach tends to be ill-suited to the objective of an optimal allocation of resources. First, there are typically too many individuals and groups whose actions must be closely controlled if an optimum is thereby to be achieved. Second, the framing of sensible directives of this general type presupposes the gathering of enormous quantities of information, usually available only to the addressees of such directives, who have every incentive to withhold it. Third, there is ordinarily no feasible way to modify such directives successively as reactions to them are evaluated. And fourth, unless the relevant technology is atypically stagnant, any detailed directives are likely to become obsolete almost as soon as they take effect – if not sooner.

In such circumstances, one may properly expect greater success with either the second model or the third. As to the second, that of modifying market incentives, the central idea is to create or simulate a regime of exchange, so that otherwise unpriced interests or resources threatened by a technological development – clean air, quiet, privacy – will receive due weight in whatever decisions are made with respect to the technology. For example, when one is dealing with a technological process in which the radius of impact in space and time is very limited, one might try to create a 'market system' by compelling all those who would benefit from the technological process in question to enter into prior arrangements with those who would be adversely affected by its application, the former purchasing in advance the right to damage certain interests of the latter. To achieve this objective, one would confer upon those interests, such as the interest in quiet, the status of prior 'rights', whether of property or of person, forbid unauthorised invasions of such rights, and enforce the prohibition by making its transgression punishable as a crime and perhaps also by empowering courts to enjoin threatened transgressions under penalty of further criminal sanctions.[2] This is what most societies typically do with respect to a small set of interests thought to require protection from all unendorsed invasion, even at the cost of giving each individual on whom the rights are conferred a potential veto over any activity which threatens violation. Whether one is dealing with a technological process as simple as that of cattle-grazing or one as complex as that of computerised information processing, the law can create a market by 'creating rights' – in the former case, by defining the 'property' rights of the owner of a field so as to incorporate a power to exclude uninvited cattle-grazers; in the latter case, by defining the 'personal' rights of the subject of an information system so as to incorporate a power to exclude uninvited users and unauthorised uses of 'private' data.[3]

The goal of forcing technology into a regime of exchange through an enforceable system of prior rights might, however, prove unattainable or inappropriate for a variety of reasons. Perhaps the affected individuals have not yet been born, or are impossible to identify in advance, or are so situated as to make an effective network of binding agreements too expensive to procure. Or perhaps the creation of prior rights of the required sort would confer excessive power upon their possessors, as in the case of a right of any single individual to insist in advance upon complete silence or upon a completely 'pure' atmosphere. In all these situations, the modification of market incentives must proceed not by actually creating a regime of exchange but by simulating the effects of such a regime through a system of liabilities, taxes, or subsidies.

Consider, for example, the case of a noisy machine in an otherwise quiet area. To give each individual within hearing range of the machine an absolute right to stop its operation would ordinarily be indefensible; but to require the machine's operator or manufacturer to compensate any such individual for the net amount by which the noise is found to have damaged him would ordinarily create the appropriate economic incentive for the development of noise-reducing technology, and would do so without imposing on any judge or administrator the great burden of extracting a mass of data from a reluctant enterprise.

It remains true, however, that reliance on voluntary private enforcement of claims to compensation, whether by individuals or in class actions, tends to be ill-suited to technological effects too weakly associated with presently existing and identifiable individuals, or too thinly spread among such individuals, to arouse their organised opposition in a timely way. But it is possible in such cases to alter economic incentives without relying on private litigation at all – for example, by subjecting enterprises employing a given technology (or enterprises responsible for its development) to taxes or other fees roughly equivalent to the marginal damage that use of the technology inflicts. This approach possesses numerous advantages over that of private damage suits. It does not rely on voluntary individual enforcement, and hence is workable for a broader range of technological effects. Being more continuous and predictable than episodic litigation, it is more likely to exert a constructive and timely influence on technological decision-making. In addition, given its automatic character, it is less likely to give rise to efforts to delay or circumvent its operation. Finally, by separating the process of penalising one party from the process of rewarding the other, it makes possible the simultaneous stimulation of both parties to seek damage-reducing alternatives when this is judged to be desirable.

Individual lawsuits, on the other hand, are not without their own compensating advantages. In their attention to the facts of the particular case, they provide a more discriminating and precise tool than the necessarily rough and approximate device of a tax on effluents or on other 'side-effects'. In involving individual litigants, they avoid the need for governmental data-gathering with respect to damages and maximise direct public participation. They assure compensation of injuries which a taxing scheme might leave unredressed; and their dramatic character might make them more useful catalysts for other forms of needed public response.

Ultimately, of course, there will be many situations for which neither actions for compensatory damage nor taxes on 'side-effects' will be appropriate means of attaining an optimal allocation of resources – as when the needed market modification is the internalisation not of costs but of benefits. Thus, when the number of potential beneficiaries of a technologically related development (such as, for example, a completely degradable and non-persistent pesticide) is very large, and when the problem of excluding non-payers from the enjoyment of the benefits is particularly difficult, the developer will invest a less than optimal amount unless government subsidises his undertaking. In such cases, the proper market adjustment will typically be the establishment of substantial economic awards for the socially useful technological development, paralleling the patent system but clearly distinguishable from it.[4]

But one should not assume that some form of market modification is invariably the best approach to chanelling technology in the direction of optimal allocation of resources. The third and final technique involves changing the decision-making structures themselves. A paradigmatic case is the merger of an upstream polluter (public or private) with a downstream user thereby internalising automatically a number of formerly external costs, assuring the consideration of effects that would otherwise have received no weight. But, apart from such relatively local-ised situations as that of a river basin (in which the benefits of combining separate operations under a central authority are likely to outweigh the costs of underspecialisation),[5] the usual possibilites of reorganisa-tion obviously fall short of complete or even partial merger. More typical is the alteration of a corporation's managerial structure – as proposed, for example, by the Campaign for Corporate Responsibility recently directed against General Motors.[6] The potentialities of such devices deserve closer consideration than they have heretofore received.[7]

Comparing the three models when the objective is not optimal allocation of resources

Thus far we have considered only the most elementary type of social objective, that of eliciting efficient patterns of technology-related choice consistent with an optimal allocation of resources. In the typical case, as we have seen, this means the creation of mechanisms to assure that resources such as clear water or silence be preserved from destruction by certain technological processes, up to the point at which the marginal cost of preserving them further would begin to exceed the marginal amount people are willing to pay for their preservation. But as soon as we cease to be bound by the amount people would willingly pay for the preservation of such amenities, we pass beyond the realm of economi-cally efficient resource allocation as a justification for legal intervention.

Among the other justifications which might be advanced, two are particularly significant. The first is the paternalistic justification which rests on such notions as the individual's temporary or permanent in-capacity to perceive and act in his own best interest, or the need to protect the individual in moments of stress, temptation or weak will. The second is the cultural or ethical justification which rests on such concepts as the threat of gradual deformation of the society and its values as a cumulative result of a sequence of voluntary choices.[8]

Justifications of either type might be invoked, for example, to support the view that all individuals should have continuous access to some collectively designated minimum level of, for example, solitude, privacy, autonomy, medical care, individuality, or intellectual activity – notwithstanding any supposed willingness to trade any of these rights, in the face of a technological option, for other valued experiences or objects.[9]

It should be noted that ample precedent exists for legal intervention of this sort. Justifications of the type considered here provide at least one plausible set of explanations for phenomena as diverse as the constitutional prohibition against slavery, the distribution of non-negotiable food stamps, the statutory prohibition against the use of heroin, or the criminal proscription of killing or mutilating a person even with his consent. And in regulating at least one area of technology – that of new drugs – American law has quite explicitly empowered government officials to define a permissible 'trade-off' between beneficial and adverse consequences which no user of the technology, however well informed, is allowed to override.

In many of the available examples of this type, it may be possible to construct a tenable 'efficiency' rationale for legal intervention. Perhaps, for example, the activities and transactions in question are forbidden on the theory that they would not have occurred if all affected individuals, present and future, could decide whether to undertake them. To the extent that this is so, we are here dealing with nothing more than a variant of the use of governmental regulation as a surrogate for voluntary agreements in situations in which the actual establishment of contractual relationships is not feasible.

In at least some of the above instances, however, more is in fact at stake, and we are indeed dealing with justifications for legal intervention quite distinct from the attainment of an optimal allocation of resources, however broadly defined. And, to the extent that this is so, one consequence is that market modification, the general approach we found most fruitful earlier is unlikely to prove helpful.[10] Instead, we will be forced to rely, despite their shortcomings, on specific regulatory directives or structural reorganisation.

This conclusion is most clearly relevant in an area which is peculiarly technological and peculiarly contemporary. I have in mind the emerging family of technological processes which promise (or threaten) to change human beings in an intimate and lasting way, and perhaps even to modify what it means to be human – such technologies as electrochemical behaviour modification, computerised monitoring of personal information, or direct genetic manipulation. It seems to me entirely plausible that developments in cybernetics and in biomedical technology – in short, developments in the technologies that act more or less directly on individual persons – will produce techniques of potential self-degradation so disturbing that a society may properly choose to preserve its cultural integrity by regulating, and perhaps by forbidding, their application – notwithstanding the frequently proclaimed value of allowing individuals to do as they wish with their lives if their choices and consequent actions do not demonstrably impinge on the welfare of other specifiable individuals.

This postulate of classical liberalism, however, does not clearly support its extension to choices which deeply affect what man *is* as well as what he *does*, or to choices which significantly *alter*, and do not merely *implement*, the value of the societies in which such choices are made. It may be that the most important types of technological process in the coming decades will call for precisely such choices, and that the most challenging role for law in this new era will not be to maximise the satisfaction of personal wants but will instead be to modulate them. As I have already indicated, this will probably mean heavy reliance on direct regulation or on structural reorganisation as the primary legal tools for the control of technological development. Reorganisation may be a more promising mode of control here than it is in the attainment of an optimal allocation of resources. One can readily imagine organising private research groups or medical committees so as to minimise the temptations to certain kinds of self-alteration.[11] The prospect of direct governmental instrusion in an area so sensitive and personal must, however, give one pause – in part as a matter of principle but in part also on grounds of limited efficiency. Our contemporary experience with hallucinogenic drugs at least suggests that governmental prohibition lacks much force in these matters. But the alternative might be to push the regulatory process back to the earliest stages of research and development, cutting off such lines of inquiry as seem most likely to lead to the biomedical technologies we fear. One may recognise that the suppression of a particular avenue of inquiry need not mean the suppression of free inquiry generally, and indeed that selective suppression may operate to forestall an unselective counteraction of a graver sort, while still regretting deeply the inroads on principle begun by such a step.

But even if I am wrong as to the issue of research regulation, the very fact that law may more and more often be confronted with a widely-felt need on the part of legislators to control what people wish to do to themselves will mean that the central legal role of such concepts as intelligent consent, voluntary choice and individual freedom may diminish as contemporary technology comes increasingly to operate directly on man himself – arguably threatening his integrity and his 'human-ness' by offering him mounting levels of pleasure or security if only he will agree to subject himself to ever subtler forms of manipulation and control. To the extent that a kind of Faustian temptation beckons twentieth-century man toward this Huxleyan dystopia, he may find it necessary to run for protection to the increasingly authoritarian use of governmental regulation. Perhaps his hardest task will then be to avoid the trap of Big Brother as he resists the call of Brave New World.

References

1. House Committee on Science and Astronautics, *Technology: Processes of Assessment and Choice, A Report of the National Academy of Sciences*, US Government Printing Office, 1969.
2. Notice that only enforceable 'rights' can be used to bribe would-be transgressors into an exchange. Mere 'liberties', conceived as freedoms from legal restraint, can only be used to threaten those who would resist their exercise.
3. In none of these cases, of course, should one fall into the error of automatically allowing the right in question to be purchased in perpetuity. For once an enterprise has been permitted to acquire a perpetual right to invade another's interests in a particular way, it may have no economic incentive to cease such invasion even if a technological advance should later make it possible for the enterprise to cease its invasion at a cost so low that those who had formerly sold their rights would, after the advance, be willing (but unable organisationally) to buy them back at a price that would then be acceptable to the seller.
4. Interestingly enough, there are reasons to believe that the United States Patent Office has occasionally refused to award patents because of its perception of undesirable side-effects. I have been told, for example, that a patent related to the 'morning-after' pill was initially denied on the ground that it would induce immoral behavior. (Interview with Dr Ralph K. Schwitzgebel, 1 June 1970, Cambridge, Mass.) The obvious ineffectiveness of such denial as a means of protecting the public, coupled with the clear impropriety of lodging such vast powers of technological censorship in a body like the Patent Office, should make it plain why such a course is ill-advised. In the converse possibility of awarding patent protection more liberally or in a more profitable form for inventions of particularly high 'social utility', perhaps the most fundamental problem – apart from the growing inappropriateness of the discrete 'invention' as the subject of an incentive system – is that the value of a patent award is intrinsically limited by the marketability of the process patented. Such a value is negligible for inventions in areas where the economic market itself would not have stimulated significant inventive activity – precisely the areas of invention which a system of positive public incentives must be particularly designed to foster.
5. M. Roberts, 'River basin authorities: a national solution to water pollution', *Harvard Law Review*, Vol. 83, May, 1970, pp. 1527–56.
6. The campaign urged, *inter alia*, the expansion of the General Motors board of directors to include three representatives of 'the public interest' and the creation of a special committee to make reports and recommendations to General Motors shareholders regarding the policies of General Motors management on such matters as safety, pollution and social welfare. General Motors Stockholders' Resolution No. 5, 22 April, 1970. Cf. M. Eisenberg, 'The legal roles of shareholders and management in modern corporate decisionmaking', *California Law Review*, Vol. 57, 1969, pp. 1, 21, 30, 180; D. Vagts, 'Reforming the "Modern" corporation: perspectives from the German', *Harvard Law Review*, Vol. 80, 1966, pp. 25, 38–40, 46, 89.
7. Even if one should conclude that reorganising corporate structure holds little promise as a cost-internalising surrogate for transactions which cannot realistically be arranged, it does not follow that such reorganisation can make no useful contribution to the broad goal of encouraging more responsible (indeed, more efficient) technological development. I suggest a single possibility, I would simply note that, despite the general public apathy in the United States about problems of automotive air pollution in the early and mid 1950s, the corporations involved were not only aware of those problems but had entered into a then-unpublicised agreement governing their research

and development efforts in the area. It is at least conceivable that the presence of so-called 'public interest' directors on the respective boards of the involved corporations, or the creation of a shareholder committee with access to categories of information now limited to management, could have forced the automotive pollution issue to surface in a timelier way and might thereby have facilitated a more effective public response – though other means are arguably better suited to this end.

8. Yet a third category of justification is available: indirect income redistribution. Occasions obviously arise on which a society properly decides to benefit some of its members at the expense of others. Such redistributive aims may at times be achieved best in connection with the development or application of a technology and the location of responsibility for the costs associated with it. It may be argued that all of a society's redistributive decisions should be implemented through the collection and disbursement of tax revenues rather than through any form of market manipulation. But political constraints may preclude that course of action in some instances and, in others, one might not even have to 'rise above principle' to reject the 'pure' tax-and-welfare route. For tax redistributions always involve some efficiency costs of their own, but a preference on distributive grounds for one cost-bearer over another (an industrial manufacturer rather than an individual consumer, for example) may entail no expected efficiency loss whatever in a particular situation.

9. Once we take this suggested step of making such rights literally 'inalienable' by forbidding even their willing sacrifice or their consensual exchange, we are obviously invoking a concept of 'rights' quite different from the concept that we employed when we spoke earlier of creating 'rights' for the very purpose of facilitating market transactions in the interests they embody. Neither the desire for economically efficient resource allocation, nor the desire for just resource distribution, would support the creation of the sorts of 'inalienable' rights proposed here; the case for them must ultimately rest on paternalistic or cultural or ethical justifications.

10. As noted above in note 8, however, market modification may on occasion be a perfectly appropriate tool for improving the distribution of income as well as for as optimal allocation of resources. It is only when one's ends are essentially 'paternalistic' or 'cultural', as I have here used those terms, that the modification of market incentives is likely to be inappropriate.

11. Particularly when these temptations are presented in the increasingly familiar context of medical experimentation on human subjects, much can be said for such structural safeguards as independent review committees or the required approval of disinterested third parties. See, e.g. Paul A. Freund, 'Legal frameworks for human experimentation' in *Experimentation with Human Subjects*, ed. Freund, George Braziller, 1969, pp. 109–10.

The politics of selecting candidate technologies for assessment

Marlan Blissett

Political judgments associated with determining candidates and priorities for technology assessment are seldom conclusive. Frequently they are based on insufficient evidence, and almost always they adversely affect some organized interest within the community. These deficiencies, however, are characteristic of all major policy decisions and do not reflect additional difficulties imposed by the nature of technology. As a practical matter, the politicial system does not regard technology as something apart from the functional activities of organized life. Consequently, the selection of technologies to be assessed depends upon their linkage to areas of generalized interest, such as health, safety, commerce, defense, labor, welfare, and the environment.

Candidate technologies have a history of being chosen from activities that are regulated by government or that are significant components of highly visible problems. The protection of the public against radioactive substances, insuring the safety and efficacy of new vaccines, restricting stack gas emissions from power plants, and limiting the legal use of electronic surveillance – to mention only a few areas of technology assessment – are deeply imbedded in issues of national scope and significance. Only rarely are technologies evaluated as isolated events with restricted social and economic impacts. The typical political strategy is to select candidates for assessment from technologies with generalized significance that affect a multiplicity of conflicting public and private interests.

The judicial process

It is precisely the generalized effects of technology that render the judicial process largely inadequate as a method of identifying candidates for evaluation. Both legal and equitable remedies are available, but their scope is narrow and their effect upon technology assessment is indirect. Money damages, a legal remedy based on tort liability, may

From Marlan Blisset, 'The politics of selecting candidate technologies for assessment', *Technology Assessment*, Vol. 2, No. 3, 1974, pp. 175–80.

be awarded only in individual cases where harm has already been inflicted. An equitable remedy, such as an injunction, can be granted only where there is no adequate legal remedy. But neither legal nor equitable remedies can adequately address major social and economic problems. A court, for example, may award damages to a worker for injuries caused by the escape of radioactive gases from a nuclear power plant; but it may not force the utility to purchase a safer reactor. Presumably, the economic risk of future accidents, coupled with safety inspections by the Atomic Energy Commission and premium review by insurance companies will induce the utility to carry out a careful assessment of its reactor operations.

Before damages may be awarded on the basis of tort liability, the plaintiff must establish causality, and this can be a considerable obstacle in the context of some of the newer technologies. The cumulative effect, for example, of small-scale nuclear applications may produce injuries that are non-specific (such as low-level radiation damage) or whose causality cannot be legally established.[1] Constrained by the necessity to establish specific causation for injury and unable to compel internalization of the social costs of technology, tort liability holds limited promise as an inducement to assessment.

Unlike legal remedies, injunctive relief, under certain circumstances, may be used to restrain technologies that are likely to produce harm. In non-regulated activities, the plaintiff must demonstrate to the satisfaction of the court that there is an affirmative prospect of actual, substantial, and irreparable injury.[2] But in instances of regulated technologies – such as atomic energy, communications, drugs, air transport and food additives – injunctive relief against violators is provided for by statute and may be invoked upon application of the administrator to the appropriate court. In all cases, injunctions must be followed by a hearing in which the defendant has an opportunity to argue the contrary. At this point, the court may insist upon a thorough evaluation of the effect of the technology upon the plaintiff; but it may not impose this requirement for society at large.

The political-administrative process

The judicial process only indirectly serves to identify candidate technologies for assessment. If private parties are unwilling to internalize court-imposed damages in their decisions to develop, market, and use technologies, the generalized effect of judicial remedies will prove insignificant.

Legislative assessments
There are, however, other decisional processes of greater scope and authority that may be used to assess technology. Perhaps the most comprehensive instrument is that of legislative action. Through the

enactment of laws, legislatures can affect the development and utilization of technology imposing statutory rules of liability, prohibiting hazardous practices, and establishing regulatory standards that govern the application of certain technologies.[3]

As general-purpose institutions, legislatures are concerned with balancing a variety of policy interests and goals and do not evaluate technologies unless they are part of an obvious social problem. The anticipation of potentially dangerous technologies is a matter that legislatures would prefer to leave to other institutions. But the diffusion of technology has become so rapid and its unintended effects so powerful that legislatures are being asked to develop early warning systems for detecting future hazards. To this point, the greatest emphasis on early detection has come from the national level, although it is not yet clear what influence Congress' new Office of Technology Assessment will have on the traditional process of legislative decision making.

The complexity of modern technology and its application to problems of national importance – especially those dealing with defense, health, communications, transportation, commerce, atomic energy, and the environment – has meant that Congress and not state legislatures has assumed the principal legislative role of assessment. Even so, Congress has not actively sought to make technology a specialized item of legislative concern. To gain a place on the legislative agenda a technology must satisfy at least three political requirements.

- First, it must be part of a controversial issue of more than local interest. Waste disposal technology in Elkhart, Indiana, for example, would not qualify as a candidate for congressional assessment unless it were part of an acute problem of regional pollution. On the other hand, strip mining of coal in eastern Montana and West Virginia is not only an issue of local and regional debate, but is part of a national controversy over ways to overcome current fuel shortages.
- Second, a candidate technology must fall within the competence of Congress and be amenable to legislative action. Congressional assessments are structured by committees that deal with established subjects such as agriculture, welfare, military affairs, foreign relations, interstate and foreign commerce, and antitrust. New technologies that are not associated with familiar problems are likely to be ignored until their application has produced a response from knowledgeable professionals, the media, administrative agencies, and interest groups. Once an indication has been given as to the extent of potential hazards and how they may be dealt with Congress can take its bearings.

The recent disclosure of a new crowd control technology that incapacitates people by disturbing their brain waves is a case in point. The device – known as photic driver – utilizes flashing infrared lights and sound vibrations to interfere with the alpha rhythms of the brain. While the application of such a technology could be extremely injurious – in some cases it could cause epileptic fits – Congress has expressed almost no interest in the matter. If past legislative practice is a guide to future action, this attitude will persist until the safety hazards are more clearly defined and the political environment has had an opportunity to suggest policy alternatives.

Third, a candidate technology must affect specific policy goals and have a relatively short time horizon. The continuing interest, for example, in the safety of nuclear reactors by the Joint Committee on Atomic Energy is directly related to a national policy commitment to promote the commercialization of nuclear power. Intensive legislative concern with nuclear safety, however, has not been entirely deliberate. In large part it is due to widespread public criticism of radiation standards and the adequacy of emergency core cooling systems. The decision of Congress to take these matters under consideration reflects both a response to outside pressures and a determination to protect a specific policy objective of considerable national importance.

Technologies that bear upon national policies are extremely diffuse, but Congress has succeeded in grappling with a number of technology-related issues that have given immediate challenge to the goals of public health (carcinogenic food additives, harmful drugs, and chemical meat processing), low-cost housing (Project Breakthrough), foreign affairs (Project Camelot), national defense (the ABM) and the future of air transport (the SST).

Regulatory assessments
The span of legislative attention tends to be comprehensive and the technologies that qualify for congressional action are always part of larger issues that confront the political system. To provide continuity of assessment at a level of detail that affects both vendors and users of technology, Congress has established regulatory policies that give administrative agencies the responsibility for investigation, review, and control. Regulatory activities that contribute directly to technology assessment are found chiefly in the fields of communication, atomic energy, occupational safety, health, commerce, air transport, food, drugs, power, and agricultural practices. Candidates for assessment are not, however, the products of systematic choice. In the majority of cases, assessment decisions are the unanticipated results of political compromises that take place among the regulatory agency, its commercial and industrial clientele, and the congressional subcommittee that monitors the agency's operations.

The principal means of assessment open to the regulatory agency are its powers to establish standards, grant or withhold licenses, and adjudicate conflicts. In established areas of technology these powers seem adequate to the task. But new or emerging technologies create uncertainties that are not easily resolved. This is due in part to the conditions of the market and in part to the lack of sufficient evidence on which to justify immediate action.

Vendors of new technologies must contend with market factors that are extremely variable. The proprietary drug industry, for example, is confronted with the instabilities of a perishable market that is characterized by a high rate of obsolescence. For many products the difference between success and failure depends upon the amount of time required for approval by the Food and Drug Administration and the arrival of a new generation of drug specialties.[4] In other industries competitive circumstances are different. Vendors of nuclear reactors do not face the prospect of rapid technological obsolescence; but their economic future could be seriously threatened as a result of a major reactor failure. Market contingencies also affect technological advances in such industries as communications, mining, transportation, and synthetic fibers – requiring a regulatory response that is sensitive to changes in user preference, pollution and safety standards, fuel shortages, and foreign substitutes.

In the application of a new technology additional uncertainties arise when a regulatory agency is forced to make crucial assessments on the basis of limited information. If the product or process has experienced a successful entrance into the market, political and economic interests will combine to make the evaluation even more difficult. The absence of large statistical samples, conflicting scientific judgments, and interest group politics have played a significant role in decisions on cyclamates, nuclear safety, tranquilizers, battery additives, pesticides, radiation release, jet aircraft noise, and chemical meat processes.

The acquisition of data on new technological applications is seldom conclusive. The typical pattern is for the sponsoring industry to carry out initial studies that are designed to meet the minimum registration, performance, and safety standards of the agency. In many cases no generally acceptable test procedures will exist and industries will be forced into a series of experimental improvisations. When an agency reviews the results, questions may be asked about the sufficiency of evidence, but further research will not be undertaken unless there is responsible opposition from members of the scientific community. Should this occur, the agency will ask the industry for additional information and request an independent assessment from the National Academy of Sciences, the National Institutes of Health, a university, a non-profit research institute, or a national laboratory with competence in the area. In most instances, the independent evaluation will point out both immediate and potential dangers if certain controls are not imposed, but a final judgment will be reserved until more data are at hand. The sponsoring industry will then counter with new evidence and challenge the assumptions used in the independent evaluation. Finally, the agency itself will have to weigh the merits of the case and chart a course of action.

The existence of incomplete or inconclusive data does not mean, however, that the agency will regard the technology in question as a candidate for continuing assessment. The selection of serious contenders is less a product of agency choice than a response to political forces that define the agency's environment. As a case in point, the evaluation of chemical residues in meat by the Department of Agriculture reveals a keen sensitivity to political interests and public pressures. In 1956–57 when hormone pellets in chickens produced widespread public fear, the Department greatly expanded its techniques for detecting stilbestrol and other growth-stimulating chemicals.[5] In the middle 1960s when the public became alarmed that drug-resistant bacteria might be spread as a result of mixing antibiotics in animal feed, the Department improved its sampling procedures for monitoring antibiotic residues.[6] When public concern quickened in 1970 over the presence of mercury in meat supplies, the Department increased its surveillance of heavy metal residues, but cut back its sampling for antibiotics and hormones.[7]

Since regulatory assessments are undertaken with vigor only after the public has been aroused, it is necessary that administrative forums be provided for issues that have not received wide publicity. The Administrative Procedure Act enables parties 'aggrieved' by agency action to have access to a trial-type hearing, although considerable controversy still surrounds the procedural role of 'consumers' and public interest groups. Agencies appear willing to hear citizen complaints and to have complainants testify as witnesses, but there is reluctance to recognize a complainant as a formal adjudicatory party. The rules of most agencies restrict participation to those who have a property or financial interest in the proceedings and to those whose presence would clearly serve to broaden the issue without causing unreasonable delay. This practice, however, has been softened somewhat by two court decisions involving citizen protest over the use of a regulated technology. In *Church of Christ* v. *Federal Communications Commission* (1966) the court ruled that 'consumers' willing to bear the expense of intervention possessed 'sufficient interest' to challenge a television renewal application.[8] And in the second case, *Scenic Hudson* v. *Federal Power Commission* (1965), the court held that an unincorporated association of non-profit conservation groups could intervene in a hydroelectric license hearing because their conduct and activities indicated a special interest in the area.[9]

Public participation in administrative proceedings is an important element of technology assessment. It alerts agencies to immediate impacts and, in some cases, serves as counterweight to the promotional bias of many agencies and provides notice that their risk-benefit calculations must conform to community values. But neither public participants nor other 'aggrieved' parties in administrative hearings are permitted to move beyond the specific issues of the case. As a result, consideration of the secondary and tertiary effects of many technologies is rarely reflected in the formal record upon which an agency must base its decisions.

Evaluation of alternatives

The lack of an effective system for anticipating second and third order consequences has hindered both regulatory and congressional assessments of technological applications. The traditional processes of congressional and administrative decision-making have been responsive to immediate pressures but remain somewhat insensitive to future possibilities. In the majority of cases, this has produced impact evaluations that have come too late to make an important difference.

The major exception to this practice – although it does not apply to Congress – can be found in the requirements of the National Environmental Policy Act (NEPA). Under the Act, federal agencies must file a detailed statement that systematically explores the secondary impacts of projects that significantly affect the quality of the human environment. Not only must alternatives to the proposed action be developed, but substantive consideration must be given to unavoidable adverse impacts and any irreversible and irretrievable commitment of resources.

In passing the Act Congress did not establish sanctions or procedures for administrative enforcement; consequently the implementation of NEPA has become largely the responsibility of the courts. Although over three hundred cases have been litigated, major decisions affecting technology assessment can be summarized under five major headings:

Public disclosure
At a minimum NEPA is a full disclosure law (*Environmental Defense Fund* v. *Corps of Engineers*. 1971) and requires that the public be given notice of all known possible environmental consequences (*Cape Henry Bird Club* v. *Laird*, 1973).

Cost-benefit analysis
Impact assessments must weigh economic and technical benefits against environmental costs (*Calvert Cliffs' Coordinating Committee* v. *AEC*, 1971) and express the results in such a way that non-experts can reach an intelligent conclusion (*Environmental Defense Fund* v. *TVA*, 1972).

Alternative actions
An evaluation must be made of alternative actions even if they are beyond the jurisdiction of the lead agency (*Natural Resources Defense Council* v. *Morton*, 1971).

Social and cultural factors
Cultural factors must be recognized as a part of the human environment (*Ely* v. *Verde*, 1971) and city residents may look to NEPA for protection against the deterioration of quality of life (*Hanley* v. *Mitchell*, 1972).

Technology development forecasts
Federal research and development programs aimed at producing new technologies with commercial applicability must submit a reasonable

forecast of the program's impact on the environment, as well as the effects of foreseeable alternatives. (*Scientists' Institute* v. *AEC*, 1973).

Court interpretations of NEPA have stimulated enormous interest in technology assessment, but they have not resolved the conflict between politics and analysis. In order to anticipate the higher order consequences of technology, decision systems must make use of analytical instruments that are different from practical or intuitive judgments. Forecasting models, computer simulation techniques, and sensitivity projections, for example, often produce glimpses of the future that run counter to public expectations and even to common sense. Under these circumstances, it is tempting to argue that analysis should be displaced by public opinion.[10] But congressional and administrative decision-makers have managed a different response. While cautious of esoteric techniques, they find postulated events useful for identifying the range of interests out of which policy options can be constructed.

Priorities

The politics of identifying candidate technologies for assessment takes place in a variety of decision forums, under conditions of imperfect knowledge, and without a clear indication of risks and benefits. Moreover, the existence of conflicting values and interests make it extremely unlikely that assessment decisions will be viewed with finality. In the face of constantly changing political conditions it is difficult to establish priorities among candidate technologies. While the political process has not developed selection criteria for relating assessment decisions to the total context of national goals and purposes, it has evolved a workable strategy of choice. That strategy – to put it succinctly – is to force decision makers to contend with multiple pressures and uncertain values and to have them choose among risks – risk to themselves, their constituents or superiors, and their environment. The typical response is to give high priority to those areas with the greatest generality of interest.

While no one is likely to deny the popularity of this approach, an important question remains unanswered: Will it be adequate for a future that demands early detection as a cost of survival?

References

1. See, for example, *Mahoney* v. *United States*, 220 F. Supp. 823 (ED Tenn. 1963) (inability to demonstrate sufficient exposure to radiation to prove causal relation to leukemia); *La Porte* v. *US Radium Co.*, 13 F. Supp. 263 (DNJ 1935) (failure to show causation in radium poisoning death of a watchdial painter); *Garner* v. *Hecla*, 19 Utah 2d 367 (1967) (denial of workmen's compensation benefits due to conflicting testimony over the cause of lung cancer in a miner).

2. 43 CJS, Injunctions, Sec. 22.
3. Harold P. Green, 'The role of law and lawyers in technology assessment', *Atomic Energy Law Journal*, Fall 1971, pp. 250–1.
4. The Science Policy Research Division, Legislative Reference Service, Library of Congress, *Technical Information for Congress*, A Report to the House Subcommittee on Science, Research and Development, 91st Cong., 1st sess., April 1969, p. 500.
5. Harrison Wellford, *Sowing the Wind*, Grossman, 1972 p. 128.
6. Ibid.
7. Ibid.
8. *Office of Communication of United Church of Christ* v. *FCC*, 359 F. 2nd 994 (DC Cir. 1966).
9. *Scenic Hudson Preservation Conference* v. *FPC*, 354 F. 2nd 608 (2nd Cir. 1965).
10. Harold P. Green, 'Limitations on implementation of technology assessment', *Atomic Energy Law Journal*, Spring 1972, p. 82.

Limitations of technology assessment

David Elliott and Ruth Elliott

Technology assessment

[. . .] One approach to the social control of technology that has met with interest in the USA is technology assessment. While not giving the citizen any new role in the process of government, this approach can introduce an extra check or control over the action of industrialists, and, to some extent, of government. In this sense it is a form of accountability. The idea is to constitute a special institution, manned by specialists, as a watchdog body, charged with monitoring public and private sector technological plans and projects, with regard to the public interest. This body would report to government (or other clients) and advise on the desirability in the long term of proposed projects. Theoretically, sanctions could then be applied to stop any project that the technology assessment body deemed undesirable. The Government might introduce legislation or taxes to control the new technology or offer tax incentives, grants or loans to make *other* choices more attractive. And of course governments can simply cut off funds to state funded research organizations and thus control projects directly. Pressure from those concerned with the evident failure of the existing planning and control system has led to the creation of an Office of Technology Assessment in the USA, and a number of environmental protection controls.

For example, Federal organizations proposing to introduce or fund technical developments are now required to file an 'Environmental Impact Analysis'. The US National Environmental Policy Act (1969) requires that 'unquantified environmental amenities and values' be considered along with technological and economic estimates of inputs to public agency decision making on projects, permits, contracts . . .[1]

In general the assessments are concerned with the effect of new technologies or products on both the physical and social environment – that is they consider the effects on working and living conditions, welfare, health as well as considering pollution, resource utilization and so on.[2]

From Chapter 5, 'Social control of technology', in David Elliott and Ruth Elliott, *The Control of Technology*, Wykeham, 1976.

Some examples of technology assessment analyses already made in the USA include projects involving rainmaking and weather control techniques, fluoridation of water supplies, water resource management techniques, and the US supersonic transport.

Studies of the effects of new drugs and food additives have also been carried out, as have analyses of the safety hazards associated with consumer products generally. Of course many of these hazards are already monitored by industry or the state.

It is sometimes, therefore, argued that there is no need for technology assessment and that existing government and commercial organizations can successfully perform the 'monitoring' function. There is, it is suggested, adequate public safety, hazard and health legislation and the government has a number of technical authorities who are charged with responsibilities in these areas. However, although there are certainly many controls, especially in the UK, there would seem to be little reason for complacency.

The recent British experiences with thalidomide should act as a warning.

The problem with the traditional approach – that is leaving assessment responsibility up to the relevant government department, or the manufacturer, is that these groups tend to have a vested interest in projects they are supporting, and so may not be able to give an objective or impartial analysis. As Wollan points out, in the case of government sponsored technology in the US: '. . . the Federal government's vested interests in the continuation of its technological programs limit its ability to provide adequate technology assessment'.[3] He argues that: 'What is needed to complement the Government's own assessment is a way to counteract the natural tendency of the government to resist vigorous and comprehensive technology assessment.[4]

An independent technology assessment body is seen as one means of doing this. Technology assessment may not replace the usual forms of control, but it could supplement them.

In Britain, many of the technology assessment functions are already carried out by Royal Commissions established occasionally to look into particular problems, and it has been suggested that this well-established device 'would seem to be a natural vehicle for executing technology assessment studies. A commission or task force could provide the political executive with a much needed overview of the development of a given technological capability.'[5]

Of course Royal Commissions may not, in practice, have a great effect on *policy*, but it has nevertheless been argued that their educative value is immense:

While commissions and task forces have been widely criticised as having only a very limited impact on the policy-making process, their educative value is rarely taken into account. The data prepared and transferred during the course of a study – the public hearings, the briefs submitted, the press coverage, and so on – all contribute to increasing the level of awareness concerning a particular issue. Hopefully, this enhanced awareness would lead to improved decision-making by the actors and the political executive, and might even (as each became more aware of the other's perspectives) lead to a consensus about the future course of the technological capability in question.[5]

Other organizations in the British context that are involved with technology policy, although with less publicity, are the Select Committee on Science and Technology, and the Central Policy Review Staff or 'think-tank', which was set up for the 1970–74 Conservative Government under Lord Rothschild, and which contributed to a Green Paper on 'A Framework for Governmental Research and Development' (Cmnd 4814). An organization more specifically committed to technology assessment is the Programme Analysis Unit, sponsored and staffed jointly by the Ministry and the United Kingdom Atomic Energy Authority, with the brief: '... to explore the wider applicability of appraisal techniques to Civil Research programmes, with the ultimate objective of improving the deployment of the UK's R and D resources and maximising the returns from Ministry and AEA investment in this area'.[6]

A major problem confronting the use of technology assessment as a 'social control' instrument, is that most of the organizations so far established, like the Programme Analysis Unit (PAU) in Britain or the Office of Technology Assessment (OTA) in America are *not* in any real sense 'independent' bodies. They are very closely allied to Government and could easily 'ossify into a "service group" which provides partial assessments'.[7]

The range and limitations of technology assessment

Whether a Government opts for the US OTA approach or expansion of the UK Royal Commission or 'task force' approach, technology assessment could obviously be a great advance on the present tendency of simply waiting for abuses of technology to lead to crises, and 'mopping up' problems *after* they have occurred. To this extent technology assessment is a preventative rather than a palliative.

Some advocates believe the technology assessment is applicable across a wide area of social policy. For example Harvey Brooks, a leading American exponent of technology assessment, sees it as a broad ranging process, not strictly limited to technological developments. For, he argues: '... decisions about technology represent only one kind of social decision which is not necessarily of greater importance than many others which do not involve technology in any direct way. There are many cases in which the alternatives to the introduction or regulation of technology may be largely non-technological in nature.'[8]

Some of these will be 'social technologies', that is procedures and techniques for assisting social and economic processes (education, communication, etc.).

Brooks emphasizes also the need for wide-ranging rather than single-issue/piecemeal investigations:

... the regulation or suppression of certain technologies may have just as great potentialities for unforeseen consequences as the introduction of new technology ... If a decision is made to forbid the introduction or further spread of a particular technology, one has to be aware of what alternative technologies may arise to take its place, or what re-adjustments in the social structure may produce undesirable effects ... This suggests the difficulties of piecemeal implementation of technological or environmental assessments.[9]

One danger of technology assessment forecast by many critics is that it might inhibit 'innovation' and progress. The problem is essentially to choose a point in the 'innovation' process at which *useful* criticism can be introduced: 'so that vested interests, sunk costs, and professional commitments do not build up a momentum that becomes difficult to reverse'.[10] If assessment takes place early enough before such pressures have built up, there need not necessarily be any 'lowered incentive to innovation. What discourages innovation is the high risk of failure due to regulation *after* a large investment has been made.'[10]

Advocates of technology assessment argue that it should have

a stimulative as well as a regulative aspect. Its purpose is to foster a more balanced development of technology as a whole in relation to social needs, not merely to exercise 'birth control' on harmful or threatening technologies. This positive role must be associated with the regulatory one because a part of the function of assessment is the consideration of a wider range of alternatives than is ordinarily turned up by present market and political mechanisms left to themselves.[11]

Brooks sees technology assessment ultimately changing the 'ground rules' of the present market structure, so as to introduce some social criteria into the innovation process, and ensure that 'certain economic activities would bear the cost of injurious effects on society'.[12]

Thus ultimately Brooks is talking in terms of trying to implement social control of technology by changing the character of the market and economic incentives rather than through direct regulation and enforcement alone. The aim is to subject technology to social control without challenging 'the basic principles of market economies'.[12]

Such approaches reflect what one critic has called 'a desire to prevent at all costs the application of environmental policies making use of direct controls which may upset the market system. Their aim seems to be to handle the eco-crisis without policies which are believed not to be compatible to the market system'.[13]

Inevitably those who believe that much radical re-structuring of the market-based socio-economic system would be required before technology could be subjected to social control are critical of these aims. Their major criticism of the market as a control mechanism is that it 'does not offer an adequate evaluation of (these) collective needs and social goods; it neither defines the necessary social aims nor their relative importance or their order of priority relative to other social objectives and constraints. Its norms and aims are based upon private net profit . . .'[14] What is required instead, is the development of new non-market derived norms and goals, techniques of assessment and mechanisms of control.

Many advocates of technology assessment, while not accepting that the market structure need be *fundamentally* changed, agree that the technology assessment approach must move beyond simplistic economic measures, such as cost-benefit analyses and towards 'a more comprehensive assessment which is capable of measuring total costs and benefits to society as a whole'.[15]

They are hopeful that, given suitable modifications of the market structure, and improved techniques of analysis, the technology assessment approach, if sufficiently broad ranging, will lead to more rational and far-sighted decision-making, since the alternative values and costs involved in any particular decision will become more visible through quantification. However, there is a danger that this concern with rationality and objectivity might be used to obscure the fact that there are value-judgments involved, and to circumvent the political process by appealing to 'scientific' decision making.

Brooks, aware of these dangers, emphasizes that: 'Although the consequences of various technological choices may be clarified by analysis there is no objective or scientific basis on which final choices can be made. The choices themselves are political, depending upon a complex interplay or bargaining process among conflicting economic, political and ideological interests and values.'[16]

He acknowledges that in fact much of the attraction of technology assessment lies in its amenability to the 'end of ideology' school of thought:

> . . . *some of the pressure for the creation of mechanisms of technology assessment is undoubtedly based on a mistaken expectation that expert opinion alone can resolve the difficult choices involved. Particularly in the American political system, the use of 'objective' or scientific analysis is very attractive as a means for legitimising political consensus, and turning aside criticism . . . This search for ways of legitimising consensus through supposedly value-free analysis is probably what has made systems analysis, cost benefit analysis, and 'planning-programming-budgeting' so popular, at least for a time, in United States politics.*[17]

While emphasizing the essentially political and value-based nature of ultimate decisions Brooks insists, however, that objective analysis still has a valuable role to perform:

Analysis can greatly clarify the relations between values and reveal fundamental conflicts and inconsistencies between simultaneously held values . . . It can also show that some conflicts between interest groups are illusory, and there are some policies from which two groups with apparently conflicting interests can both benefit. Technology assessment can lead people to rethink their own value preferences by revealing the relative cost of various options.[18]

However, Brooks here seems guilty to some extent of indulging in the same over-emphasis on the rationality of decision-making processes that he has criticized in others. Is it in fact realistic to assume that *powerful* groups will change their own values and goals merely because it is rationally demonstrated that these goals could carry high costs for other groups? Certainly experience to date with technology assessment in the US suggests the contrary. Some studies that have been undertaken in the US 'indicate that the federal government's vested interests in the continuation of its technological programmes limit its ability to provide adequate technology assessment. In the field of weather modification, agencies are reluctant to explore in depth the need for regulation of their own operational programmes. In the SST projects, the Federal Aviation Agency has been unable to ask the kind of questions about engine noise that might challenge basic assumptions about the plane the agency is developing. In the case of fluoridation, the Public Health Services advocacy has interfered with its responsibility for continuing assessment of its original endorsement'.[19]

Such experiences suggests that it is naïve to separate technology assessment into two discrete parts: an objective apolitical process of technical investigation, and a political decision-making process on the basis of this evidence. As we have already illustrated, techniques used in such investigations are quite clearly *not* value-free; moreover vested interests and dominant values can have a profound effect on the kind of questions asked and the kinds of alternatives considered during the technical investigation process.

In spite of this, however, the belief in the neutrality of the technical process is widespread. Technology assessment is, according to one advocate: 'Neutral and objective, seeking to enrich the information for management decisions . . . Technology assessment is a tool for the renewal of our basic decision-making institutions, the democratic, political process, and the free-market economy.'[20] In the light of such statements, it is easy to see how technology assessment could become yet another tool for legitimizing the inequities of the *status quo*.

Similarly, although the technology assessment institution may in theory be an independent body, with no prior commitment to the values and priorities of any particular social group, it is hard to see how this 'independence' could in fact be maintained in practice.

Such agencies frequently tend to become 'a functional unit in a self-perpetuating industrial system. Each complementary part of the unit learns to respond to the system's needs. Seen in this light, an agency is not so much captured and enslaved as it is integrated, it adjusts to a system whose *status quo* it helps to protect.'[21] At the most practical level, any institution must receive funds from somewhere. At the level of *values*, it might be argued that given the manifestly unequal balance of power in our society at present, what is needed is an organization that will positively *emphasize* the values, goals and priorities of under-represented sections of society, rather than assume a position of 'neutral indifference' to all social groupings.

Neutrality, as has been suggested in previous chapters, has a disturbing tendency to imply an endorsement of the *status quo*.

For the kinds of reasons presented here, some critics of technology assessment have seen it as an attempt to merely *absorb* protest by setting up yet another branch of central government with only token independent power.

Such arguments have led to suggestions for considerable public participation in technology assessment, in order to *attempt* to promote a more balanced consideration of competing demands and interests. For example Mitchel has commented that: '. . . technology assessment should be diffused throughout society, involving a wide variety of social and economic interests, rather then being confined to central government'.[22] Tony Benn, then Labour Minister for Trade and Industry, argued that the use of sophisticated techniques by a group of experts supposedly representing a wide range of interests is no substitute for more direct democratic control, and carries with it 'dangers of human manipulation'.

To say this, is to challenge the expert trying to impose political decisions on us, head on; to query his credentials, and to encourage the same disrespect for him that good democrats have always shown to those who purport to dispense revealed truth. The language surrounding the decisions that have to be made may be complicated. The scientific factors or engineering problems may be complicated too. But unless the public insists upon deciding or approving the objectives which are to be striven after, it will abdicate all power over its own future.[23]

As it is, the technology assessment approach relies almost entirely on specialist technologists, who are asked to assess the 'effects of technology' in the public interest. To rely on a core of experts to perform these assessments seems to be a further step toward centralisation of power.

Many critics of technology assessment would prefer more decentralized forms of control and surveillance. Benn has proposed that the community should have greater access to technical and financial resources so that interested groups could perform their own technology assessment. He suggests that: '. . . some research council funds should be specifically allocated to trades unions and other recognised community groups to allow them to sponsor relevant research into the best means of safe-guarding the interests of their members'.[24] The idea of providing public support for independent technology assessment by pressure groups has also been suggested in the US context, where the idea of 'citizen assessment associations' has been put forward. In true American fashion it has been suggested that funds could be raised from 'bonds' so that people could help support the CAA's activities and philanthropically 'invest in the social future'.[25]

A number of voluntary groups motivated by a belief in the need for community involvement in TA, have recently come together in the US to form the National Council for the Public Assessment of Technology, the idea being to allow the non-expert a voice in the TA process.[26] Others are less sure that such decentralization is possible within our existing complex technological society, arguing that it is '. . . becoming increasingly difficult for a democratic society to control . . . complex technological systems and do it through the decentralised, socially responsive decision making that is at the heart of the democratic system'.[27]

In similar vein, Brooks argues that our 'technological and social decisions form an increasingly complex network of interactions which require a consistent approach to policy, that is difficult to reconcile with participatory democracy in the decision process'. Consequently 'we may be faced with the reality that the feasibility of participatory technology may be least at the very time when the affluence and perception of individuality produced by the massive application of technology make the desire for participation greatest'.[28]

A substantial number of technology assessment advocates still maintain that assessment by 'experts' with merely a 'broad accountability' to the public interest is the only feasible and 'rational' way to control technological development. 'On some grave public issues an aroused public will get emotional and will have an impact. But I think that on the vast majority of issues, it is the industrial leaders and other special interests, working quietly with congress in the background that have major impact.'[29] To many of those who prefer to leave decisions in the hands of experts, the danger is of *too much* rather than too little popular control. As Dr Leon Green of Lockheed Aircraft Corporation has remarked: 'The principal danger is not that new technology will be furtively imposed upon a blissfully ignorant public without adequate assessment but rather that it will be over-assessed to the point of harassment by hysterical (and hardly democratic) scientific Philistines, principally from the sinister side of the political spectrum.'[30] While such attitudes to technology assessment prevail, one cannot dismiss the fear expressed by Tony Benn that the technique could become 'a new mask behind which new men of power plan new ways of imposing their will on a new generation of new serfs'.[31]

The danger is that all technology assessment involves is the erection of a counter bureaucracy to oppose the existing bureaucracy. The two may in fact over time become inseparable. This is not a true 'adversary' situation, representing the clash of power and interests, but the absorption and institutionalization of conflict into a 'system-maintaining' structure.

References

1. M. Baram, 'Technology assessment and social control', *Science*, Vol. 180, No. 4085, p. 467.
2 One specialized technique that is being developed is 'energy accounting'; a technique which involves assessing the likely energy resource costs of any technological system or process. This is likely to gain in importance as it becomes urgent to utilize dwindling energy reserves efficiently. The creation of an 'Advisory Council on Energy Conservation' in Britain by the 1974 Labour Government will no doubt hasten these developments. Research into energy priorities is also central to the Energy Technology Support Unit at Harwell.
3. M. Wollan, 'Controlling the potential hazards of government sponsored technology', *George Washington Law Review*, Vol. 36, July 1968, p. 1134.
4. Ibid.
5. M. Gibbons and R. Voyer, 'Technology assessment: bias-free analysis', *New Scientist*, 24.5.1973, p. 468.
6. The Programme Analysis Unit 1967–1971, PAU 1971, Chilton, Didcot, England.
7. Derek Medford, *Environmental Harassment or Technology Assessment*, Elsevier Scientific Publishing Company, 1973, p. 121.
8. H. Brooks, 'Technology assessment as a process', *International Social Science Journal*, Vol. 25, No. 3, 1973, p. 248.
9. Ibid., p. 249.
10. H. Brooks, et al., OECD Report 1971, 'Science, growth and society', in N. Cross et al., *Man-made Futures*, Hutchinson, 1974, p. 139.
11. Ibid, pp. 141–2.
12. Ibid., pp. 144–5.
13. K. W. Kapp, 'Environmental disruption and protection', in K. Coates (ed.), *Socialism and the Environment*, Spokesman Books, 1974, p. 17.
14. Ibid., p. 18.
15. Ibid., p. 19.
16. H. Brooks 'Technology assessment' p. 251.
17. Ibid.
18. Ibid.
19. M. Wollan, op. cit., p. 1134.
20. R. A. Carpenter, Chief of the Library Reference Service, US Congress, quoted in *Technology Assessment, Superfix or Superfixation, Science for People*, No. 24, Nov. Dec. 1973.
21. H. S. Kariel, *The Decline of American Pluralism*, OUP, 1967, p. 91.
22. J. Mitchel, 'The consumer movement and technological change', *International Social Science Journal*, Vol. 25, No. 3, 1973, p. 367.
23. Tony Benn, 'Technology assessment and political power', *New Scientist*, 24.5.1973, p. 489.
24. Ibid., p. 490.
25. E. R. Mottur, 'Technology assessment and citizen action', in R. Kasper, ed., *Technology Assessment*, Praeger, 1972.

26. See Hazel Henderson, 'A philosophical conflict: re-examining the goals of *knowledge*', in *Public Administration Review*, Oct. 1974.
27. E. R. Mottur, quoted in R. G. Kasper, op. cit., pp. 278–9.
28. H. Brooks, 'Technology assessment', p. 255.
29. Quoted in R. G. Kasper, op. cit., p. 226.
30. L. Green, 'Technology assessment or environmental harassment' in R. G. Kasper, op. cit., p. 198.
31. Tony Benn, op. cit., p. 490.

Technology assessment and social control

Michael S. Baram

The emerging concepts of corporate responsibility and technology assessment are, to a considerable extent, responses to problems arising from technological developments and their applications by industry and government. These problems appear in the relatively discrete sectors of consumer protection and occupational safety and in the diffuse sectors of community quality of life and the national and international environments.

Consumer protection

As products have become more sophisticated and defects in them less easily detected by the consumer, the common-law principle of caveat emptor, 'let the buyer beware' has been largely abandoned by the courts, and the principle of strict corporate liability has been frequently adopted.[1] Federal and state legislation and regulatory agencies for consumer protection have multiplied with this shifting of responsibility. Nevertheless, common law, legislation, and regulation pertaining to product safety have been largely ineffective '. . . federal authority to curb hazards in consumer products is virtually non-existent . . . legislation consists of a series of isolated acts treating specific hazards in narrow product categories. . . . Despite its humanitarian adaptations to meet the challenge of product-caused injuries, the common law puts no reliable restraint upon product hazards'[1]. As a result, Ralph Nader and other crusaders have mobilized citizens against specific technological developments embodied in hazardous products and processes – such as the Corvair and various food additives.

The 92nd Congress enacted the Consumer Product Safety Act, thereby creating an independent commission with the authority to develop mandatory safety standards for many product categories and to carry out related functions to protect consumers.[2] However, regulation of automobiles, drugs, boats, foods, and other product categories is

From Michael S. Baram, 'Technology assessment and social control', *Science*, Vol. 180, No. 4085, May 1973, pp. 465–73.

excluded and left to existing programs. The commission is expected to maintain the regulatory agency tradition of reliance on industrial testing and reports; and 'except for the availability of [commission] information and the opportunity for litigants to argue the fact of compliance or noncompliance with mandatory Government standards, the law is expected to have little effect on products liability litigation'[3]. It is too early to determine whether or not the law will bring about an effective regulatory program.

Occupational health and safety

The incidence of harm to workers, the difficulties of employee recovery under the common law, and the inability of the judicial system to internalize such 'costs' sufficiently to bring about a preventive approach by corporate management are among the factors that led to workmen's compensation laws and insurance programs,[4] and agency standards for occupational hazards. The National Labor Relations Act,[5] and most recently the Occupational Safety and Health Act[6] have provided frameworks for decision-making on automation and hazardous technological developments. Nevertheless, high injury rates persist in several industrial sectors[7] as old and new technology continues to create lethal environments for employees – for example, 'The National Academy of Sciences reports a study showing that the life-span of radiologists is five years shorter than the national average . . .'[8] (p. 13).

The introduction of new automation technology has traditionally brought about strong union opposition because of impacts on job security.[9] Now, impacts on employee health provide new bases for opposition. As a result, some new, highly automated plants have been shut down – Rio Tinto's lead processing plant in the United Kingdom and General Motors' Vega plant in Lordstown, Ohio, have recently suspended operations until the economic and the physical and mental health effects of new automation technology on employees could be determined and diminished.[10]

Community quality of life

The impacts of industrial and government technology on health, land use, esthetics, and other aspects of community quality of life[11] have finally aroused organized citizen opposition. Government transportation and energy programs are now persistently opposed by local communities. Corporations that have traditionally provided the economic base for communities are now increasingly confronted by litigants seeking compensatory damages, restraining orders, and injunctions; by newly aggressive local officials responding to citizen complaints and invoking long-dormant police powers against noise, smoke, and other nuisances; and by state and federal officials enforcing air and water quality programs. Despite judicial reluctance to enjoin ongoing industrial activity that concurrently provides local economic benefits and environmental degradation,[12] the expanding enforcement of public nuisance and pollution control laws has recently brought about a number of plant closures.[13]

Nevertheless, the economic objectives of states and local communities and the fear of job losses and other dislocations that would arise from project or plant shutdowns will continue to determine the pace at which community quality of life is rehabilitated and environmental degradation controlled.[14] The complex task of resource management must be undertaken by state and local governments. How else to reconcile the objectives of economic and social opportunity – housing, economic development, transportation, and so on – with enhanced community quality of life – open space, recreation, esthetically pleasing surroundings, population stability? The reconciliation of such diverse objectives will not be possible until the consequences of technology can be systematically assessed, until rational siting and land use guidelines have been established, and until state and regional planning find a viable political structure.

National environmental quality

Ehrlich, Commoner, and other early crusaders may have been critically received, but nations are now embarking on serious, more effective pollution control programs. In the United States, the new water pollution control program has been designed to achieve use of the 'best practicable' pollution control technology by 1977, the 'best available' technology by 1983, and a national 'no pollution discharge' goal by 1985.[15] The air quality program provides authority for federal control over new stationary sources of air pollution, over automotive emissions, and over all sources of air pollutants hazardous to human health.[16] New legislation has established federal authority to limit the noise emissions of numerous corporate products;[17] and laws to tighten up control over pesticides and hazardous materials have again been enacted.[18]

The national commitment now authorizes control over most forms of pollution caused by technological processes, ensuring more rigorous analysis, regulation, enforcement, and citizen participation. Nevertheless, many technology-created pollution problems remain – the management and disposal of radioactive waste, toxic materials, sludge, and solid waste. In addition, new technologies such as weather modification and marine resource extraction are now being developed and experimentally applied, and they will undoubtedly create new problems and new legislation in our already 'law-ridden society'[19] (p. 32). The pattern is obvious and disturbing: the development of a technological advance, insistence upon its application by interest groups in industry and government, utilization, the appearance of environmental problems, legislation, regulation, and extensive litigation to control environmental impacts.[20]

Assumptions

These problems of consumers, employees, communities, and nations are the results of the processes we use to develop, apply, and regulate our technology – of our methods of social control. Social control is, in turn, the result of complex interactions of underlying political, economic, and cultural forces.

What is to be done? We can continue to grapple with the problems as they crystallize, using the established and ineffective patterns of post hoc legislation, regulation, and litigation. On the other hand, we can boldly attempt to alter the underlying forces or causes, and their interactions, but this calls for information we do not have and demands an acknowledgement that the forces at work in different political systems are yielding substantially similar problems.[21]

The most feasible strategy appears to be one of intervening in those decision-making processes of the public and private sectors that bring about technological applications; such intervention would take the form of introducing new frameworks for planning and decision-making. The development and use of coherent frameworks for technology assessment and utilization could meet many of the demands for corporate and governmental responsibility. Clearly, the use of such frameworks will affect the underlying social forces not directly confronted and will entail considerable reliance on established legal and regulatory procedures.[22,23]

The task of developing frameworks for technology assessment and utilization must be undertaken in full recognition of several realities.

1. Application of any such framework to a particular technological advance will yield differences in opinion and information from professionals, as well as from concerned citizens.
2. Continuing research, monitoring experiments, and changing designs will not necessarily resolve such differences, but will generally reveal the transscientific nature of decisions to be made about the further development and utilization of a specific technological advance: for example, the decisions will ultimately involve value-based consideration of the probable harm of the advance and the scope, magnitude, and acceptability of that harm.[24]
3. Receptors – consumers, employees, and citizens generally – will find elitist decision-making and compensatory solutions to possible harmful effects inadequate, and they will actively seek to participate in the planning, design, and implementation stages of the technology application process.
4. A multiplicity of inadequate decision frameworks for technology

assessment and utilization already exist and are employed by, for example, Congress, regulatory agency officials, corporate management, insurance ratesetters, courts, and organized citizen's groups.

Given this statement of the problem and these assumptions, it appears that the task is to somehow 'get it all together' – to develop an understanding of how technology interacts with society and its institutions of social control: to demonstrate that citizens, corporations, and public institutions are all interrelated in specific patterns and thereby share responsibility for rational planning and decision-making; and to shape a common conceptual framework that can be readily applied by each decision-maker, in order that the different results can be compared meaningfully and used to choose knowledgeably among alternatives.

Developing a coherent framework

Technology is dependent upon processes that occur in four interrelated contexts: basic research, applied research, the development of prototypes for testing or experimentation, and ongoing production and utilization. Although it is difficult to pinpoint the path of any specific development, it is clear that most technology (in the form of processes, products, or techniques) in use today was brought about by the interactions of people and findings in these four contexts.[25]

Within each context different levels and kinds of resources, or inputs are required – for example, manpower, funds, time, facilities, education, and materials – but large social and economic commitments and irreversible commitments of natural resources are usually made only when the development and experimentation phase is undertaken. These large commitments lend an inevitability to the technological advance, because few courts and federal agencies have been willing to halt major socioeconomic commitments, irrespective of hazards to individuals or society.[26]

The technology that emerges subsequently brings about social and environmental effects, or outputs – direct and indirect, primary and secondary, beneficial and detrimental, measurable and unmeasurable. Whether one uses nuclear power or the snowmobile as an example of current applications of technology, several classes of effects are apparent. These include effects on health (mental and physical, somatic and genetic), economy (individual and corporate, local and national, international), environment (pollution, disruptions of ecosystems), resources (availability of materials, land, and waters for competing uses), values (changes that are ultimately reflected in new law and policy), and sociopolitical institutions and processes (structural and substantive changes). As these and other effects are aggregated, they determine the quality of life.

We have no quantifiable information on many of these effects; nor can we accurately predict potential effects, their synergism, or the inter-

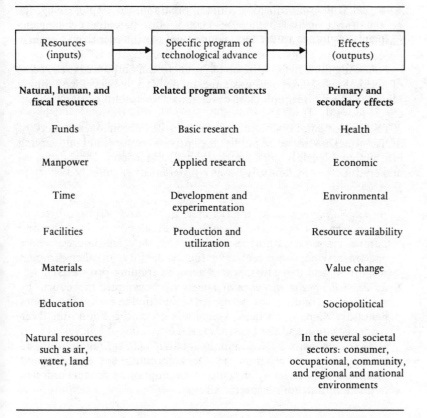

Fig. 1. Resources (inputs) and effects (outputs) of technological developments.

vention of exogenous forces such as population migration or natural disasters. We do not have devices sophisticated enough to monitor and assess many of these effects, nor do we have articulated goals or indices to measure progress toward such goals.[23] Decisions on goals, indices, and effects are now, and will probably always remain, transscientific.

But we have learned one thing well – that impacts and amenities which are unmeasurable or unquantifiable are nevertheless real and should be as integral to decision-making as quantifiable technical and economic considerations. At the federal level, this has been clearly expressed in the National Environmental Policy Act (NEPA) of 1969,[27] which requires that 'unquantified environmental amenities and values' be considered along with technological and economic or quantitative inputs to public agency decision-making on projects, permits, contracts, and other major actions when such actions are likely to result in significant environmental impacts. Agencies are now struggling with this new requirement as they develop environmental impact assessments, which are subsequently exposed to the public for review before agency action. Public response to over 3,000 impact statements during the past 2 years has ranged from acquiescence, to intervention in agency proceedings, to political pressure, to extensive litigation.[28]

Following this brief discussion of inputs to and outputs of the process of technological advance, a simple model can be developed which relates a specific technological development to resources (inputs) and effects (outputs) (Fig. 1).

The implementation of each program will depend on a variety of decision-makers in both public and private sectors and at varying jurisdictional levels – local, state, regional, and federal. These decision-makers function as controls on any program in essentially two ways (Fig. 2):

1. *by controlling resources* (for example, public and private sources of manpower and funds for research and development; land use and natural resource authorities; federal and state legislatures, whose enactments may be essential to the availability of other program resources; and educators, who determine training programs);
2. *by controlling the detrimental effects* (for example, the courts by means of preliminary or permanent injunctions or awards of compensatory damages; federal agencies, such as the Food and Drug Administration and the Environmental Protection Agency, and their state counterparts by engaging in standard-setting, regulation, and enforcement; and program managers, corporate management, and insurance rate-setters by bringing about program or product redesign to abate or ameliorate specific effects).

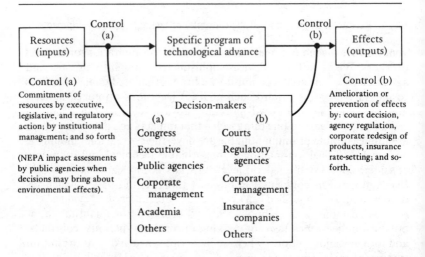

Fig. 2. Decision-makers.

To further develop this model, some of the major influences on decision-makers who control technological developments must be determined. These influences (Fig. 3) include information on:

1. resource availability;
2. technical and economic feasibility;
3. actual and potential effects; and
4. operational-institutional values, which are comprised of the common law, legislation, economic and social policy, institutional management policies, and other 'given' values that have been recognized and accepted by decision-makers as of the time any specific decision is made regarding further program development. These include diverse and often conflicting laws and policies – for example, NEPA (to foster the conservation and rational use of resources) and the oil depletion allowance (to foster rapid exploitation of resources).

To complete this general model, the social dynamics of any program of technological advance must be considered further – specifically, the responses of individual citizens and organized interest groups to perceived resource commitments and program effects (Fig. 4). These responses can be manifested through institutional procedures for changing the laws and policies that influence decision-makers – a lengthy process requiring extensive aggregation of voters or shareholders and generally undertaken in order to influence future decisions, not the particular decision that provoked the response.

Responses can also be manifested through formal, adversarial procedures to challenge decision-making – for example, injured consumers can go to court and disturbed environmentalists can intervene in agency proceedings or seek judicial review of agency decisions. Finally, a variety of informal procedures can be employed to feed back responses to decision-makers – such as demonstrations, employee absenteeism, product boycotts, consumer choice, or quasipolitical campaigns. The environmental and consumer protection movements serve as vivid examples of these new pressures on decision-makers, pressures new only in their intensity.

Citizens responding to perceived detrimental effects or resource misuse comprise a diverse group of consumers, shareholders, unions, crusaders, and citizens' organizations, ranging from those with national objectives (for example, the Sierra Club) to those with local or self-interest objectives (for example, labour unions, airport neighbors). The responses manifested through institutional, formal-adversarial, or informal procedures for exerting pressure on decision-makers may, in time, become so widespread or aggregated that they will be incorporated into the common law or form the basis for new management policy or legislation and, as such, become part of the matrix of operational-institututional values. This has already occurred to a considerable

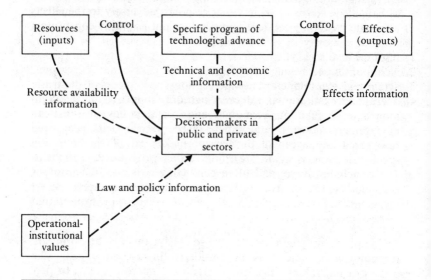

Fig. 3. Information flows to decision-makers.

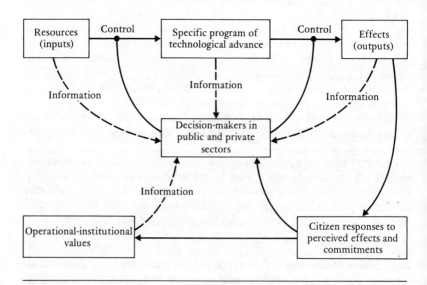

Fig. 4. Summary of influences on decision-making.

extent with regard to environmental and consumer protection responses.

Although the sector of society that responds adversely to the effects of a specific technological development does not normally constitute a democratic majority in its early stages, the issue raised by such responses deserve serious consideration, and the procedures for eliciting such responses are being strengthened by the courts and legislatures. First, the responses represent new perceptions, new 'pieces of the truth' that were either unknown to, ignored, or lightly considered by decision-makers. Second, they represent market and political influence that can be magnified by use of the media. Third, although they may be ignored at first, these responses will continue to appear in various forms and may bring about delays that are more costly after a program has been started (the utilities and the Atomic Energy Commission, for example, are now finding this out as they attempt to further the nuclear power program: plant construction and operation are running more than 2 years behind schedule, with greatly increased costs, because of extensive litigation and hearings,[29] which resulted from an earlier failure to consider citizens' concern about thermal and radioactive waste disposal, reactor safety, and related ecological and health issues. Fourth, such responses are based on real concerns, will often find larger public support, and eventually could result in stringent legislation or judicial findings that decision-makers would have to live with.[30]

Finally, a citizenry that expresses a diversity of interests is the most effective mode of promoting the accountability of decision-makers to the full social context in which they operate. Too often, decision-makers in all institutions have failed to inform the public about the bases and risks of decisions, thereby precluding feedback of larger social issues and humanistic concerns in their effort to promote institutional or self-interest objectives.[31] But the benefits of an informed and responsive public have now been adequately demonstrated. Cars will be cleaner by 1975; the Army Corps of Engineers will not continue to dam rivers and spend public funds without more rigorous analysis of impacts and needs; the Food and Drug Administration will begin informing the public of the chemical contents and quality control criteria of specific consumer products they regulate; maximum permissible exposures of workers and the public to power-plant radiation have been falling. These are some of the recent 'accountability' benefits that are being derived from public pressure.

Decision-making in both public and private institutions supporting technological programs and applications is becoming more complicated and less efficient, in the institutional, short-term sense; but long-term efficiencies, in terms of larger social interests such as public health, can be expected. In more pragmatic economic and political terms, it has become increasingly apparent that it is in the long-term self-interest of decision-makers and their institutions to be open and responsive to the interests of the public. As David Rockefeller has defined the issue for the private sector:[32]

The question really comes down to this: Will business leaders seize the initiative to make necessary changes and take on new responsibilities voluntarily, or will they wait until these are thrust upon them by law? Some adjustments are inevitable . . . there may have to be new laws to force consideration of the quality-of-life dimension so that more socially responsive firms will not suffer a competitive disadvantage. It is up to the businessman to make common cause with other reformers . . . to initiate necessary reforms that will make it possible for business to continue to function in a new climate as a constructive force in our society.

In the public sector, opposition to projects and the failing credibility of programs have prompted several agencies to increase citizen participation in program planning and design – beyond the environmental impact statement requirements of NEPA.[33]

The model I have presented (Fig. 4) does not provide any answers, but it can be used for several purposes: to widen the perceptions of planners, designers, and decision-makers responsible for specific technological advances and applications; to depict the interrelationships of resources, effects, decision-makers, institutions, and citizens; to develop policy, management, or program alternatives in the corporate, congressional, and public agency sectors that support and regulate technological development and utilization; and to assess, with public participation, the impacts of technological developments before they are utilized. Above all, the model articulates an accounting system, or framework, for decision-making that is dynamic and that can be used by all of the decision-makers, irrespective of their interests. The model has also proved helpful in the development of curricula and research: by making possible the ordering and integration of diverse perspectives and events and by providing an understanding of the patterns of technological development, application, and impacts, as well as social responses to technology. This understanding extends to technology in general, as well as to developments in such specific areas as mariculture, housing, and bioengineering.[34]

Reforms in process

A number of recent legal developments can be related directly to the model, particularly to the sector designated 'citizen responses to perceived effects and commitments' of technology. For citizen responses to be responsible, the flow of information to the public about effects and commitments – actual and potential – must be coherent and balanced, and it must present alternatives with their uncertainties in comparable terms. For citizen responses to be meaningful, the processes of planning, design, and decision-making must be accessible to citizens and open to their concerns.

For example, NEPA requires federal agencies to assess environmental impacts before 'major actions' are taken. These actions range from the Atomic Energy Commission's approval of a construction license for a nuclear plant to be built by a utility, to the funding of increments of the highway program by the Department of Transportation, to authorization by the Department of Agriculture for the use of herbicides and pesticides. The responsibility for assessment is broad and must include full consideration of five issues:[35]

1. potential environmental impacts;
2. unavoidable adverse impacts;
3. irreversible commitments of resources;
4. short-term use considerations versus long-term resource needs; and
5. alternatives to the proposed action.

Draft and final impact assessments are made available to other governmental officials and to the public for review and further development under guidelines established by the Council on Environmental Quality.[36,37] Although NEPA does not provide veto power to any official, even if the project poses real environmental hazards, the act does provide new information to the public – by exposing the extent to which environmental effects are being considered by the agency – and provides an enlarged record for judicial review of agency decisions. Obvious deficiencies in an agency's procedure, the scope of its statement, or the content of its statement will, on the basis of experience since NEPA was enacted, result in citizen intervention in agency processes, political opposition, and litigation. Many projects proposed and assessed have been delayed, and, in some cases, projects have been abandoned. Other projects have proceeded after being redesigned to ameliorate those effects on the environment that generated controversy,[23] (pp. 221–67).

Most projects involve applications of existing technology, but a few involve the development of new technologies – for example, the Department of Transportation's air cushion vehicle, the Atomic Energy Commission's liquid metal fast breeder reactor, cloud seeding experiments of the National Science Foundation and the National Oceanographic and Atmospheric Administration, and the use of polyvinyl-chloride containers, to be approved by the Internal Revenue Service, for alcoholic beverages.[38]

NEPA does not expressly require consideration of social, health, or economic impacts or of secondary effects such as subsequent population migration and land development. These considerations are frequently ignored or treated in cursory fashion, even though they are integral to comprehensive assessment of project impacts and decision-making. NEPA does not impose assessment and exposure processes on industry or the private sector, but, whenever a utility, corporation, or other private institution is the applicant or intended beneficiary of federal agency funds, license, or other 'major action', its proposal is subject to the NEPA process. There have been suggestions that NEPA be extended directly to the private sector, but as yet these have not been seriously considered at the federal level. However, variants of NEPA have been adopted by several states, and more states are expected to follow suit.[39] Because of state and local control of land use, state versions of NEPA have the potential for directly affecting land development activities in the private sector. This potential has been realized in California, where the state supreme court has determined that the state's Environmental Quality Act requires county boards of supervisors to conduct environmental assessments before issuing building permits for housing projects and other land developments to the private sector.[40] Similar requirements may apply to the private sector in Massachusetts, where the new environmental assessment requirements are imposed on 'political subdivisions' as well as on state agencies and officials.[41]

Therefore, the model can be further developed by adding environmental impact assessments by public decision-makers at the point where resources are to be committed to certain types of projects that apply 'old' technology, as well as to certain activities that will involve the further advance or application of new technology. Concomitantly, the flow of information to citizens has been enhanced.

The development of impact statements is a meaningless exercise unless they are actually used in decision-making.[42] It is difficult to use impact statements because of the diversity and the essentially unquantifiable nature of the new factors they present – since most agency decision-making depends on quantification of technical and economic factors.[37] The use of impact statements in the last stage of a project, such as the awarding of construction contracts, is deceptive. The earlier stages of planning and design may not have included assessment, thereby precluding citizen inputs at a time when more important changes in project plans and alternatives could have been accomplished. In other words, effective use of impact assessment techniques and citizen feedback can be more readily achieved in the earlier, less tangible stages of a project – precisely when most agencies prefer to plan and design without public intervention. Hopefully, litigation and subsequent judicial review will impose the NEPA framework earlier in agency processes.[43]

Further difficulties with the NEPA process have become apparent. There is an inherent conflict in the requirement that the agency proponent of a project assess it and discuss alternatives. After all, the agency has already selected an alternative and has undertaken the impact assessment essentially to justify its choice. Subsequent discussion of alternatives is too often a superficial process of setting up 'straw alternatives' for facile criticism. Clearly, independent review of all the alternatives, including the proposed agency action, would be desirable. However, independent review would also require the structuring of new agency procedures and independent institutions for assessment.[44]

Finally, the problem of dealing with unquantifiable impacts remains. The assignment of values and weights to environmental and social amenities may either be arbitrary or intentionally designed to produce decisions that had been predetermined by agency officials.

Despite these difficulties and the numerous conflicts and increased costs that now attend agency programs, NEPA is slowly forcing wiser environmental practices, more sensitive agency buraucracies, and more effective roles for citizens. It is possible that the NEPA process could eventually provide the basis, not for conflict in the courtroom or at agency hearings, but for negotiation in good faith between interested parties over points of dispute as revealed by the environmental assessment.[45] The resolution of labor-management conflicts under the National Labor Relations Board provides useful experience that should be reviewed for possible application to the NEPA context.

A major extension of NEPA practices to the assessment of new technology may have been accomplished with the passage of the Technology Assessment Act of 1972.[46] This law established within the legislative branch an Office of Technology Assessment (OTA) to '... provide early indications of the probable beneficial and adverse impacts of the applications of technology and to develop other coordinate information which may assist the Congress. . . .' The office is required to undertake several tasks[46] (sect. 3):

1. identifying existing or probable impacts of technology or technological programs;
2. where possible, ascertaining cause and effect relationships;
3. identifying alternative technological methods of implementing specific programs;
4. identifying alternative programs for achieving requisite goals;
5. estimating and comparing the impacts of alternative methods and programs;
6. presenting findings of completed analyses to the appropriate legislative authorities;
7. identifying areas where additional research or data collection is required . . .
8. undertaking . . . additional associated activities. . . .

Assessments to be carried out '... shall be made available to the initiating ... or other appropriate committees of the Congress ... [and] may be made available to the public. . . .'[46]

The law does not distinguish between technological developments in the public agency and private sectors and presumably includes technology being developed with private funds. Although provided with the authority to subpoena witnesses, OTA '... shall not, itself, operate any laboratories, pilot plants, or test facilities.' The broad language of the assessment requirements and the way in which assessments are used by Congress effectively preclude a substantial replication of the litigation and other conflicts that have characterized the NEPA experience.

Political conditions will inevitably determine the initiation of OTA studies and their use by congressional committees, and it appears that the public will, in general, be unable to secure judicial review to promote accountability of OTA and Congress.

The burden of formulating guidelines to describe when OTA should be called upon by Congress and prescribing procedures for providing information to the public clearly lies with the OTA board and advisory council. Above all, it appears essential that OTA develop and articulate a coherent framework for all technology assessments to be undertaken. Such a framework would prevent OTA assessments from becoming skillfully contrived, ad hoc case studies, which would be essentially closed to the introduction of important information from citizens and interest groups. OTA therefore has the additional burden of laying out a framework that will replace the multiple, partial models employed by different interests, that will promote inputs from interdisciplinary and humanistic sources, and that will clearly present, in a replicable format, the quantifiable and unquantifiable costs and benefits of new technological developments and applications.

Procedures to enhance the flow of balanced information on technological developments to the public will inevitably face the problem of information manipulation and secrecy practices. 'The public's need for information is especially great in the field of science and technology, for the growth of specialized scientific knowledge threatens to outstrip our collective ability to control its effects on our lives.'[47]

Secrecy on the part of public agencies and the executive branch is still common practice to protect decision-making processes from public criticism, despite the 1967 Freedom of Information Act.[48] However, sustained public pressures for the release of non-classified information have made such secrecy more controversial and somewhat more difficult to justify. The recent passage of the Federal Advisory Committee Act may bring about the diminution of another important form of secrecy in the public sector – agency advisory committee proceedings and recommendations, which are used in setting standards and other decision processes.[49]

The common law of trade secrets is similarly invoked to protect corporate information – presumably from the competition (the common law basis for the concept),[50] but increasingly from the public and government. The Environmental Protection Agency has been unable to secure information on the quantities of polychlorinated biphenyls (PCB's) made and sold by the one American manufacturer, despite evidence that PCB's are now part of the international pollution problem.[51] In other industrial technology sectors, however, congressional legislation has provided the government with access to information and procedures normally cloaked by trade secrecy. For example, section 206(c) of the Clean Air Act[16] provides that the Environmental Protection Agency may:

... enter at reasonable times, any plant or other establishment of such [auto engine] manufacturer, for the purpose of conducting tests of vehicles or engines in the hands of the manufacturer or ... to inspect ... records, files, papers, processes, controls, and facilities used by such manufacturer in conducting tests ... [regarding motor vehicle and engine compliance with EPA regulations].

A similar section in the 1972 Water Pollution Control Act,[15] (sect. 308) also provides the Environmental Protection Agency access to secret information held by water polluters. It appears that Congress is now aware of trade secrecy as an obstruction to pollution control and is willing to begin limiting the antisocial uses of secrecy to some extent.

Finally, trade secrecy, in its present forms, will certainly obstruct the development of meaningful 'corporate social audits' that David Rockefeller and other industrial leaders have called for. Legal sanctions for corporate secrecy obviously must be challenged if corporate responsibility and technology assessment are to be realized.

Beyond secrecy lies the problem of corporate advertising for new products and technological processes. Here, too, developments in the courts and regulatory agencies indicate that better information must be provided the public. The rapid evolution of the 'Fairness Doctrine' now means that radio and television broadcast licensees must make reasonable and fair presentations of the contrasting sides of a controversial issue, once such issue has been raised (usually by advertising) on licensee broadcast time. As expressed in a recent law review note: 'This obligation is incurred even at the licensee's expense if no sponsorship is available ... [although] the licensee has discretion to determine 'how the contrasting sides will be presented and who will be the spokesman'[52] (p. 109).

The doctrine has been applied by federal courts to cases of product advertising (cigarettes, large-engine automobiles, and high-test gasolines) in which it was felt that only one side of a controversial issue – the effect of such products on public health – was being presented by Federal Communications Commission (FCC) licensees in the form of advertisements. In the case of cigarettes, *Banzhaff* v. *FCC*,[53] the court noted that its ruling for equal time for countercommercials or presentations promoted the first amendment policy of fostering the widest possible debate and dissemination of information on matters of public importance. In the case of commercials for automobiles and high-octane gasolines, the court noted, 'When ... the hazards to health implicit in air pollution are enlarged and aggravated by such products, then the parallel with cigarette advertising is exact ...'[54] and ignored possible impacts on advertising and licensees as it sent the case back to the FCC for redetermination.

The idea that broadcast licensees should present balanced information on advertised but controversial technological processes or products is now a reality. Once again, the flow of information to the public, as

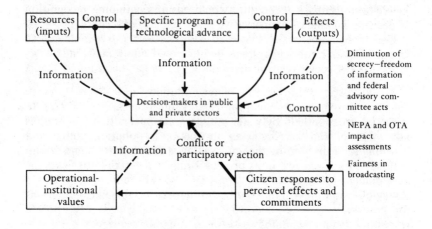

Fig. 5. Summary of influences and recent developments for decision-making.

indicated on the model (Fig. 5), is being enhanced and new corporate attitudes and advertising practices should follow. (The NEPA, OTA, secrecy, and 'Fairness' developments can now be depicted on the model.)

How will this enhanced flow of information be used by citizens responding to the effects of technology? What will be the nature and forms of the resulting new pressures on decision-makers?

On the model, the broad arrow from citizens to decision-makers represents not a flow of information, but adversarial processes in courts and agency proceedings. For decision-makers to learn from an endless series of adversarial processes is a slow, costly, and painful task that benefits only lawyers. The task facing the public sector and corporate decision-makers who are responsible for applications of technology is to transform this relationship from an adversarial one to one of joint decision-making and negotiation of differences in good faith among all interested parties – in short, to establish an ongoing dialogue and joint effort at assessing and planning the uses of technology.[55] This effort will require new institutional management procedures, the development of more sophisticated assessment techniques, the articulation of assumptions by decision-makers, an opening up of project or program planning and design stages, and, ultimately, structural and substantive changes in the political system.

'Who speaks for the public?' will become a central issue – one that the federal agencies and the courts are now grappling with in the context of NEPA.[56] Perhaps technology itself may provide some assistance here. Citizen-feedback technology exists, has been used experimentally, and has demonstrated a remarkable potential for both informing citizens and eliciting opinions and information useful for decision-making.[57] The enhanced process orientation that could result from applications of the recommended model, improved information flow, and new citizen-feedback techniques would ensure continuing recognition in decision-making of the pervasive social impacts of technology.

Can these numerous, fragmented developments in technology and in our legal and political systems be integrated into a coherent framework for the social control of technology? It has been noted that[58] (p. 729):

> ... *two major intellectual developments of the seventeenth century occurred almost simultaneously in law and science. The first was the drive for systematic arrangements and presentation of existing knowledge into scientifically organized categories ... the second ... was the concern with degrees of certainty or ... probability. .... By the end of the seventeenth century ... traditional views ... had been upset and new methods of determining truth and investigating the natural world had replaced those that had been accepted for centuries ... there was a strong movement toward arranging both concepts and data into some rational ordering that could be easily communicated and fitted into the materials of other fields so that a universal knowledge might emerge ... traditions of legal history and legal argumentation that assume the law's autonomous march through history are seriously in need of correction. ...*

It is now time to replicate this experience, develop a coherent framework for the social control of technology, and ensure that forthcoming processes of technology assessment and utilization will be systematic and humane.[59]

References

1. *Final Report of National Commission on Product Safety*, Government Printing Office, 1970, pp. 73–9.
2. Public Law 92–573 (1972).
3. *US Law Week*. Vol. 41, No. 16, 1972, p. 1061.
4. See, for example, J. Sweet, in *Legal Aspects of Architecture, Engineering and the Construction Process*, West, 1970, sect. 30.07, pp. 634–7.
5. 29 US Code 151.
6. 29 US Code 651. See *Job Safety and Health Act of 1970*, Bureau of National Affairs, 1971, for collection of relevant materials.
7. D. Cordtz, *Fortune*, Nov. 1972, p. 112.
8. As discussed by F. Grad, in *Environmental Law*, Bender, 1971, pp. 1–115.
9. *Harvard Law Review*, Vol. 84.
10. Coverage in the media has been extensive. See the 1971 and 1972 issues of the *Observer* and the *New York Times* – for example, *New York Times*, 7. 3. 1972, p. 17.
11. *Man's Health and the Environment*, Department of Health, Education, and Welfare, 1970, pp. 97–125.
12. *Boomer* v. *Atlantic Cement Co.*, 26 New York 2nd ser. 219, 257 New Eng. 2nd ser. 870 (1970) provides a classic example of judicial caution.
13. See 'Economic dislocation early warning system reports' of the Environmental Protection Agency, (mimeographed).

14. Note, for example, the numerous requests for variances from air pollution control requirements by industry and chambers of commerce that are now being processed and granted.

15. Public Law 92-500 (1972).

16. 42 US Code 1857, as amended by Public Law 90-148 (1967), Public Law 91-604 (1970), and Public Law 92-157 (1971).

17. Public Law 92-574 (1972).

18. Public Law 92-516 (1972).

19. *Legal Systems for Environment Protection*, legislative study No. 4 (UN Food and Agriculture Organization, 1972), pp. 23-32.

20. Congressional recognition of the relationship between technological advance and environmental deterioration is expressed in Title I, Section 101(a) of Public Law 91-190 (1970).

21. C. S. Russell and H. H. Landsberg, *Science* Vol 172, 1971, p. 1307; M. I. Goldman, *Science* Vol. 170, 1970, p. 37.

22. The Council on Environmental Quality has partially defined the task (23, p. 343): 'The contemporary world is to a great extent determined by technology.... The scale and speed of technological change may well have outstripped the ability of our institutions to control and shape the human environment.... It is important to understand the emerging technologies of the future and their implications for the environment and our way of life.... Predicting what and how new technologies will shape the future is a difficult task.... Even more difficult than predicting future technological developments is assessing what the full impact of any particular technology will be.... Despite the difficulties of assessing technology, it is essential that it be done.... We must develop the institutional mechanisms capable of making technology assessments....' Implicit in the council's proposal is the need for new methods to be employed in the development of assessments and the need for assurance that such assessments will indeed be used in decision-making in relevant public and private institutions.

23. Council on Environmental Quality, *Environmental Quality: Third Annual Report*, Government Printing Office, 1972.

24. A. Weinberg, *Science* Vol. 177, 1972, p. 27.

25. See, for example, *Technology in Retrospect and Critical Events in Science*, National Science Foundation, 1968.

26. B. Portnoy, *Cornell Law Review*, Vol. 55, 1970, p. 861.

27. 42 US Code 4321.

28. See *102 Monitor*, the monthly report of the Council on Environmental Quality, for listings of environmental impact assessments and periodic reviews of litigation related to NEPA. Also see (*23*, pp. 221-67) for a comprehensive survey of NEPA implementation.

29. No data available at this time. Statement based on conversations with professionals, familiar with nuclear power program.

30. See, for example, *Calvert Cliffs Coordinate Committee* v. *Atomic Energy Commission*, 449 Fed. Rep., 2nd ser. 1109 (DC Cir. Ct 1971).

31. As Senator Sam Ervin (DNC) has said 'When the people do not know what their government is doing, those who govern are not accountable for their actions – and accountability is basic to the democratic system. By using devices of secrecy, the government attains the power to 'manage' the news and through it to manipulate public opinion. Such power is not consonant with a nation of free men ... and the ramifications of a growing policy of governmental secrecy is extremely dangerous to our liberty' (*The Nation*, 8.11.1971, p. 456).

32. Boston *Globe*, 5.5.1972, p. 17.

33. See *Congr. Rec.*, 5.10.1972, p. 517059 regarding the Corps of Engineers and *Policy and Procedure Memorandum 90-4* (Department of Transportation, 1972) regarding the federal highway program.

34. The model is being used in the presentation of 'Law and the social control of science and technology' and 'Legal aspects of environmental quality', two graduate courses, and in several research projects at MIT by the author.

35. Public Law 91–190 (1970), Sect. 102 (2) (c).

36. *Fed. Reg.* Vol. 36, p. 7724, 23.4.1971.

37. Council on Environmental Quality, 'Memorandum for agency and general counsel liaison on NEPA matters' (mimeographed), 16.5.1972.

38. See the *102 Monitor* of the Council on Environmental Quality for abstracts of draft and final impact assessments, some of which grapple with new technological developments.

39. See *102 Monitor* Vol. 1, No. 6, July 1971, p. 1, for action by six jurisdictions. Since this review, Massachusetts has adopted its version of NEPA: Chap. 781 of Massachusetts Acts of 1972, amending Chap. 30 of Massachusetts General Laws. Connecticut is now considering similar action.

40. *Friends of Mammoth* v. *Mono County*, 4 Environ. Rep. Cases 1593, Calif. S. Ct. (1972).

41. Chap. 30, Massachusetts General Laws, sect. 62.

42. In *Calvert Cliffs Coordinating Committee* v. *AEC* (*30*), the court's ruling included discussion of the 'balancing process' that agencies must undertake in project decision-making to comply fully with NEPA, in addition to procedural compliance in the development of impact assessment: 'The sort of consideration of environmental values which NEPA compels is clarified in Section 102(2) (A) and (B). In general, all agencies must use a "systematic, interdisciplinary approach" to environmental planning and evaluation "in decision-making which may have an impact on man's environment". In order to include all possible environmental factors in the decisional equation, agencies must "identify and develop methods and procedures . . . which will insure that presently unquantified environmental amenities and values be given appropriate consideration in decision-making along with economic and technical considerations". "Environmental amenities" will often be in conflict with "economic and technical considerations". To "consider" the former "along with" the latter must involve a balancing process. In some instances environmental costs may outweigh economic and technical benefits and in other instances they may not. But NEPA mandates a rather finely tuned and "systematic" balancing analysis in each instance'.

43. See, for example, *Stop II 3 Association* v. *Volpe*, 4 Environ. Rep. Cases 1684 (1972), where the US District Court for Hawaii held that highway project design work and further test borings be enjoined until an impact assessment has been developed and used, since such work 'would increase the stake which . . . agencies already have in the (project)' and reduce any subsequent consideration of alternatives.

44. M. Baram and G. Barney, *Technology Review*, Vol. 73, No. 7, 1971, p. 48.

45. The 'Leopold Matrix' is a useful mechanism for promoting rational discussion and systemic resolution of project impacts by the proponents and opponents of a project in a nonadversarial setting. The matrix disaggregates impacts, calls for designation of probability of magnitude and significance of each impact, and can be completed by each of the interested parties in a project controversy. Comparative analysis of the results reveals important areas of difference of opinion and enables the parties to consider a variety of strategies for reducing these differences, such as design change or the need for concurrent projects to offset specific impacts. For example, waste water from a housing project may be one of the bases for community opposition, yet state and federal funds and programs may be available to reduce the problem. See *A Procedure for Evaluating Environmental Impact*, Circular No. 645, US Geological Survey, 1971. Also see P. Bereano (unpublished manuscript, 1971) for application of the 'Leopold Matrix' to technology assessment.

46. Public Law 92–484 (1972). For the text of the bill and relevant background, see US Senate, Committee on Rules and Administration, subcommittee on computer services, *Office of Technology Assessment for the Congress* (92nd Congr. 2nd sess., 2.3.1972).
47. *Soucie* v. *David*, 2 Environ. Rep. Cases 1626 (DC Cir. Ct., 1971).
48. 5 US Code 552.
49. Public Law 92–463 (1972) and Executive Order 11686 (1972). Also see US House of Representatives, committee on Government Operations, *Advisory Committees* (92nd Congr., 2nd sess., 4.11.1971).
50. M. Baram, *Harvard Business Review*, Vol. 46, No. 6, 1968, p. 66.
51. *Chlorinated Hydrocarbons in the Marine Environment*, National Academy of Sciences, 1971. p. 17: 'Recommendation: Removal of obstacles to public access to chemical production data. Among the causes contributing to the lack of available data on the chlorinated hydrocarbons is a legal structure that allows manufactures of a given material, when there are no more than two producers, the right to hold their production figures as privileged information.* The panel recognizes the economic rationale that deters the release of production figures by such manufacturers and understands that our government is charged by law with the protection of their proprietary interest. Indeed, we approve the principle that governmental action should not artificially affect competition. However, we also feel that there are times when it is not in the public interest for government to maintain as privileged data that are necessary for research into the state of our environment and for an assessment of its condition. In that regard, we recognize the possibility that it is not always competitive concerns alone that determine the less than candid posture assumed by industry concerning production figures. We recommend that the laws relating to the registration of chemical substances and to the release of production figures by the Department of Commerce and the Bureau of the Census be reexamined and revised in the light of of environmental deterioration. The protection afforded manufacurers by government is an artificial obstacle to effective environmental management, particularly with reference to the polychlorinated hydrocarbons. In view of other impediments – technological, methodological, and financial – such protection is clearly inappropriate.'
* For example, the Monsanto Chemical Company has refused to release its production figures for PCB's, although requested to do so by many scientists and government officials.
52. B. Wiggins, *Natural Resources Journal*, Vol. 12, No. 1, 1972, p. 108.
53. 405 Fed. Rep. 2nd ser. 1082 (1968); certiorari denied, 396 Supreme Ct. 824 (1969).
54. *Friends of the Earth* v. *Federal Communications Commission*, 2 Environ. Rep. Cases 1900 (DC Cir. Ct., 1971).
55. Of course, the achievement of a consensus is not sufficient to ensure responsible decisions: there must also be an integration of technical perspectives on long-term material and individual needs, which may have been ignored by the parties to the consensus. Such needs are usually too remote (for example, teratogenic effects) or hidden (for example, ground water depletion) to be accorded full consideration by project proponents and citizen adversaries.
56. See *Sierra Club* v. *Morton*, 45 Supreme Ct. 727 (1972), wherein the Supreme Court provided the latest answer to when '. . . a party has a sufficient stake in an otherwise justiciable controversy to obtain judicial resolution of that controversy. . . .' The court noted that injury other than economic harm is sufficient to bring a person within the zone of standing; that merely because an injury is widely shared by the public does not preclude an individual from asserting it as a basis for personal standing; that injury sufficient for standing can include esthetic, conservational, and recreational injury, as well as

economic and health injury. But the court noted that '. . . broadening the categories of injury that may be alleged in support of standing is a different matter from abandoning the requirement that the party seeking review must have himself suffered the injury . . .' and that '. . . a party seeking review must allege facts showing that he is himself adversely affected . . .' in order to prevent litigation by those '. . . who seek to do no more than vindicate their value preferences through the judicial process.'

57. T. Sheridan, 'Technology for group dialogue and social choice', MIT report to the National Science Foundation on grant GT 16 'Citizen feedback and opinion formulation', 1971; and D. Ducsik, N. Lemmelshtrich, M. Goldsmith, E. Jochem, 'Class exercise simulating community participation in decision-making on large projects: radiation case study' (unpublished manuscript, 1972).

58. B. Shapiro, *Stanford Law Review*, Vol 21, 1969, p. 727.

59. I wish to thank Dennis W. Ducsik, a doctoral candidate in the department of civil engineering at MIT who is pursuing an interdisciplinary program in environmental resource management and technology assessment, for his help as a research assistant in the project and in the development of this article. I also wish to acknowledge the support of the National Endowment for the Humanities (grant No. EO-5809-71-265).

Public involvement
in technology

Technical power and people

Tony Benn

The structure of government within the nation state, as now organized, is unlikely to survive in its present form. It evolved in response to circumstances very different from those that now exist and, as is evident, it is proving itself incapable of coping adequately with the amount of power that mankind now has at its disposal. It is both too small to exercise really effective human control over the destiny of its own citizens in a tiny and dangerous world; and it is too big and too clumsy an instrument to deal with the rapidly changing and diverse needs and values of people in the communities where they live and work.

This is the inescapable conclusion to which one is driven by even the most superficial examination of the impact of the technological revolution through which we are passing.

This process of political obsolescence has been going on for a long time; and it began to accelerate with the development of weapons systems that extended the range of warfare beyond the heavy artillery and relatively light and slow aircraft which were in use up until the Second World War. With the advent of nuclear weapons and intercontinental missiles, the nation state was forced to surrender its basic claim, on the allegiance of its people – namely, that it served as a necessary and effective instrument for defending its citizens against assaults from the outside. Modern weapons led to the move towards the bloc system of defense which represents, even for the senior partners in each bloc, a permanent erosion of their national independence and sovereignty. And it was recognized at about the same time that the ultimate logic of modern weaponry required the establishment of some world organization like the United Nations, with the implication that one day it would develop into an embryonic world government, however long it took to reach that state. Meanwhile the paralysis of the superpowers when they try to use their military arsenals is only too apparent.

But it is not only the emergence of external forces that have brought into question the credentials of the nation state. Technology has had

From Anthony Wedgwood Benn, 'Technical power and people: the impact of technology on the structure of government', *Bulletin of the Atomic Scientists*, Dec. 1975.

an equally dramatic impact on the lives of the citizens, in both less developed and highly developed societies. Their experience of modern life, amplified by the mass media, rendered more intelligible by improved education and made progressively more vulnerable and fragile by the interdependence that is inseparable from economic development, has led to demands being pressed from below which the modern state with a centralized power structure may be incapable of meeting quickly enough to avert intolerable strain, and possibly violent upheaval. Thus the second claim of the nation state that it can effectively protect a society against the risk of internal disorder or distintegration is also in doubt. Looking around the world the stresses in many countries can be seen to be dangerously above the safety level.

Nor is it only in terms of military or civil insecurity that the nation state has found itself on the defensive. Industrial development – especially by the multinational corporations – far exceeds the scale of operation of industry a generation ago, and the power of these new companies, not to mention their rate of growth, now exceeds that of many nation states. Governments of even quite advanced societies can no longer, therefore, claim to be wholly effective in safeguarding the interests of their citizens against possibly harmful decisions taken by these firms.

Moreover instantaneous worldwide communications available on more and more television channels means that the nation state can no longer guarantee to erect on its frontiers effective censorship that filters out unacceptable foreign ideas and preserves the sort of broad identity of views, culture and outlook that could be said to represent its way of life as embodied in the consensus on which its society worked.

The death-throes of the self-contained nation state may last for a very long time, but the process of transformation in the constitutional structure of society is as inevitable for the nation state as it is for any firm which finds technological change destroying its old management structure and requiring it to adapt itself accordingly.

The emergence of international managements controlling military and industrial power has now virtually ousted the shareholder or stock-holder as a center of power and has simultaneously stimulated greater demand for popular power.

In this process the role of science in society has come to occupy a central ground of argument between the new bureaucracies that see it as an agent for promoting their own aims and purposes, and people who increasingly see science both as a threat to their survival and, if properly used, as one of the key instruments for solving the problems that press on them most directly. Thus science has been drawn out of the academic atmosphere from which it drew its inspiration and original funding, and into the vortex of political controversy.

Science as instrument for political domination has given birth to the military-industrial complex which is immensely powerful in both the communist and noncommunist worlds. Enormous sums of money are made available from general taxation to develop new weapons systems which it is claimed will preserve a favorable power balance for those nations that are ready to pay the bill and spare the necessary qualified manpower.

But meanwhile, from below, more and more voices are being raised to divert these same resources to meet the needs of development and to improve living conditions. It is not just modern war with its inevitable killing that is becoming unacceptable, but the growing conviction that war-making absorbs money and skill on such a scale that, were it to be turned to constructive purposes, the causes of many conflicts that lead to war might be eliminated.

The same tug of war is evident in civil industrial developments. The bureaucracies which govern large firms (sometimes supported by governments) are forever seeking to maximize their return on capital invested by using science to make more sophisticated products and by employing complex techniques of persuasion to create a demand for them; at the same time, the public is beginning to question the whole process. First, they are concerned with the side effects that may follow from the unchecked economic growth that has up to now been regarded as an unmixed blessing. Second, they are beginning to wonder whether there are not other needs to be met than those which express themselves through market forces. The conflict between private and public transport in major cities is one example, and the whole structure of educational provision with its tremendous concentration on graduate and postgraduate work is another.

National governments are caught between these two formidable forces which are pulling in opposite directions. They know – because it is their business to know – that large and efficient managements will be required if the delicate balance in any world system is to be maintained. To this extent they are necessarily in close and continuing contact with the big organizations concerned.

At the same time, especially in societies where the vote has been granted, national politicians are painfully aware of the pressures coming from their electorates conveying, however, imperfectly, the problems and aspirations of ordinary citizens.

National governments are thus the fuse box connecting two conflicting realities. A great deal of current passes through that fuse box, and the heat is intense. If it blows, there could be a total blackout and a total breakdown. President Truman once said: 'If you don't like the heat, get out of the kitchen.' But somebody has to stay in the kitchen at least until we can find a cooler way to cook.

Until recent years the centralized bureaucracies seemed to be having it all their own way. They generated technology, and controlled the use to which technology was put. The public was so astonished by the new scientific miracles and felt so humble in the presence of the experts in science and technology who masterminded these achievements that they hardly questioned the purposes to which this power was being put.

Henry Ford was seen as a man who had put technology at the service of man. Military scientists were seen as key figures through whom security could be achieved and our enemies vanquished. Technical decisions were uncritically accepted as lying outside the capabilities of ordinary people to question and they stood back while the experts decided. Thus it was that President Kennedy's historic decision to put an American on the Moon by 1970, or the Anglo-French Treaty to build the supersonic airliner, were accepted without public debate. Both these ventures were seen as glorious examples of man's freedom deriving from his new-found power to control nature.

But once freedom – in this case scientific freedom – had been won, people started to question how that freedom should be used. It may take a highly skilled chemist to develop a contraceptive pill or a brilliant engineer to develop a new system of communication. But the use to which either is put involves the application of a scale of values which it is entirely within the capability of everybody and anybody to apply for himself. The problems of the control of technology in a scientifically permissive society can therefore be seen to be no more complex than any other value judgment which democratic societies now accept and that electors and voters are qualified to take.

Indeed, there is now growing evidence that more and more people are quite independently coming to the same conclusion and this is expressing itself in more forceful demands from below. These demands are not new ones, but what is significant about them is that for the first time the technology capable of satisfying them now exists.

Take first the demand for sufficiency from those who are still experiencing poverty – both the poor in developed societies and the even greater number of poor in societies that have not developed. These people are different from their forefathers in that they know that other people have escaped from poverty and that the technology that made escape possible is available to them. It is one thing to be poor when there is no choice, but it is another to accept what may appear to be an unnecessary poverty. This is the cause of the revolution of rising expectations in both developing and developed societies. As living standards rise expectations seem to keep well ahead of them and produce the curious phenomenon of levels of personal dissatisfaction rising in parallel with affluence.

The demand for greater equality is also gathering force, similarly fanned by the mass media. This is not merely a demand for greater economic equality, but also for racial and sexual equality which sees in discrimination an entrenchment of unacceptable privilege and a perpetuation of a more fundamental oppression. The use of resources including scientific resources to secure greater equality is highly relevant, especially in the educational field.

The worldwide demand for educational reform touches directly on the control of science. More and more people are becoming skeptical of the established objective of education to educate elites, including scientific elites. Even if looked at from a purely practical point of view it would appear that the main barriers to human advance lie more in our failure to apply well-established techniques than in our tardiness in evolving new ones. For example, millions more lives could be saved by raising the general level of simple health services than by pouring millions of pounds or dollars into perfecting heart transplants or other sophisticated surgical operations. There is even a curious convergence of view between a community which doesn't quite know how to employ the many PhDs emerging from graduate schools, heavy with honors but short of experience, and the students who everywhere are discontented because their studies are so academic and appear to lack 'relevance'. This feeling is shared on both sides of the Iron Curtain and there are more similarities between modern thinking on this in China and the United States than there are between the old school academic establishments in both these countries and the communities they are supposed to serve. Educational bureaucracies are already finding themselves on the firing line along with the military industrial complex as this pressure begins to build up.

The demand for greater popular power – or participation as it now tends to be called – follows from the demands described above. Where the franchise has not yet been won, it is being demanded; and where it has been achieved, there is a mounting pressure for further democratization of decisionmaking.

This pressure is not really new at all. It is as old as political philosophy itself, but what is new is that it is being extended far beyond the simple demands of the Founding Fathers of the American Republic or the French Revolution, or the modest advocates of universal adult suffrage. More and more people are coming to suspect that democracy has slipped through their fingers while they were busy watching science proving its apparently limitless capability.

The new bosses

Now, all of a sudden, people have awakened to the fact that science and technology are just the latest expression of power and that those who control them have become the new bosses, exactly as the feudal landlords who owned the land, or the capitalist pioneers who owned the factories, became the bosses of earlier generations. Ordinary people will not now be satisfied until they have got their hands on this power and have turned it to meet their needs.

This may sound like a very revolutionary doctrine, and so indeed it is. But once we understand what is happening, it is no more frightening than the demand for power that emerged in the past as a popular clamor for political democracy.

What we lack are the institutions capable of realizing that demand in today's world, and making it effective. It must necessarily lead to the strengthening of international and supranational institutions big enough to encompass the totality of man's needs as he gradually learns that brotherhood has moved from a moral aspiration to an essential pre-requisite of survival. We are mainly short on imagination bold enough to extend our sense of responsibility to embrace the area of our common interest. This imaginative leap is difficult for the old and the middle aged, but it comes quite naturally to the young. Their view of the Spaceship Earth with its people living closely together will in time replace the distortions of Mercator's flat projection showing every country highly colored within its political fronters – just as Galileo's view of the universe replaced the flat concept of the Ptolemaic astronomers.

Popular pressures

Nationally, the demand will express itself in more subtle ways. The pressure for open government which reveals the choices before they are made will intensify. Decisions affecting the use of science and technology, whether by governments, corporations or universities, will become increasingly the subject of critical scrutiny, as has been shown most vividly by the recent economic and environmental debates and decisions on the development of the supersonic transport. People may still argue as to whether the decision was right or wrong, but no one can doubt that it was taken openly and that the decisive pressure came from below in sufficient strength to overturn the wishes of an Administration and the aerospace industry, both of which wanted to go ahead.

Similarly, the environmental pressures that have built up over recent years can be seen as having a political significance greater even than the actual cause which the environmentalists espoused. They can be seen as a direct political demand under the classification of technology assessment aimed at securing a proper consideration of the consequences of all decisions before they are reached, so that the side effects can be taken into account at the time of the basic decision. This is a move to better and more democratic decisionmaking, and if it can be made a permanent feature of political life, it will be far more important even than the improvement of the environment. It may, in fact, serve to check the wildest environmentalists who are now pressing for unrealistic policies which could have unexpected industrial and human side effects.

But the pressure for democratization will not stop there. It is bound to extend to the democratization of industrial power, through workers' control, educational power and the power of the mass media which, by their control of information output, can play a decisive part in shaping society.

We are presently so conscious of the centralizing forces that derive from technological change and of the huge new and powerful bureaucracies that they have created that many people tend to be despondent, to believe that ordinary human influences are quite powerless and the cause of democracy is irretrievably lost as man surrenders to the new power centers. The emergence of countervailing power from the grass roots is less easy to recognize. It is dispersed so widely, its exercise is so uncertain, and the time scale of its successes is so long that many people do not believe it really exists. At the moment it may be only a potential power, but its potentiality is far greater than most people realize. We have not yet learned to organize ourselves to use the power that has fallen into our hands because we are not fully aware of it and because it requires us to think about our system of government in quite a different way.

The study of civics or political institutions as most of us learned about them at school, or through the mass media, always focuses upon the formal structure of the nation state. We are told how accountability has been secured by freedom of speech and the vote. But even this interpretation stresses what our leaders do and say. Policy and changes of policy are presented to us as coming from the top.

Change from below

But is that really how our political system works? I greatly doubt it. There is an interpretation of political change under which one can argue that it is change from below that has been and is really significant and can, over a period, be decisive. Certainly, the demand for the vote was a demand that came from the grass roots and was reluctantly conceded by the political leaders of the time. The demand for human rights or racial equality has never been particularly acceptable to those in authority in societies which denied these rights. The groundswell demand for free trade unions or socialized education or socialized medicine in a welfare state was not thought up in the corridors of power. They bubbled up in the community, lapping around the foundations of the establishment until they acquired sufficient momentum to swamp the opposition in Congress or Parliament. By this means, too, the environmentalists captured the White House and Number 10 Downing Street, making it clear that they would no longer tolerate the barbarities of technology. The new movement for women's rights has also gathered force outside the system and is already making progress within it against the entrenchment of male privilege.

It is arguable from this that the historic function of the politician is to capitulate, and that the good politician capitulates only to forces that he has helped to create by education and argument and by his encouragement of those who are trying to extend the area of human responsibility.

Indeed, the task of statesmanship today requires leaders to be more than bureaucratic administrators of vast governmental machines. For anyone who looks around him and, even more, anyone who looks ahead should see one fact staring him in the face. The amount of power that the technological revolution has created far exceeds the capability of even the most inspired, dedicated or brilliant leaders to control unaided.

In June 1940, when the seemingly unconquerable German Army stood poised on the French coast ready to attack Britain, Winston Churchill pledged himself to carry on the struggle 'until, in God's good time, the new world with all its power and might steps forth to the rescue and liberation of the old'. That is exactly the position confronting the statesman of today as he observes the massive and menacing power of technology which encompasses us. He must carry on the struggle until, in God's good time, the people with all their power and might step forth to the rescue and liberation of mankind.

Only a massive dispersal of power conveying responsibility beyond and within the nation state to those upon whose wise exercise of it our survival depends can possibly redress the balance in favour of the people in their battle to gain control of the machine. To pretend otherwise would be an illusion – an illusion we can ill afford to nourish.

Science, technology and democracy

Leslie Sklair

The *problem* of the control of science and technology [. . .] is notoriously difficult: even the most democratically minded in the most democratically organized societies appear to believe that science and technology cannot properly operate or develop under conditions of democratic control. That is, the ideal of a participatory democracy seems not to apply to the case of science and technology.

The reason for this, at first sight, is simple enough. Scientists and technologists are usually highly trained people whose knowledge and skills have been earned after years of study and practice. They are, in a word, experts, and like many experts in our society they have not only specialized information but they have also specialized languages in which to communicate with each other. Almost every new development brings with it a new vocabulary of terms or symbols. All of this conspires to isolate scientists from other men and to insulate science from the societies in which it is carried out. The case is different but not, I would maintain, totally dissimilar, for technologists and technology. [. . .] Technology is the expression of the practical institutionalization of science and it is through technology that most people experience the institutionalization of cognitive science. For example, we are all familiar with electric lighting and cooking appliances, and many of us have a fair knowledge of the principles of electricity as they apply to these appliances. The same holds true for the operation of, and principles behind, the internal combustion engines and the mechanical systems which contribute to the near paralysis of our cities most days. At this level, in fact, we are a remarkably sophisticated society, and the least educated members of advanced industrial societies have a vast fund of technical expertise and knowledge without which, of course, it would hardly be possible to survive. We rarely consider our talents in this respect precisely because these things are the bread and butter of modern life. It appears, then, to be perfectly possible to translate the content of science and particularly technology in order for the instructions for millions of devices, processes, and machines to be understood and operated by the public at large. This is clearly because at the stage

Extracts from Chapter 7 of Leslie Sklair, *Organized Knowledge*, Paladin, 1973.

when a product is ready to be marketed and sold to the general popula-tion the scientists and technologists responsible for its development (or some other relevant technically competent persons) are forced to do this translation. The ordinary consumer, therefore, is deemed to be competent to buy wisely and to use properly the fruits of science and technology. But at this point, in most cases and in most societies, the process stops. Beyond consumption the ordinary consumer is not generally deemed to be able to appreciate what goes on in science and technology; the private language remains untranslated and the esoteric knowledge remains uninterpreted.

As I have already said, this raises political as well as technical ques-tions. The problems of control of science and technology in modern society are a special case of the general problem of democracy, I shall argue, and not, as others have argued, simply irrelevant to the general problem of democracy because the masses do not and could not be expected to understand sufficient science and technology to make in-telligent decisions about them. This latter argument rests on the same fallacy as the argument used by many élitist theorists and those who consider all but the most superficial forms of democracy to be hope-lessly inefficient. That the masses could understand enough about science and technology in order to participate in decision-making in this area is not an *assumption* of my argument; it is a proposition that I shall support with evidence. This is necessary if my original concern, that technical possibilities should respond to the aspirations of men, is not to rely on the benevolence and enlightened despotism of scientific and technological élites; instead aspirations ought to guide technique because men can freely choose the structures of the societies they want.

The first part of the argument concerns the issue of how much and what kinds of science and technology people must know in order to make intelligent decisions. There are probably genetic limitations on the numbers of people in any population that are capable of becoming, even in the very best environment, theoretical physicists or molecular biologists, but even this much is by no means certain. In any case, very few people would agree that one actually has to be a working physicist or biologist to make sensible decisions of policy in these fields and in their applications. The reason for this is that it is probably impossible to be a working scientist or technologist, with all that this entails, and at the same time to devote more than a small fraction of the available time and energy to policy-making bodies. It is one thing for a working scientist to be a sometime member of a Science Advisory Board, it is quite another thing for him to be a full-time science or technology policy-maker as such. As with the laboratory administrator [. . .] the opportunities that such jobs allow for scientific research may well be rather limited. Further, the generalist, who has a greater knowledge of a variety of fields than the specialized researcher, is often seen to be the most suitable candidate for the important policy posts throughout the world. Clearly, then, one does not have to be a working scientist to be a policymaker in science and technology, if we are to judge by present experience, and perhaps it might even be a disadvantage to be one.

The generalist proposal, that policy-making in science and technology should be in the hands of those with a broad outlook covering many fields, looks at first to be altogether more plausible. This brings to the fore the debate around the criteria for scientific choice which has occupied many writers for many years. If the criteria for scientific choice are exclusively technical (scientific and/or technological), then the view that only scientists and technologists should be permitted to make these decisions gains great credence. If, on the other hand, the criteria for scientific choice are both technical and non-technical (social, political, economic, or any mixture of these or others), then it is very difficult if not impossible to maintain that scientists and technologists alone should be empowered with these decisions. The generalist, thus, is the man who not only has a broad knowledge of the whole of science and technology but also has some understanding of what is often termed 'the social relations of science and technology'. And it follows that, in many instances, the people who know most about the impact of particular pieces of science and technology are the people who actually experience it in their day-to-day lives, and it is totally unlikely that these people will happen to be scientists or technologists, whether specialists or generalists, in more than a small fraction of these cases. [. . .] The idea of informed public debate is at the very heart of the notion of democracy I wish to propound. This implies neither that everyone should know everything about everything – a patently ridiculous requirement – nor that everyone should be equally interested in everything – a patently unrealistic requirement. What it does imply, at the least, is that everyone should be given an opportunity to find out about those things that most affect his life, and that society be organized in such a way that people are positively encouraged to have an interest in these things. *Interests* may be used in a significantly ambiguous manner in this discussion: it is in our interest (to our advantage) to be interested in (unapathetic about) many things. Just as people may be interested in things which are not necessarily in their interests, it is even more true that people are very often not interested in things which are most certainly in their interests. For example, it is often said that certain types of young people nowadays are interested in 'the drug scene' and that this is not in their (best) interests; on the other hand it is often said that the very low turnouts in local government elections show that the majority of voters are uninterested in matters which will affect their vital interests. We may label these interpretations of interest in both senses as the 'official' or the observers' view.

The participants' view might look very different. The young man or woman using certain forms of what many reliable medical authorities consider to be relatively harmless drugs for amusement or paths to creative experience, might well regard those who assert their right to legislate what is and is not in his 'best' interests with some suspicion. Why, it may be asked, are alcohol and tobacco tolerated and their use in moderation deemed not contrary to the best interests of most of the population, whereas certain other drugs are banned ? The answer to this question is complex and clearly includes such factors as the tax revenue that alcohol and tobacco bring in, the probability that most of those responsible for the bans either smoke tobacco or drink alcohol or do both and few if any of them have ever experienced the drugs they ban, and the general opposition to the various drug cultures stimulated by the mass media (and misleadingly undifferentiated so as to prevent any legal distinction between hard and soft drugs from being easily acceptable). In both senses, then, the interests of the lawmakers and those whose actions are being affected by the laws can differ considerably.

The case of apathy in local elections may be similarly understood. The manifest point of having elections at all is to give people the choice between a variety of alternative candidates and policies. In the Free World democrats often sneer at the socalled elections in totalitarian countries such as the Soviet Union and Egypt where unopposed candidates are returned to the most important state offices with majorities of between 99 and 100 per cent. Apathy at election time in their own countries, therefore, is seen by these democrats as a shameful waste of rights and opportunities. The citizen who does not vote, however, may see the matter quite differently. He may see himself as a member of a tiny minority against a monolithic majority, with no chance of a change, and so the election is a foregone conclusion and it is not worth the effort to cast his vote. More likely the apathetic voter will fail to distinguish the *real* difference between the candidates, for he may feel that none of the alternatives will represent his interests. Perhaps he has voted in the past for different parties in response to the promises of one and then another, and nothing very much has happened to improve his situation. His apathy, then, is a rational act (or non-act), for if he believes that none of the candidates will do much for him then it is simply not worth voting. His best interests will not be served by a time- and energy-consuming interest in local politics as it stands, and he might either attempt to change the system, or failing that he might, as perhaps a majority of people do, withdraw from any meaningful participation in local political processes.

This latter issue illustrates one of the crucial problems of democracy and one that has its parallels with the questions of science and technology policy with which I am primarily concerned. It is not enough to ensure that there are no formal prohibitions on participation in political affairs for the creation of a healthy democracy. It is likewise not enough to ensure that there are no formal prohibitions on learning for the creation of an informed public. For the creation of a healthy democracy and an informed public which is an essential part of it, as opposed to naïvely *laissez-faire* liberalism – the invisible hand in the velvet glove – there needs to be a positive encouragement to citizens. Let us take the case of big science policy and look at what does happen and what could happen.

Effectively, the man in the street, the ordinary elector, has no direct say in big science policy-making and very little indirect say. [. . .] Most research and development is paid for either by governments, from taxes, or by private industrial firms, often in terms of a percentage of profits or turnover. In America, which accounts for about two-thirds of non-Communist R & D expenditure, most of the funds spent in the 1960s by the Federal government went for space and military purposes. I have already discussed the contract system and it is clear that the application of the 'public interest' in circumstances such as these raises serious doubts as to the operation of truly democratic principles. But at least the Apollo project did achieve its major objective, unlike many expensive military projects. In 1969 it was reported that Senate investigators were examining the failure of projects on which over $9,000 million had been spent. The eventually cancelled B-70 bomber had lost $1,500 million; $512 million were lost on a nuclear-powered aircraft; the Dyna-Soar space plane lost $405 million; and the Navajo and Skybolt missiles had consumed more than $1,100 million between them. 'All of these projects were totally abandoned. But [said the correspondent] in no case were they abandoned before the companies involved were paid in full for their efforts.'[1]

This appears to be only the tip of the iceberg. Underestimation of costs of major defence contracts is the rule rather than the exception, and it is tempting fate to have a system which encourages privately owned specialist companies, a large proportion of whose business comes from government and especially military contracts. This may not be totally unrelated to the fact that among the top executives of these firms are to be found unusually high numbers of retired military personnel. However one looks at it, public control over the choice of big science projects and expenditure leaves something to be desired. I have given these rather shocking figures not simply to insinuate abuse, although I must confess to a natural suspicion whenever public funds are privately disposed of, but also to show that either those responsible for making big science policy in these extremely expensive fields are criminally negligent and/or incompetent in a not inconsiderable number of cases. Criminality will be punished by the law where it is detected and guilt sustained (it may be noted that this type of fraud is somewhat less risky than, say, robbing banks), though the incompetent may be more difficult to dislodge. In any case, the gist of my argument is that with a little training most of us, adequately motivated, could hardly do worse than many science and technology planners apparently do. What lesson can we derive from this?

Keeping people out of science

In the first place, there would seem to be an excellent reason for those at present in control of big science and its funding to let it be widely understood that the issues involved were so technical and the knowledge required was so esoteric that only a select few could be considered competent to carry out this work and make the crucial decisions. In mock democratic spirit they might claim that 'society' or 'the people' or 'public opinion' decides what should be done, in general terms, and they, the experts, go ahead and make sure that it is done. The role of the public, therefore, is restricted to the provision of a general mandate for action. But, as we have seen, and as few citizens in the advanced industrial societies would wish to deny, there is rarely if ever any real debate about big science or its consequences, precisely because the issues are deemed to be too technical for the layman and sometimes even for the politicians themselves. The only choice that is given is in terms of the typically false dichotomy between growth and stagnation or between defence and destruction. The methods of the parties in the major democracies may differ, sometimes very considerably, but in the contemporary world the alternatives to more science and technology are conceived in such a way that reasonable and intelligent people, if they accept the premises, could not fail to agree to the technocratic or quasi-technocratic conclusions. And the very possibility of a critical scrutiny of the premises is rendered most unlikely, not by any formal prohibition (for that is not the way of enlightened democracy) but by a discouragement from all sides and an official climate of support for the professional, the expert, and the neutrality of technical information and decision-making. Therefore, whether it is to protect a lucrative racket or to protect a position of privilege, or whether it is simply to prevent the uninitiated from interfering with his work, the science policy-maker has every reason to dissuade members of the public from the view that the processes of making the decisions of big science are of legitimate concern to the unqualified.

There is another, rather more general reason why it is to the advantage of certain groups in advanced industrial societies that there should be little if any public discussion about science and technology or public participation in the decisions that are made about big science. [. . .] I refer of course to the assumption that we want a society in which large proportions of our national product go towards research and development in order to increase our national product even more, presumably in order to be able to invest yet more in R & D, and so on . . . I shall only say at this stage that countries where most people are well fed and well housed and somewhat educated are in a different position with respect to this matter than poor countries. E. J. Mishan, in a recent book which elaborates many of these points, has aptly labelled this assumption 'growthmania' and, like every mania, if most people suffer from it then those that do not are apt to be considered if not maniacs themselves, then at least a little odd.

We have isolated some potential motives that those responsible for big science policy might have for excluding the rest of the population from their deliberations. As I have said, there is no intention on my part to suggest any sort of conspiracy theory that might argue that these policy-makers deliberately mislead the public, obstruct the efforts of anyone trying to discover what they are doing, or that they systematically attempt to abuse the considerable powers that they possess.

Obviously, all of these things do happen here as in most other similar institutions; the point is that the exclusion of the public from decision-making in this and other areas does serve a set of interests which can be traced to a particular group of people, which is not to say that their interests necessarily conflict dramatically with those of the public.

When we add up these factors, the social image of the expert whose knowledge and talents are asserted to be inaccessible to ordinary men and women, plus the sheer immensity of big science and its curious detachment from day-to-day existence, plus the vested interests that those in a position to help the public to come to terms with the problems have in maintaining the system as it is, it is hardly surprising that the population at large is not only as good as disenfranchised in matters of science and technology but also that it seems not to mind very much. Even on the infrequent occasions on which public opinion is aroused by technical issue, e.g. the Anglo-French Concorde project or the *Torrey Canyon* oil tanker disaster in Britain, the antiballistic missile system (all \$20,000 million of it) or the great Nevada radiation cloud leak in the United States, it is either too late for the outcry to make much difference, or decisions are taken in any case which pay only the scantest attention to what the people might want.

Bringing people into science

Situations such as these force political decisions on us, and these are decisions which indicate how serious we are about democracy. I have already suggested that there are good reasons for not leaving all the decisions about big science in the hands of the big scientists, whether specialists or generalists, though of course it would be foolish to exclude them from participation in such decisions simply because they are big scientists or administrators. Indeed, it is clear that those who are technically trained and competent have the essential role to play that all specialists in all societies might play, namely to tell us what is possible and impossible, likely and unlikely. The crude objection to science policy-making (often distinguished from technology policy-making) – that new knowledge is unpredictable and so we cannot plan science – is so philosophically weak as to be laughable, except for the fact that many liberal-conservative philosophers and scientists appear to accept it as an impeccably logical argument. For their benefit one may briefly suggest that science policy, like any other type of policy, does not pretend to certainty, neither does it pretend to magical powers of prophecy. Nevertheless, if vast sums of money are devoted to a particular branch of science, then the likelihood of advances there are greater than if it is neglected; if large numbers of mathematically trained researchers are attracted to biology rather than physics, then we can expect certain types of developments in the bio-medical sciences; and finally, if we build a 300 GeV intercontinental accelerator, then we can be sure that certain types of new particles will be identified. It is in a rather occasional and special sense that new knowledge is utterly unpredictable. Therefore, scientists and technologists will be able to make intelligent predictions about the consequences of their work, and though it would be unreasonable to expect them to be totally accurate all the time, it is reasonable to expect them to be very accurate some of the time and fairly accurate most of the time.

In the only case study known to me of a serious experiment involving lay advisory committees on research – in the US Department of Agriculture – it was said that 'the advisory committees did not destroy the freedom of the scientist'.[2] It is, however, impossible to generalize from this experience for my purposes here because the lay advisors turned out to be mainly the large-scale producers and their representatives; neither the small men nor the consumers appeared to be able to achieve membership. Current experiments with methods of technology assessment in the USA, USSR, and China might well, in the next few years, provide further relevant information.

Before any of the philosophers or scientists or other defenders of Western civilization go into paroxysms of rage at the notion of science by public committee, let me at once note both that this is in no way implied by what I say and that if indeed anyone thinks that it is, then it only proves how deeply ingrained are some attitudes in the minds of some of our most educated citizens. And let me also reiterate the distinction I have made between little science for purely cultural reasons and big science as a public responsibility. (Not that culture cannot have unintended consequences – who would have thought that the Beatles would become significant earners of foreign currency for a hard-pressed economy, and be rewarded in traditional British fashion for their efforts.) Where small sums of money are granted to scientists in order that they might have the leisure and a little equipment or research assistance to follow their hunches, it would be as ridiculous to expect them to spend a lot of time and effort at first justifying and then explaining the success or failure of their work to interested members of the public as it would be to expect recipients of small grants for poetry or painting to do the same. However, where very large sums of public money are concerned and where significant manpower consequences will arise from the carrying out of the project, it is as reasonable to expect the scientists and technologists to justify what they intend to do publicly as it would be to expect the architects and designers involved in the rebuilding of a city centre to do the same. The analogy is altogether too near the bone as many people who have visited some of our towns and cities might agree. All too often private profit – usually largely risk free – rather than civic need provides the motivation for urban redevelopment as it does for big science.

Once we have established (or at least planted the seed of) the notion that big science can in some meaningful fashion be planned, and that the planners need not always and at every stage be scientists or technologists themselves, and that public involvement is desirable, we are left with the apparently insurmountable problem of making science and technology intelligible to a willing public. I am assuming, no doubt thus betraying a naïvely Utopian prejudice, that in the unlikely event that both big scientists and the authorities were to make great efforts to demythologize big science, and were to succeed in showing the public that decisions in this area could be democratically reached if certain cognitive conditions were satisfied, the public would be willing to receive instruction in technical matters. It might be worth considering some sort of test for the citizen which he had to pass in order to win a place on one of the Councils of Public Discussions on Decisions in Big Science, in much the same way as people nowadays have to pass driving tests before they can be allowed to drive cars on the public highway.

This is not a study in the sociology and politics of education, and so I can only point out some general reasons why this problem of instructing the public in technical matters appears to be insurmountable, and the recommendations that I shall make will seem rather piecemeal. Apart from the vested interests of those at present in control, which results in the tendency to withhold from all but a very few popularizers of science a modicum of professional respectability, let alone high esteem, the phenomenon of 'the opposition to science and technology' must not be ignored. Indeed, the low prestige that the science community accords to its popularizers is often related to the ambivalent feelings that many people in advanced industrial societies appear to have about big science. The link, of course, is the Frankenstein or the ecological catastrophe syndrome. It is not difficult, with a little knowledge of current developments in a few selected fields, to present a convincing enough case for the probability that the new biology will create monsters or that big science in general will poison our atmosphere or melt our ice-caps. What makes this so easy to do is the fact that the alarmist position, especially on pollution, is in many cases more than justified by the available technical evidence. Popularizers who point this out, and who help to stimulate anti-scientific attitudes, are thus regarded by those whose work is thereby brought into the public eye in a critical fashion as interferers and troublemakers. It is usually easier to rebuff such attacks by impugning the scientific credentials of the popularizer than by meeting his arguments.

All of this will tend to put obstacles in the way of an improved public comprehension of scientific matters, and to see why this is so it is necessary to reflect for a moment on the nature of the mass media. In general it is true to say that whenever controversy is generated in large-circulation newspapers or magazines or on television rational argument and a careful weighing of the evidence are less often decisive in the resolution of the debate than are the personalities of the protagonists and their respective public relations skills. (These latter factors are also important even in some purely academic disputes.) When these tendencies lead to sensationalism and large undocumented claims and to blanket *ad hominem* refutations the cause of popularizing science is ill served. Exposure to science and its disputes does not always necessarily lead to an informed public for the simple reason that if the exposure leaves behind a mess of false ideas and misleading impressions then perhaps those exposed are worse off than they were before. Studies of the presentation of science and technology in the mass media, from Britain and America, give little indication that the picture I have drawn is unduly pessimistic, though there are, of course, honourable exceptions.

Education, whether or not it starts in the home, is supposed to continue in the school, and undoubtedly it is in the school that the future citizen will be most influenced with respect to an interest in and a willingness to learn about science and technology. [. . .] As far as the majority of children are concerned – those who leave school around fifteen years of age and have no further formal education, and who make up the majority of the electorate – the situation is often irreparable although [. . .] at some levels all who can operate satisfactorily in an advanced industrial society will have an historically unique collection of technical skills and knowledge. But these are mostly, as it were, 'after the event' skills and knowledge, and what is necessary for real public participation in big science decision-making is that the mass of the population should have the confidence and the desire to come into the process *before* it is too late to do anything about what is happening.

Most very expensive projects, especially civil and military aviation ones, provide examples of this. The defence of the Anglo-French Concorde is increasingly of the variety: well we've spent so many millions of pounds on it already, we may as well finish it. Perhaps the first law of R & D economics (Realpolitik) might be expressed as: where there are risk-free profits to be made free enterprise will encourage governments to throw good money after bad! As the US military examples I have already quoted suggest, projects tend to be cancelled after vast sums of public money have been spent on them and not before. It is little wonder then that people who are interested enough in these problems and who take the trouble to instruct themselves on the issues involved become discouraged and disappointed in the potentialities of the democracies in which they live. And it is no wonder at all that most of the population appear to assume that there is very little point in bothering about these problems, for their chances of influencing decisions in these areas are practically nonexistent.

Broadly, education has its positive and negative dimensions. It is only realistic to speak about the education of young people and adults in the various aspects of science and technology which clearly do affect their lives if certain political possibilities are opened up to them. It is perhaps the case that there are some people who have a desire to learn on a wide front as part of their genetic apparatus, but it is certainly the case that environmental variables strongly influence the individual's desire to learn in general and that the social organization of the school, the neighbourhood, and the wider political community in which the individual is located, can make a very great difference to his basic educability. If the experiences of those nations with widespread educational systems teach us anything, they teach us that given favourable conditions a large proportion of the population of every nation is capable of assimilating the knowledge and skills necessary for modern living, and a lot more besides. There is no reason *a priori* why well-planned education could not be very effective in any context to a level where people could at least have an intelligent opinion on problems raised. I am *not* suggesting for a moment that the people collectively do the science or technology; I *am* suggesting that they could have an appreciation of what is being done.

Already, in circumstances of great public disquiet, like the furore that greeted the decision over the siting of a third airport for London, and the fairly regular uproars over contaminated food, relevant groups do organize and try to act collectively. Where the level of public alarm is high, then we may assume that the potential for education is present although, as I have suggested, this need not always have totally desirable consequences.

The ideal state of affairs, accordingly, would be as follows. A proposal is made and, after some not altogether random though informal public and private discussions, it is deemed to be worthy of serious consideration. If it is a very expensive proposal and one that would need support on a variety of levels, financial, educational, political, and so on, then it might enter some formal process whereby information about it could be made readily available and displayed in places where people are liable to see it rather than where they are not. There would seem to be no reason why people who lived in the same street or in the same block might not meet informally though purposively to discuss the proposal and perhaps to call on local 'experts' who could be relied upon to answer questions about it and to explain it. These local groups might be loosely organized, say through local schools or police stations or pubs, into larger units where further discussions might take place and people might benefit from the views of people very different from themselves.

To the protests of the 'realists' who would reject such a scheme out of hand with the objection that the vast majority of people would not take the trouble to attend these meetings or that under conditions of perpetual consultations nothing would ever get done, there are simple answers. First, if people were given the opportunity that a nationally sponsored and supported scheme such as I describe could offer, and they chose not to take advantage of it on several occasions and permitted important decisions to be taken without their participation, then they would have less cause for complaint than they have now. In this case, a valuable experiment in practical democracy would, in my view unfortunately, have failed. But to find out we must try it.

Second, the thesis that it is massively inefficient and time-wasting is unconvincing because, as things stand at present, major proposals do in fact take many years of committee work, expert consultation, and often political debate in parliaments and in other high places before decisions are reached. While all this top-level activity is going on it would be quite possible for the public to become involved in the processes of deliberation, debate, mutual education, and finally representation in the actual decision. It must be borne in mind that in complex situations simple yes–no decisions are rather unlikely to be the most important. It is far more likely that many choices will have to be made between a variety of alternatives and that with a wider body of decision-makers we can expect even more alternatives. Again, all or nothing decisions, though sometimes called for, probably occur less frequently than decisions which imply branching paths. For example, a major proposal like the Channel tunnel scheme contains a large number of related problems, each of which might have a set of alternative solutions, and each of these solutions might create new sets of problems and so on. At every point the path has branches and each branch in its turn becomes a new path with its branches. So it is not a matter of 50 million British citizens or 200 million Americans having a big meeting and saying yes or no to one specific proposal, but a fairly long-term multi-faceted process whereby ordinary people might become involved in those parts of the decision-making which they felt to be most closely related to their interests.

In the Channel tunnel example everyone in Britain and France would have at least a minimal financial interest if the money were to come from their taxes. The communities at each end of the proposed tunnel, both actual and potential, would have an interest in terms of the changes in their patterns of living that such a scheme would inevitably bring. The engineering problems involved in such a venture and the alternative methods put forward are clearly technically complicated to a high degree, but it is difficult to believe that they are so complicated that the general principles behind the choices of those putting forward the plans could not be explained and illustrated to the untrained public. If, for example, the adoption of one method meant that a massive investment in one type of engineering would be necessary and that this would in all probability constrain the development of other types of engineering, and perhaps make it probable that other projects in the future would use this method, then – apart from the engineering and technological merits of the method, which are obviously matters of great importance – the possible consequences of all this for, say, the ordinary consumer of domestic appliances in ten years' time might also be taken into account.

These considerations are especially relevant in the development of new materials. Plastics provide a good illustration of the problems in this area. At first, hard-wearing, almost indestructible, and now possibly entirely indestructible plastics seemed a great boon to all and sundry. They quickly found a multitude of uses both as improvements on existing materials and, in response to the insatiable desire of manufacturers to enlarge their markets, in entirely new ways. Now, of course, we are faced with the phenomenon of literally millions of un-wanted, useless, or obsolete objects which we cannot get rid of precisely because of the quality which originally had made them so wanted and useful – their indestructibility. Thus we see the essentially ambivalent nature of scientific and technological progress.

The moral of this story for the Channel tunnel proposal is that the more ordinary people who have no particular reason for favouring one or other of a variety of proposals and subproposals the more likely it is that these little flaws might be spotted. If a massive investment were required to develop, say, a material capable of withstanding enormous water pressures and also transparent so that travellers could watch the fish, and if it were likely that to recoup some of the R & D costs all sorts of other uses were to be suggested for it so that our civilization would be likely to utilize it in every possible case, then it would be only sensible to put it before as wide a panel as possible in order that the benefit of the total national experience might be directed to consider possible snags.[3]

To repeat my earlier claim: if we are serious about the ideal of a participatory democracy, then all of these suggestions would not seem as ridiculous as they undoubtedly will do to many responsible people in advanced industrial societies. It is, nevertheless, legitimate to ask whether or not public participation in the formation and evaluation of big science policy would result in different decisions in fact being taken. Even if my notions of participatory democracy find sympathy here and there could it not be argued that the end result would not be so unlike what we now have? Science and technology, perhaps, would continue very much as before. This view is often expressed with the implicit and sometimes explicit belief that science and technology have an intrinsic dynamic, an internal mechanism which ensures to a greater or lesser extent that they will continue to develop once a certain take-off stage has been reached. Thus, the argument goes, other than a certain educational and/or therapeutic effect, public participation in the decisions of big science would not significantly change its progress one way or another. Leaving aside the very real importance of the education and/or therapy involved – and these may be absolutely crucial and sufficient reason for the whole thing in any case – the argument about the intrinsic dynamic of science and technology seems to me to be the next line of defence of those who find the idea of the democratization of science and technology unpalatable, but who might admit some of the points I have made. For the intrinsic dynamic view has a most important bearing on what I have termed 'alternative futures'. And this is where big science and our theories of social change collide, for though science and technology were always supposed to provide us with a future full of so many exciting alternatives, it often appears to be the case that big science, while providing some alternatives, cuts out many more.

References

1. Harlow Unger, *Sunday Times*, 19.10.1969.
2. L. C. Mainzer, 'Science democratized; advisory committees on research', *Public Administration Review*, **18**, 1958, pp. 314–23.
3. In his otherwise very enlightened book, *Scientific Knowledge and Its Social Problems*, Raverty (1971) finds no place for the public in these matters.

Why public participation is essential in technology assessment

Joseph F. Coates

The spread of bureaucracy in both the public and private sectors of American society is one of the most important characteristics of our age. A combination of economic and technological forces produces a web of increasingly complex problems all closely interrelated. The pressure of these forces toward bigness and the accumulation of the so-called 'critical mass' fosters bureaucracy both within government in all branches and at all levels as well as in the private sector, in industry, and even the educational, professional, and non-profit communities. A significant aspect of the process of bureaucratization is the symbiotic relationship between the public and the private bureaucracies.

As bureaucracies grow bigger, power flows to the center into the hands of an elite technocracy. Whether by intent or by circumstance, technocrats tend to gather unto themselves the intellectual, organizational, and financial resources which permit them to make the critical decisions governing the whole society. There is a long-term trend toward an information-dependent society which, of necessity, puts a high premium on education, knowledge, information, intellectual elitism, and specialization. This is true not only for advanced science and high technology but also for some of the seemingly more routine applications. A good deal of expertise is needed to run a sewage system, a social security program, a water works, a power grid, or a fire department.

Bureaucratization induces a number of qualities inimical to the basic concepts of democracy and free society. Bureaucracies tend to be secretive, self-serving, non-imaginative, non-risktaking, and susceptible to functional lying. They lack a nervous system commensurate with their size and responsibility. In their relationships with the public, bureaucracies withhold certain kinds of unpalatable information or deliver information in such a way that it distorts facts. Bureaucracies find it even more difficult than individuals to deal with bad news. Although they are intended to be the servants of the public, in fact, bureaucracies mature into instruments freighted with various kinds of impediments limiting responsiveness to commonwealth interests.

The traditional means by which citizens have participated in decision

From Joseph F. Coates, 'Why public participation is essential in technology assessment', *Public Administration Review*, Jan.–Feb. 1975.

making by governments, aside from the electoral process itself, have been the courts, lobbying, and public hearings. These channels have fallen far short of a satisfactory mechanism for involving the citizenry in decisions affecting their welfare.

The courts tend to focus mainly on procedural rather than substantive issues. Even when they do address substantive issues, the intellectual structure of the law does not match with considerations that should enter into management of a highly technologized society. The span of responsibility of the courts is not likely to be congruent with the domain of real world impacts. In contrast with the breadth of issues involved, the framework offered by the courts is likely to be parochial, limited, time-bound, and circumscribed in outlook.

Lobbying is, by nature, a special interest activity. The formation of citizen lobbies and broadly based consumer interest groups is a relatively recent phenomenon. The power they wield does not rival that of the established and well-financed special interest lobbies clustered in Washington and the state capitals. The activity of the special interest lobbies, separate or together, is not congruent with the broad interests of the general public.

Hearings are forums in which special interest groups seek to dominate. Whether of an adversary or advocacy nature, hearings lend themselves to special pleading. More often than not, they are short-term, local, and highly circumscribed. Collectively, the witnesses rarely cover all important issues and perspectives. Hearings have the added disadvantages of being time-consuming, expensive, and redundant.

In summary, the three traditional means through which citizens have participated in making decisions on using technology to meet society's needs are all inadequate as a clear expression of public interest. Furthermore, the public is not yet up to the task of representing its interests. In the first place, there is no such thing as 'the Public'. On any particular issue, citizens divide up according to perspectives and interests. A representational cross-section of public opinion is easy to grasp as a theoretical concept but difficult to transfer to reality. When new issues of a technological nature arise, as for example the environmental-energy confrontation, it is not easy to identify and mobilize the public interest or even a representative collection of various public interests. Public attitudes have not kept up with the fast pace set by technological change. It is a major task to draw forward in a timely fashion these latent and inchoate publics, to cause them to rise from their low levels of consciousness in a search for answers to complex current issues. The groups that *are* well organized and active are likely to suffer from certain characteristics which disqualify them as representatives of the broad commonweal. They are usually ideologically oriented, closed, and single-focused.

By contrast with these traditional procedures for citizen participation, technology assessment is a class of policy studies which systematically examine the effects on society that may occur when a technology is introduced, extended, or modified with special emphasis on those consequences that are unintended, indirect, or delayed. The issues with which technology assessment is concerned are issues of the future. But there is no constituency for the future. No group can lay claim to representing the commonweal for time yet to come. Nor, for that matter, are there experts in the problems of the future. The experts in the recognized disciplines are likely to provide suboptimal advice reflecting their predispositions and biases. With all due respect to the futurists and the value of their efforts to forecast future trends, their specialization has not yet reached the point of scientific expertise. But future studies are becoming more sophisticated and more useful to the policy process.

The United States and other industrialized nations now find themselves caught up in a technological revolution in which every new technology produces new ignorance. The bureaucracies that control our fate, whether public or private or an inseparable mix of the two, seek to ride the turbulent current of change. But, as noted above, they are ill-prepared to face up to bad news. Technology assessment is all too likely to yield bad news, along with the good. Those who manage the bureaucracies are tempted to pretend to not to hear or hope that the bad news will go away.

What can public participation do to bring more rationality into this disordered scene? On many different fronts, different publics are being awakened. The collective movement of public interest groups represents perhaps the most promising new development within our political system. But the movement can go in either of two directions. It can become a constructive force for directing change or a destructive force for arresting change. It can cooperate with those in control of the bureaucracies in efforts to shape the future or it can challenge the bureaucracies in a confrontation doomed to stand-off and stalemate.

In order to assure that the movement goes in a positive direction there needs to be responsible leadership on the part of those guiding the citizen groups and, equally important, a responsive attitude on the part of those who guide the bureaucracies. Obviously, it would be unrealistic to expect complete harmony and reconciliation. Tension and conflict will be essential to the resolution of the issues involved in technology assessment. Adversary proceedings will almost certainly be required as a part of the process of public participation. But they should be better grounded in understanding.

If the input of citizen groups to the technology assessment process is to have any significant effect, those who are active in these groups must be informed in areas of complex scientific and technological matters. To interface with the technical experts and impact their decisions, the representatives of the public must themselves be knowledgeable in substantive matters. The educational process will be demanding over sustained periods of time. Fortunately, there is growing evidence that many groups and individuals are willing to make the kind of effort and sacrifice necessary to give new meaning to citizen participation.

The political impact of technical expertise

Dorothy Nelkin

Technologies of speed and power – airports, power generating facilities, highways, dams – are often a focus of bitter opposition. As these technologies become increasingly controversial, scientists, whose expertise forms the basis of technical decisions, find themselves involved in public disputes. This 'public' role of science has generated concern both within the profession and beyond; for a scientist's involvement in controversial issues may violate the norms of scientific research, but have considerable impact on the political process. As scientists are called upon to address a wider range of controversial policy questions,[1] 'problems of political choice [may] become buried in debate among experts over high technical alternatives'.[2]

This paper will discuss some of the implications of the increasing involvement of scientists in controversial areas. What is the role of experts in public disputes? How are they used by various parties to a controversy, and how do scientists behave once involved? Finally, what is their impact on the political dynamics of such disputes?

The role of experts

Scientists play an ambivalent role in controversial policy areas. They are both indispensible and suspect. Their technical knowledge is widely regarded as a source of power. 'The capacity of science to authorize and certify facts and pictures of reality [is] a potent source of political influence.'[3] Yet experts are resented and feared. While the reliance on experts is growing, we see a revival of Jacksonian hostility toward expertise, and of the belief that common sense is an adequate substitute for technical knowledge.[4]

The authority of expertise rests on assumptions about scientific rationality; interpretations and predictions made by scientists are judged to be rational because they are based on 'objective' data gathered through rational procedures, and evaluated by the scientific

From Dorothy Nelkin, 'The political impact of technical expertise', *Social Studies of Science*, Vol. 5, 1975.

community through a rigorous control process. Science, therefore, is widely regarded as a means by which to de-politicize public issues. The increasing use of expertise is often associated with the 'end of ideology'; politics, it is claimed, will become less important as scientists are able to define constraints and provide rational policy choices.[5]

Policy makers find that it is efficient and comfortable to define decisions as technical rather than political. Technical decisions are made by defining objectives, considering available knowledge, and analyzing the most effective ways of reaching these objectives. Debate over technical alternatives need not weigh conflicting interests, but only the relative effectiveness of various approaches for resolving an immediate problem. Thus, scientific knowledge is used as a 'rational' basis for substantive planning, and as a means of defending the legitimacy of specific decisions. Indeed, the viability of bureaucracies depends so much on the control and monopoly of knowledge in a specific area, that this may become a dominant objective.[6] Recent technological disputes, however, suggest that access to knowledge and expertise has itself become a source of conflict, as various groups realize its growing implications for political choice.

The past decade has been remarkable for the development of 'advocacy politics';[7] consumer advocates, planning advocates, health care advocates and environmental advocates have mobilized around diverse issues. Key slogans are 'accountability', 'participation', and 'demystification'. These groups share common concerns with the 'misuse of expertise', the 'political use' of scientists and professionals, and the implications of expert decision making for public action. Table 1 presents some statements of these concerns by various groups: radical scientists who have organized to develop 'science for the people'; consumer advocates concerned with corporate accountability; advocacy planners who assist communities in expressing their local needs; and environmentalists and health professionals who demand 'demystification of medicine'.

Their criticism reflects a dilemma. The complexity of public decisions seems to require highly specialized and esoteric knowledge, and those who control this knowledge have considerable power. Yet democratic ideology suggests that people must be able to influence policy decisions that affect their lives. This dilemma has provoked a number of proposals for better distribution of technical information; expertise, it is argued, is a political resource and must be available to communities as well as to corporations, utilities or developers.[8] The increasing importance of technical information has also prompted analyses of the behaviour of scientists as they are diverted to applied and controversial work.

For example, Allan Mazur suggests that the political (i.e. non-scientific) context of controversies crucially affects the activities of scientists, the way they present their findings, and thus their ultimate influence on decisions. Despite norms of political neutrality, claims

Mazur, scientists behave just like anyone else when they engage in disputes; their views polarize and as a result the value of scientific advice becomes questionable. Thus, disputes among experts may become a major source of confusion for policy makers and for the public.[9] Guy Benveniste, focusing on the use of scientists by policy makers, suggests that 'technical' decisions are basically made on political or economic grounds. Expertise is sought as a means of supporting particular policy programmes; the selection of data and their interpretation are thus related to policy goals.[10] Similarly, King and Melanson argue that when knowledge is employed in the resolution of public problems, it is shaped, manipulated, and frequently distorted by the dynamics of the policy arena.[11]

These analyses emphasize the politicization of expertise. Details of two recent disputes in which 'experts' were used by both project developers and critics provide an opportunity to develop these arguments, and then to explore the impact of experts on the political process. One of the disputes concerns the siting of an 830 megawatt nuclear power plant on Cayuga Lake in upstate New York; the other is the proposed construction of a new runway at Logan International Airport in East Boston, Massachusetts.

The power plant siting controversy began in June 1967, when the New York State Electric and Gas Company (NYSE&G) first announced its intention to build Bell Station.[12] Groups of scientists and citizens, concerned with the thermal pollution of Cayuga Lake, organized themselves to oppose the plant, and demanded that NYSE&G consider design alternatives that would minimize the damage to the lake caused by waste heat. They forced the utility to postpone its application for a construction permit, and to contract for additional research on the environmental impact of the plant. In March 1973, following consultants' recommendations, NYSE&G announced a power station plan that was essentially the same as its earlier controversial design. The company, however, was now armed with data from one and a half million dollars' worth of environmental research supporting its claim that the heat from Bell Station would not damage the lake. Yet once more there was concerted and well-informed public opposition, this time focused on radiation hazards. Four months later the company was forced to abandon its plan.

The proposed new 9,200-foot runway at Logan Airport was part of a major expansion plan that had been a source of bitter conflict in East Boston for many years.[13] Located only two miles from the centre of downtown Boston in an Italian working-class community, this modern convenient airport is a source of extreme irritation, fear, and community disruption. The expansion policies of the Massachusetts Port Authority (Massport) have been opposed, not only by airport neighbours but also by Boston's city government and by state officials concerned with the development of a balanced transportation system. Here, as in the Cayuga Lake power plant siting debate, knowledge was used

Table 1. Public concern with expertise

Radical scientists	Consumer advocates	Environmentalists	Advocacy planners	Medical critics
On the misuse of technology				
[we] feel a deep sense of frustration and exasperation about the use of [our] work. We teach, we do experiments, we design new things – and for what? To enable those who direct this society to better exploit and oppress the great majority of us? To place the technological reins of power in the hands of those who plunder . . .	What is needed is a sustained public demand for a liberation of law and technology to cleanse the air by disarming the corporate power that turns nature against man.	Many believe that the advantages of our technology compensate for environmental degradation . . . Some have faith that the laboratories that have delivered miracles can also provide the tools to remedy any problems man may face. But with technology's gifts to improve man's environment has come an awesome potential for destruction.	Advocacy planning may be one of the channels of action through which people may try to humanize their technical apparatus; to prevent the exercise of bureaucratic power from leading to a new diffuse despotism, in which power appears in the image of technical necessity.	Psychiatry and psychology are used as direct instruments of coercion against individuals. Under the guise of 'medical methods', people are pacified, punished, or incarcerated.
On the use of expertise				
Skills and talents of potentially enormous usefulness have been bent to destructive ends to guarantee expansion and protect imperialism. For the sake of the ruling	Too many of our citizens have little or no understanding of the relative ease with which industry has or can obtain the technical solutions . . .	It doesn't require special training to keep a broad perspective and to apply common sense. Thus, for every technically knowledgeable [person] there is a layman	Even without administrative power, the advocate planner is a manipulator . . . The planner may not be the first to identify 'problems' of an urban area, but he	Professionals often regard themselves as more capable of making decisions than other people, even when their technical knowledge does not contribute to a

class scientists and engineers have been turned into creators of destruction by the mechanisms of an economic and social system over which they can exert no control.		activist . . . In fact, the technologist's training can stand in his way. There is a growing awareness that civilized man has blindly followed the technologists into a mess.	puts them on the agenda and plays a large part in defining the terms in which the problem will be thought about – and those terms in effect play a large part in determining the solution.	particular decision . . . Professionalism is not a guarantor of humane, quality services. Rather it is a code-word for a distinct political posture.

On expertise and public action

What we can hope is not that scientists can provide the people with an objective approach to build a better world, but that in the better world built by the people, scientists will be able to work in a more objective fashion, unfettered by elitism and the worst competitive aspects of present-day science.	An action strategy must embrace the most meticulous understanding of the corporate structure – its points of access, its points of maximum responsiveness, its specific motivational sources and its constituencies.	The importance of the environmental movement's potential rests not only in what tangible results it can accomplish, but in its acting as a catalyst to start people working together. Alliances possible by organizing around environmental concerns stagger the mind of the seasoned community organizer.	Any plan is the embodiment of particular group interests . . . any group which has interests at stake in the planning process should have those interests articulated . . . Planning in this view becomes pluralistic and partisan – in a word, overtly political.	Medicine should be demystified. . . . When possible, patients should be permitted to choose among alternative methods of treatment based upon their needs. Health care should be deprofessionalized. Health care skills should be transferred to worker and patient alike.

Sources: These statements are quotations from editorials and the popular literature circulated by such groups as SESPA, Nader's Raiders, Earth Day groups and the Health Policy Advisory Centre.

as a resource both by Massport, seeking justification for its expansion plans, and by those opposed to such plans. Massport's staff was backed by consultants who claimed that without expansion the airport would reach saturation by 1974, and that the new runway would cause no environmental damage. The opponents, primarily from the adjacent working-class neighbourhood of East Boston, used technical advice provided by the city of Boston. Following pressure from the governor as well as from the mayor, Massport eventually deleted the proposed runway from the master plan for future airport development.

While this paper will focus on similarities in the dynamics of these two disputes, it is necessary first to point out important differences. The community opposed to the power plant was a college town; the dispute was a middle-class environmental conflict, sustained by expertise from scientists in a nearby university who also lived in the area. In contrast, the opposition to the airport came primarily from a working-class neighbourhood dependent on expertise provided by government officials who, for political and economic reasons, chose to oppose the airport development plans.

The technical aspects of the two disputes were also quite different. The power plant issue was embedded in a set of vague uncertainties and intangible fears about radiation; airport expansion posed the concrete and direct threat of increased noise and land purchase. The main area of technical conflict in the former case was the potential environmental impact of the new power plant and the experts involved were mostly scientists and engineers. In the latter case the controversial issue was the validity of projections – whether the runway was really necessary at all – and the dispute involved economists and lawyers as well as engineers.

Despite such differences, the two cases have a great deal in common: the use of expertise, the style of technical debate, and the impact of experts on the political dynamics of the dispute are remarkably similar.

The use of expertise

Opposition to both the power plant and the airport developed in several stages. The developers (utility manager, airport manager) contracted for detailed plans on the construction of their proposed facility. As they applied for the necessary permits, affected groups tried to influence the decision. The developer in each case argued that plans, based on their consultants' predictions of future demands and technical imperatives concerning the location and design of the facility, were definitive, except perhaps for minor adjustments necessary to meet federal standards.

In the power plant controversy, scientists from Cornell University who lived in the community were the first to raise questions about the NYSE&G plan when it was announced in 1967. By mid-1968, their activity had built up sufficient political support to persuade NYSE&G

to postpone its plans, and to undertake further environmental research.

A new sequence of events began in March 1973, when NYSE&G again announced its intention to build the plant and claimed that it was imperative to begin construction promptly. The company's consultants, Nuclear Utilities Services Corporation, had prepared a five-volume technical report. NYSE&G placed copies in local libraries, circulated a summary to its customers, and invited comments. The report supported NYSE&G's earlier plan for a plant involving a General Electric boiling water reactor with a once-through cooling system. The study concluded that cooling towers (which had been recommended by power plant critics in 1968) were economically unfeasible in the size range required for the plant, unsuited to the topography of the area, and would have a tendency to create fog. To develop an optimum design for a once-through cooling system, consultants designed a jet diffuser to provide rapid mixing of the heated discharge with the lake water. With this system, they argued that the plant would have an insignificant effect on the aquatic environment of Cayuga Lake. The consultants only briefly concerned themselves with the issue of radioactive wastes on the grounds that this was not a problem unique to Cayuga Lake; the report only stated that the effect would be substantially below current radiation protection standards.

NYSE&G organized an information meeting attended by 1,000 citizens, and for two hours summarized the highly technical material supporting its plans. This, however, was followed by two and one-half hours of angry discussion, and the utility's president announced that if public protest was likely to cause delay, they would build the plant at another site. He hoped, however, that the decision would be 'based on fact and not on emotion'.

The first organized response came from twenty-four scientists who volunteered to provide the public with a review and assessment of the utility's massive technical report.[14] Their review was highly critical and NYSE&G's consultants responded in kind (see below). Meanwhile, citizens' groups formed and the community polarized, as the company posed the issue in terms of 'nuclear power *or* blackouts'.

The airport case also involved experts on both sides of the controversy. Opposing forces mobilized in February 1971, at a public hearing required by the Corps of Engineers in order to approve Massport's request to fill in part of Boston Harbour. One thousand people attended and for ten hours scientists, politicians, priests, schoolteachers and others debated the priorities which they felt should govern airport decisions. Massport's staff was backed by consultants, who claimed that without the runway the airport would reach saturation by 1974. Consultants provided a brief environmental statement arguing that the new runway would have no direct detrimental effects of ecological significance. The only environmental costs would be the elimination of ninety-three acres of polluted clam flats and two hundred and fifty acres of wildlife preserve – which constituted a hazard in any case because birds interfere with jets. Furthermore, because of the added flexibility, the runway would relieve noise and congestion caused by an expected increase in aircraft operations. Massport's claims were later buttressed by an environmental impact statement commissioned from Landrum and Brown, Airport Consultants, Inc. at a cost of $166,000. The study documented Massport's contention that the new runway was essential for safety and would be environmentally advantageous; it emphasized the positive contributions of Logan Airport – its economic importance to the City of Boston, and the reduction of noise that would result from increased runway flexibility.

The opposition was organized by a coalition of citizens' groups called the Massachusetts Air Pollution and Noise Abatement Committee. The issues raised were diverse. Neighbourhood people spoke of the discomfort caused by aircraft operations, and of Massport's piecemeal and closed decision-making procedures. Environmentalists feared the destruction of Boston Harbour, and planners related airport decisions to general urban problems. Legal, economic, and technical experts became involved as the Mayor's office and the Governor evaluated Massport's claims. As in the power plant case, the conflict polarized as Massport posed the issue in terms of 'airport expansion *or* economic disaster'.

The style of technical debate[15]

In both cases the technical debate involved considerable rhetorical licence, with many insinuations concerning the competence and the biases of the involved scientists.[16] NYSE&G emphasized that the need for a nuclear power plant on Cayuga Lake was 'imperative', that there would be a serious energy shortage if they did not proceed immediately with the plan, and that the impact of the plant on the local environment would be 'insignificant'. NYSE&G insisted on their unqiue technical competence to make this decision. 'Our study is the most comprehensive study ever made on the lake. Opponents can create delays but are not required to assume responsibility.' . . . .

However, the Cornell critics called NYSE&G's data 'inadequate', 'misleading', 'non-comprehensive', and 'limited in scope and inadequate in concept.' Some of the critics provided data from other research that contradicted NYSE&G's findings. They emphasized that there was simply not enough known about deep-water lakes to assess the risks.

NYSE&G consultants countered by claiming that Cornell critics were unfamiliar with the scope and requirements of an environmental feasibility report; in particular, that the critics' review failed to distinguish between the goals of pure and applied research. 'From an academic position a complete ecological model that predicted all possible relationships would be desirable, but this was neither feasible nor necessary for assessing the minor-perturbations caused by one plant.'

In fact, each group used different criteria to collect and interpret technical data. The two studies were based on diverse premises which required different sampling intervals and techniques. NYSE&G consultants, for instance, claimed that their water quality studies focused on establishing base-line conditions to predict the changes caused by the power plant; Cornell studies focused on limiting factors, such as the impact of nutrients on lake growth.

Scientists attacked each other with little constraint. Cornell reviewers accused NYSE&G consultants of value judgments that led to 'glaring omissions', 'gross inadequacies', and 'misleading interpretations'. Consultants referred to the Cornell report's 'confusion resulting from reviewers reading only certain sections of the report', and 'imaginative, but hardly practicable suggestions'. The NYSE&G president accused the Cornell reviewers of bias: 'It is of some interest that many of the individuals who participated in the Cornell review have taken a public position in opposition to nuclear plants. Philosophical commitment in opposition to nuclear generation may have made it difficult for these reviewers to keep their comments completely objective'.[17]

A similar style of debate characterized the technical dispute over the airport runway. Expansion of Logan was recommended by consultants as 'the best opportunity to realize a reduction of current social impact'. Failure to expand the airport as proposed would cause delays, increase air pollution, reduce safety margins and have a 'drastic' and 'immeasurable' impact on the local economy – 'an impact which the Boston area could not afford'. Massport's environmental report described and rejected, one by one, alternatives proposed by airport opponents. Banning specific types of aircraft 'interferes with interstate commerce'. Limiting maximum permissible noise levels is 'legally questionable', since the airport functions as part of a coordinated national system. A surcharge for noisy aircraft would be 'useless' as economic leverage, since landings fees represent a negligible percentage of total airline expenses. Setting night curfews is 'precluded' by the interdependence of flight schedules and aircraft utilization requirements: it would relegate Boston to a 'second-class' airport and have 'disastrous effects' on service to 65 per cent of the 267 cities served by Boston. Moreover, 70 per cent of the cargo business would be 'negatively affected'. Soundproofing neighbouring houses and building would be 'economically prohibitive' and have little effect. The *only* feasible solution to noise and environmental problems, according to the consultants' report, was an expanded runway system that would permit increased flexibility. Massport insisted on the validity of its expertise: 'We are closer and more knowledgeable than any other group no matter what their intention may be, on what Logan Airport . . . what Metropolitan Boston, what the entire state of Massachusetts and New England needs.'[18] And Massport consultants suggested their agreement with their client when, in a technical analysis of the airport's economic impact, they stated: 'It is inconceivable that an enterprise of this magnitude can be treated other than with the most profound respect.'[19]

Airport opponents called the Massport technical reports 'the logical outcome of efforts directed toward narrow objectives'. City consultants contended that authority to restrict aircraft noise was in fact limited neither by the FAA nor by the Massport enabling act, and that the FAA actually encouraged airport operators to restrict airport noise independently. They argued that Massport's assumptions concerning anticipated demand for increased airport capacity were questionable and in any case were subject to modification by consolidating schedules and dispersing general aviation flights. Massport's own raw data suggested that with a reasonable adjustment Logan Airport could accommodate a considerable increase in actual business, for aircraft were operating at an average of just under half capacity. Moreover, projections were based on the growth pattern of the 1960s. The decrease in air travel demand in 1970 could have been regarded either as a new data point or as an anomaly. Massport chose the latter interpretation, ignoring the 1970 slump. Their projections also ignored the possibility of competitive alternatives to air travel.[20]

Massport's figures concerning the economic impact of expansion and the consequences of a moratorium on expansion were debunked by critics as 'blatant puffery'. As for Massport's contention that the new runway would be environmentally advantageous, city representatives concluded that an expanded airfield would only expose new populations to intolerable noise. Instead, they recommended measures to increase capacity at Logan through scheduling adjustments and efforts to distribute the hours of peak demand by economic controls such as landing fees.

Differences were to be aired at a second round of public hearings scheduled for 10 July 1971. However, on 8 July, following a task-force study that recommended alternatives to expansion, Governor Sargent publicly opposed the construction of the new runway. Under these circumstances, the Corps of Engineers was unlikely to approve the project, so Massport withdrew its application for a permit and temporarily put aside its plans for the runway. A year and a half later, in February 1973, Massport deleted the proposed runway from the master plan for future airport development. Citing projections that were close to those used by airport opponents two years ealier, the Port Authority claimed that re-evaluation of future needs indicated that the new runway was no longer necessary.

Both disputes necessarily dealt with a great number of genuine uncertainties that allowed divergent predictions from available data. The opposing experts emphasized these uncertainties; but in any case, the substance of the technical arguments had little to do with the subsequent political activity.

The impact of expertise on political action

In both the airport and power plant controversy, it was the *existence* of technical debate more than its *substance* that stimulated political activity.[21] In each case the fact that there was disagreement among experts confirmed the fears of the community and directed attention to what they felt was an arbitrary decision-making procedure in which expertise was used to mask questions of politicial priorities

This relationship between technical disputes and political conflict was most striking in the power plant case. Cornell scientists assessed the NYSE&G report with the intention of providing technical information to the public. They focused almost entirely on the issue of thermal pollution – the effect of the plant's heated effluent on Cayuga Lake. The citizens' groups, however, were most concerned with the issue of radiation. They had followed the considerable discussion in the press and in popular journals about the risks associated with the operation of nuclear reactors – risks that had not been as widely publicized at the time of the first controversy in 1968. Thus, the thermal pollution issue (which had dominated earlier controversy) became, in 1973, a relatively minor concern. Citizens, in contrast to the scientists who were advising them, focused on problems of transporting and disposing of nuclear wastes, on the reliability of reactor safety mechanisms, on reactor core defects that would allow the release of radioactive gases, and on the danger of human error or sabotage.

When the citizens' committee first met to establish a position on the issue, its newsletter concentrated entirely on the reactor safety issue.[22] This set the tone of subsequent discussion, in which three possible courses of action were considered: that the committee oppose construction of any nuclear plant on Cayuga Lake until problems of reactor safety and disposal of radioactive wastes were resolved; that it take up its 1968 position and oppose only the *current design* of Bell Station; or that it support NYSE&G plans. The first proposal, one of total opposition, won overwhelming support. The emphasis of citizens' groups thereafter was on the risks associated with nuclear power, despite the fact that the technical debate dealt mainly with the problem of thermal pollution.

The disputes between scientists, however, served as a stimulus to political activity. In the first place, the criticism by Cornell scientists neutralized the expertise of the power company. Simply suggesting that there were opposing points of view on one dimension of the technical problem increased public mistrust of the company's experts, and encouraged citizens to oppose the plant. Second, the involvement of scientists gave moral support to community activists, suggesting that their work would be effective. The citizens' groups called attention to NYSE&G's statement that if there were concerted opposition, the company would not go ahead with its plans. The ready support of local scientists led to substantial expectation in the community that the effort involved in writing letters and going to meetings would not be wasted.

As for the details of the technical dispute, they had little direct bearing on the dynamics of the case. Citizens trusted those experts who supported their position. People who supported NYSE&G voiced their trust in the consultants employed by the power company: 'Let us allow the professionals to make the decisions that they get paid to make.' And power plant critics used expertise only as a means to bring the issue back to its appropriate political context. The case was one of local priorities, they claimed; it was not a technical decision: 'To say that our future is out of our hands and entrusted to scientists and technicians is an arrogant assumption ... We suggest that the opinions of area residents who care deeply about their environment and its future are of equal if not greater importance'.[23]

In the airport case, the technical arguments served primarily to reinforce the existing mistrust of Massport among those opposed to airport expansion, and they were virtually ignored by those who supported Massport. Opinions about the necessity of the runway were well established prior to the actual dispute. In East Boston, Massport employees and local sports clubs which were supported by an airport community relations programme defended the Port Authority's plans for a new runway and maintained their trust in Massport's competence. 'In terms of efficient and competent operation, Massport is head and shoulders above other agencies.'

Airport opponents, while benefiting from the advice provided by experts from the City of Boston, claimed the issue was a matter of common sense and justice. They defined the problem in terms of values (such as neighbourhood solidarity) which are not amenable to expert analysis. 'We need no experts. These people will verify themselves the effect of noise. .... Massport is extremely arrogant. They do not have the slightest conception of the human suffering they cause and could not care less.'[24]

Airport critics pointed out various technical errors and problems of interpretation in Massport's predictions and environmental impact statements; but this simply re-confirmed the community's suspicion of Massport, and further polarized the dispute. Later, these same experts who were sympathetic to East Boston's noise problem failed to convince the community to accept a Massport plan for a sound barrier. Despite advice that this would help to relieve their noise problem, the community chose to oppose construction of the barrier. Local activists feared that this was a diversion, and that if they accepted this project the community would somehow lose out in the long run. Thus, they disregarded expert opinion that this was a favourable decision, and the old mistrust prevailed.

Summary and conclusions

The two conflicts described above, over the siting of a power plant and the expansion of an airport, have several aspects in common. One can trace parallels, for instance, in the way the developers used expertise as a basis and justification of their planning decisions; how experts on both sides of the controversy entered the dispute and presented their technical arguments; and how citizens affected by the plan perceived the dispute. Similarities are evident in public statements, as developers, experts and citizens expressed their concerns about various aspects of the decision-making process. These are compared in Table 2. These similarities, especially with respect to the use of scientific

Table 2. Perspectives on decision making and expertise

	Power plant dispute	**Runway dispute**
Developers		
On responsibility and competence for planning	Our study is the most comprehensive study ever made on the lake. Opponents can create delays but are not required to assume responsibility.	We are closer and more knowledgeable than any other group no matter what their intention may be, on what Logan Airport . . . what Metropolitan Boston . . . what New England needs.
On public debate	We have adopted a posture of no public debate.	We have competent staffs . . . I can't see any sense in having a public hearing . . . If it is to be by consensus that the authority operates . . .
Experts (consultants)		
On impact of project	Alternate approaches would have undesirable effects on the human environment . . . the proposed design should produce no significant impact. Actual individuals would be exposed to much lower doses than that due to normal habits.	Adverse environmental impact will result from failure to undertake this project as contrasted with the impact if the Authority proceeds. Noise measurements of typical urban noise conditions . . . show that street level background noise overshadows taxi-way noise.
On planning	Although an ecological model might be desirable from an academic viewpoint it is not felt to be necessary to provide an adequate assessment of the impact of the minor perturbation introduced by the proposed plant.	A master plan would be nothing more than an academic exercise . . . a study of this magnitude could never be justified for a small project of this nature.
Experts (critics)		
On developers' data	Statements and conclusions were not justified and must therefore be regarded as nothing more than guesses . . . The data base is not only inadequate, but misleading.	Analysis of the economic impact of Logan Airport shows demonstrated 'blatant puffery' in the figures appearing in the report.

(cont.)

Table 2 (*cont.*)

Citizens (project supporters)		
On decision-making responsibility	Let us allow the professionals to make the decisions that they get paid to make.	In terms of efficient and competent operation, Massport is head and shoulders above other agencies.

Citizens (project opponents)		
On decision-making responsibility	To say that our future is out of our hands and entrusted to scientists and technicians is an arrogant assumption . . . We suggest that the opinions of area residents who care deeply about their environment and its future is of equal if not greater importance.	We need no experts. These people will verify themselves . . . Massport is extremely arrogant. They do not have the slightest conception of the human suffering they cause and could not care less.
On decision-making process	Were they using the power the people gave them to support their own feelings or those of private concerns? There is representative government in our country, but it sure isn't in our county.	What is really on trial here is not just the Port Authority, it is really the American system. Will it listen to spokesmen for the people and the people who speak for themselves?

Sources: These perspectives are direct quotations from public hearings, letters or transcripts of meetings.

knowledge, suggest several related propositions which may be generalizable to other controversies involving conflicting technical expertise:

First, *developers seek expertise to legitimize their plans and they use their command of technical knowledge to justify their autonomy.* They assume that special technical competence is a reason to preclude outside public (or 'democratic') control.

Second, *while expert advice can help to clarify technical constraints, it also is likely to increase conflict,* especially when expertise is available to those communities affected by a plan. Citizens' groups are increasingly seeking their own expertise to neutralize the impact of data provided by project developers.[25] Most issues that have become politically controversial (environmental problems, fluoridation, DDT) contain basic technical as well as political uncertainties, and evidence can easily be mustered to support or oppose a given proposal.

Third, *the extent to which technical advice is accepted depends less on its validity and the competence of the expert, than on the extent to which it reinforces existing positions.* Our two cases suggest that factors such as trust in authority, the economic or employment context in which a controversy takes place, and the intensity of local concern will matter more than the quality or character of technical advice.[26]

Fourth, *those opposing a decision need not muster equal evidence*. It is sufficient to raise questions that will undermine the expertise of a developer whose power and legitimacy rests on his monopoly of knowledge or claims of special competence.

Fifth, *conflict among experts reduces their political impact*. The influence of experts is based on public trust in the infallibility of expertise. Ironically, the increasing participation of scientists in political life may reduce their effectiveness, for the conflict among scientists that invariably follows from their participation in controversial policies highlights their fallibility, demystifies their special expertise and calls attention to non-technical and political assumptions that influence technical advice.[27]

Finally, *the role of experts appears to be similar regardless of whether they are 'hard' or 'soft' scientists*. The two conflicts described here involved scientists, engineers, economists and lawyers as experts. The similarities suggest that the technical complexity of the controversial issues does not greatly influence the political nature of a dispute.

In sum, the way in which clients (either developers or citizens' groups) direct and use the work of experts embodies their subjective construction of reality – their judgments, for example, about public priorities or about the level of acceptable risk or discomfort. When there is conflict in such judgments, it is bound to be reflected in a biased use of technical knowledge, in which the value of scientific work depends less on its merits than on its utility.

References

1. See discussion of the increased demands for expert decision-making in Garry Brewer, *Politicians, Bureaucrats and the Consultant*, Basic Books, 1973. Also, Dean Schooler, Jr., in *Science, Scientists and Public Policy*, The Free Press, 1971, suggests that in the past, scientific influence has concentrated in government entrepreneurial areas such as space exploration, or in policy areas defined in terms of national security. The participation and influence of scientists has traditionally been rather minimal in policy areas with redistributive implications, e.g. social policy, transportation, and other issues subject to social conflict and competing political interests. As the public seeks technical solutions to social problems, and as scientists themselves become engaged in controversial public issues, this pattern is changing.
2. Harvey Brooks, 'Scientific concepts and cultural change', *Daedalus*, Vol. 94, Winter 1965, p. 68.
3. Yaron Ezrahi, 'The political resources of American science', *Science Studies*, Vol. 1, 1971, p. 121. See also Don K. Price, *Government and Science* (New York University Press, 1954).
4. For a discussion of the historical tradition of resentment of experts in the United States see Richard Hofstadter, *Anti-intellectualism in American Life* (Knopf, 1962).
5. See Robert Lane, 'The decline of politics and ideology in a knowledgeable society', *American Sociological Review*, Vol. 31, Oct. 1966, pp. 649–62, and Daniel Bell, *The End of Ideology*, The Free Press, 1960.

6. See discussion in Michel Crozier, *The Stalled Society*, Viking Press, 1973, Chapter 3. A vivid example of the importance of this tendency to monopolize knowledge occurred during the 'energy crisis' with the realization that the large oil companies had nearly exclusive knowledge on the state of oil reserves.

7. I am using this term to describe a phenomenon that Orion White and Gideon Sjoberg call 'mobilization politics', in 'The emerging new politics in America', in M. D. Hancock and Gideon Sjoberg (eds.), *Politics in the Post Welfare State*, Columbia University Press, 1972, p. 23.

8. Note for example the system of 'scientific advocacy' proposed by John W. Gofman and Arthur R. Tamplin, *Poisoned Power*, Rodale Press, 1971. A similar system is suggested by Donald Geesaman and Dean Abrahamson in 'Forensic science – a proposal', *Science and Public Affairs (Bulletin of the Atomic Scientists)*. Vol. 29, Mar. 1973, p. 17. Thomas Reiner has proposed a system of community technical services in 'The planner as a value technician: two classes of utopian constructs and their impact on planning', in H. Wentworth Eldridge (ed.), *Taming Megalopolis*, Vol. 1, Anchor Books, 1967. Based on systems similar to legal advocacy and expert witness in the courts, such proposals are intended to make technical advice more widely available to citizens' groups – usually through provision of public funds to underwrite the cost of expertise.

9. Allan Mazur, 'Disputes between experts', *Minerva*, Vol. 11, April 1973, pp. 243–62.

10. Guy Benveniste, *The Politics of Expertise*, Glendessary Press, 1972. See also Leonard Rubin, 'Politics and information in the anti-poverty programs', *Policy Studies Journal*, Vol. 2, Spring 1974, pp. 190–5.

11. Lauriston R. King and Philip Melanson, 'Knowledge and politics', *Public Policy*, Vol. 20, Winter 1972, pp. 82–101.

12. For a history and analysis of this controversy see Dorothy Nelkin, *Nuclear Power and its Critics*, Cornell University Press, 1971; 'Scientists in an environmental controversy', *Science Studies*, Vol. 1, 1971, pp. 245–61; and 'The role of experts in a nuclear siting controversy', *Science and Public Affairs*, Vol. 30, Nov. 1974, pp. 29–36.

13. Documentation of this conflict can be found in Dorothy Nelkin, *Jetport: The Boston Airport Controversy*, Transaction Books, 1974.

14. Two hundred copies of the critique were sent to libraries, citizens' groups, faculties at universities and colleges in the area, officials in state and federal agencies, political representatives in local, state and federal government, and newspapers.

15. Unless otherwise noted, the quotations that follow are from local environmental reports, memos, letters and public hearings. They are statements by the opposing scientists involved in the controversy.

16. Mazur, op. cit. note 9, also documents the use of rhetoric in technical debates.

17. William A. Lyons, 'Recommendations of the executive Offices of New York State Electric and Gas Corporation to the Board of Directors' (13 July 1973).

18. Edward King, Massport Executive Director, Testimony at US Corps of Engineers' 'Hearings on the application by the MPA for a permit to fill the areas of Boston Harbour', 26.2.1971, mimeograph, p. 101.

19. Landrum and Brown, Inc., *Boston-Logan International Airport Environmental Impact Analysis*, 11.2.1972, section ix, 3.

20. A systematic critique of Massport's data was made by a commission chaired by Robert Behn (Chairman of Governor's Task Force on Inter-City Transportation), 'Report to Governor Sargent', April 1971.

21. For further discussion of this point, see Nelkin, 'The role of experts in a nuclear siting controversy', op. cit., note 12.

22. CCSL (Citizens Committee to Save Cayuga Lake), *Newsletter*, 6 (April 1973). This newsletter reprinted in full a selection of well-informed articles – notably those by Robert Gillette in *Science*, Vol. 176, 5.5.73; Vol. 177, 28.7.1972, 8.9.1972, 15.9.1972 and 22.9.1972; and Vol. 179, 26.1.1973.
23. Statement by Jane Rice cited in the *Ithaca Journal*, 14.5.1973, p. 1.
24. These statements are from testimony at US Corps of Engineers' Hearings, op. cit. note 18. The ultimate expression of this kind of sentiment was, of course, the remark alleged to have been made by former Vice-President Spiro Agnew, responding to the report by the US Presidential Commission on Pornography and Obscenity: 'I don't care what the experts say, I *know* pornography corrupts!'
25. For further discussion of the tactics of using expertise within the fluoridation controversy, for example, see Robert Crain et al., *The Politics of Community Conflict*, Bobbs Merrill, 1969; and H. M. Sapolsky, 'Science, voters and the fluoridation controversy', *Science*, Vol. 162, 25.10.1968, pp. 427–33.
26. The relation between beliefs and the interpretation of scientific information is analyzed in S. B. Barnes, 'On the reception of scientific beliefs', in Barry Barnes (ed.), *Sociology of Science*, Penguin Books, 1972, pp. 269–91.
27. See discussion of how controversy among scientists influences legislators in Barnes, ibid.

The consumer movement and technological change

Jeremy Mitchell

Discovery of the consumer

In its current form, the consumer movement represents a reinterpreta-
tion of an idea that is itself far from new. In 1928, Beatrice Webb was
proclaiming that the fundamental distinction between the two types of
organization represented by 'associations of producers' on the one
hand and 'associations of consumers' on the other was '. . . perhaps the
most pregnant and important piece of classification in the whole range
of sociology'. As the archetype of an association of consumers, Mrs
Webb chose the Co-operative Movement of Great Britain, whose
origins dated back to 1844 and which was the precursor of consumer
co-operative movements throughout the world.

However, in its origins, the co-operative movement was not really a
consumer association at all. It was strongly inspired by the syndicalist
ideals of the self-governing workshop. Industrial self-government was
the primary aim. The device by which the share capital was owned
by – and profits attributed to – the consumer customers of the co-
operative societies came about virtually by accident.

The claim of some of the pioneers that if co-operation '. . . is loyally
supported and infinitely extended it will solve all social problems,
destroy poverty, eradicate crime, and secure the greatest happiness to
the greatest number'[1] (quoting, J. T. W. Mitchell) now sounds very
hollow. The fact that the consumer, in a co-operative society, is the
formal owner of the means of distribution seems to have little significance in practical terms. By analogy, it can be compared with the
consumer's formal ownership of the means of production in a nationalized industry, or the individual shareholder's formal ownership of a
joint-stock company. We have learned from Drucker and others about
the divorce of control from ownership in large-scale enterprises, and
this appears to be just as true of consumer co-operatives as it is of
enterprises where the capital is held by shareholders in a more conventional way.

Extracts from Jeremy Mitchell, 'The consumer movement and technological
change', *International Social Science Journal*, Vol. 25, No. 3, 1973.

It is, however, no criticism of the consumer co-operative movement to say that despite its strength and the volume of its retail sales, its aims and methods did not equip it to respond to a new set of consumer's needs which began to be identified in the third quarter of the twentieth century (somewhat earlier in the United States).

Changing market

What form do these new consumer needs take? What has happened during the third quarter of the twentieth century to bring them such prominence? First, there are those which have arisen from changes in the character and structure of the market for consumer goods and services. With many products, there has been an extensive proliferation of home-produced and imported models, under a wide variety of brand names, with different specifications and prices. For example, the December 1972 issue of *Which?* the magazine of the Consumers' Association, giving the results of a comparative test on slide projectors, reported finding hundreds of different slide projectors in the shops, ranging in price from under £10 to nearly £200. How can the consumer make a sensible choice in such a situation?

Another market factor is the increased real purchasing power available to the consumer, which has brought with it associated problems of choice. For the first time, a significant proportion of consumers was no longer preoccupied with the problems of subsistence, but found that relative prosperity brought with it difficult questions of resource allocation.

The third set of market factors is associated with the various imperfections of the market which seem to put the consumer in a disadvantageous position in relation to the producer and distributor. As Galbraith has pointed out, the concept of consumer sovereignty, in which producers respond to the instructions of the consumer about the types of goods and services that he needs and the prices that he is prepared to pay for them, no longer seems to be appropriate:

The mature corporation has readily at hand the means for controlling the prices at which it sells as well as those at which it buys. Similarly, it has the means for managing what the consumer buys at the prices which it controls. This control and management is required by its planning. The planning proceeds from use of technology and capital, the commitment of time that these require and the diminished effectiveness of the market for specialized technical skills.[2]

An important aspect of the management of specific demand by large corporations is the management of information about goods and services. While many countries have systems of statutory or voluntary control of advertising, there is considerable freedom of manœuvre for the large corporation within any limits that may be laid down. It is the advertiser who decides what shall be said about his product, who decides which characteristics shall be emphasized and which omitted, and who is able to mobilize and deploy the skills of the public relations and advertising professions. The communication of information about consumer goods and services is now an established industry in its own right, with its own technology, and its successes – and some failures – have been fully documented.[3,4]

Technological factors

Another group of factors consists of those which are technological in character. This is an area in which economic theory has so far made a negligible contribution. In their comprehensive review of the literature of technical progress, Kennedy and Thirlwall[5] deal with the effects that technical progress has on macroeconomic growth – the various attempts that have been made to quantify the rate of technical progress as a determinant of output growth – and with the actual process of technological change as it affects the production function in different industries and firms. Consumer behaviour in response to technological change receives little or no attention, as the literature is non-existent.

This traditional neglect of technology and the consumer in economics has been explained

. . . by the fact that the emergence of new commodities and changes in the character of commodities have become important for consumer commodities only in recent decades. Prior to this, innovation and technological change were largely confined to the means of production rather than the means of consumption. Inventors and innovators were concerned with making existing commodities more efficiently rather than with making more efficient commodities.[6]

Ironmonger himself constructs a time-table of the introduction of new goods to the United Kingdom. What is noticeable about this time-table is the quickening of pace which took place towards the end of the nineteenth century (e.g. tramways, electroplate, telephones, motor-cycles, canned and preserved foodstuffs), and the subsequent increasing acceleration. In the 1950s, the examples include television; synthetic fibres; detergents; frozen foods; motor-scooters; long-playing records; colour film; magnetic recording; ball-point pens; polythene.

Need for information

Among these new goods, there are those whose performance is to a greater or lesser extent competitive with traditional goods. Textiles made from synthetic fibres compete with those made from natural fibres. Other goods, such as television receivers, are totally new and cannot be said to compete with existing goods in any meaningful sense. The significant factor so far as the consumer is concerned is that in both cases his existing stock of information is irrelevant. What he knows about wool, cotton and linen has little bearing on the characteristics and performance of nylon. Faced with buying a television receiver for the first time, he has no relevant knowledge which he can bring into play.

The end result of changes in consumer goods and services induced by technology is therefore the same as that brought about by changes in market factors. The consumer is short of information which will enable him to take rational decisions – either to buy or not to buy, or to buy product A rather than product B. This is the most significant consumer need in developed Western societies at the present time, and the need which has stimulated the development of the consumer movement in its contemporary form.

Development of consumer testing organizations

To find a single date for the start of the consumer movement, one must go back to 1928, when *Your Money's Worth*, by Stuart Chase and F. J. Schlink,[7] was published in the United States. Eirlys Roberts[8] describes the authors' aim as being to harness the work done by the National Bureau of Standards and other public agencies for the open benefit of the taxpayer who was ultimately responsible for financing their work. The National Bureau of Standards was engaged in an extensive programme of testing goods and services for the United States Services and government departments. The results of these tests saved the United States Government something of the order of $100 million a year. Why should they not be available to the individual citizen?

One of the authors, Schlink, founded a club with subscribing members, which was turned into an association called Consumers' Research. Consumers' Research carried out comparative tests on consumer products and also drew on some of the work carried out by members of the American Standards Association.

A second American organization, Consumers Union, was founded in 1935, by a staff breakaway from Consumers' Research. In the long run, it was the more successful of the two, and is now the largest consumer organization in the world, with more than 1 million subscribers to its magazine.

The American consumer movement was founded during the years of depression. It might be expected that economic depression would provide a sharp stimulus to the development of consumer organizations. When money is short, there should be a strong incentive to spending it as efficiently as possible. In practice, this has not proved to be the case. In the United States, the membership of Consumers Union only began to expand rapidly in the years of prosperity following 1946. In the

United Kingdom, Consumers' Association was born in 1957 on the crest of a wave of expansion of consumer goods and services, and its membership has risen to 600,000. In both countries, the development of the consumer organizations has been strongly associated with the market factors that have already been noted: proliferation of varieties and brands, and increased real purchasing power creating a mass market for goods and services above the subsistence level.

The primary purpose of both Consumers Union (United States) and Consumers' Association (United Kingdom) is to convey information to members and subscribers. This information is based mainly, but not exclusively, on the results of comparative tests. More recently, the information base has been extended to include a systematic assessment of the experience of members in relation to the durability, reliability and servicing of cars and other major durables. Organizations of this kind can be called information co-operatives. They provide their members with information which is unobtainable elsewhere. It is not just a question of releasing for the consumer information held by government (as Chase and Schlink had hoped to do) or by manufacturers. Very often the consumer testing organizations are engaged in generating new information about consumer goods and services. When a report is published comparing, say, washing machines or refrigerators, much of the information relating to the performance of the durables may be as unfamiliar to the manufacturers as it is to consumers.

Consumers Union (United States) and Consumers' Association (United Kingdom) have been cited as examples of organizations which meet the consumer's needs for information largely by conducting and reporting the results of comparative tests. They are the largest and among the oldest of the consumer testing organizations, but they now have their counterparts in a number of other countries, notably in North-Western Europe – including the Netherlands (Nederlandse Consumenten Bond), Belgium (Association des Consommateurs), Sweden (Konsumentinstitutet) and Norway (Forbrukerrådet). Consumer testing organizations in smaller countries face particular difficulties, because a certain minimum absolute level of membership is necessary to establish a testing organization as viable. Collaboration in joint multinational testing projects is helping to overcome some of these difficulties.

There are ways in which comparative testing is unable to meet the consumer's needs for information. The proliferation of types and brands of a particular product, mentioned earlier, sometimes means that it is in practice impossible to provide information which covers the full extent of the market. Inevitably, also, there are time lags involved in providing information about changed or new products when they come on to the market.

A more important weakness of consumer testing information is that it is usually provided in a form (i.e. periodical journals) which is not well adapted to use at the moment when it is needed – just when a purchase is about to be made. With major durables, where the purchase can be planned in advance, this weakness can be overcome, but it remains serious for higher frequency purchases.

More generally, consumer testing information cannot provide for the wide range of consumer goods and services which are neither branded nor standardized. Fresh food, textile piecegoods, glass, pottery, repair services – these and many others are not really susceptible to the provision of information based on comparative tests.

Informative labelling

Two other types of consumer organization have developed whose role in providing information is complementary to that of the comparative testing organizations. The first is concerned with the provision of informative labelling. By agreement with the consumer organization concerned, manufacturers attach labels to their products which present information, in a standardized form, about composition, performance and care. The consumer therefore has information available when he needs it most, at the moment of buying. On the other hand, there are limits both to the types of goods and services that are suitable for informative labelling, and the amount of information that can be conveyed in this form. Information labelling has made most progress in Sweden (Varudeklarationsnämnden), though a scheme had been launched by the government-sponsored Consumer Council in the United Kingdom a little while before the council itself was abolished by the government in 1970.

Quality certification

The other complementary type of consumer organization provides quality certification. Again, by agreement with the organization, manufacturers are allowed to fix a quality certificate which indicates that the product concerned meets certain minimum levels of composition or performance, established and verified by the consumer organization. The amount of actual information available to the consumer is, inevitably, small and non-comparative, but, as with informative labelling, it is provided when the consumer needs it most. Qualité France is an example of a well-established quality certification organization.

These three types of consumer organization – comparative testing, informative labelling and quality certification – have come into existence to meet, in various ways, the consumer's needs for information. One feature they share is that it is the more sophisticated consumers (in terms of, for example, high social class, high income and late terminal education age) who are most likely to be aware of their own information deficiencies and of the possibilities that exist for compensating for these. Consumer organizations are characteristically information co-operatives run by the educated middle class primarily for the benefit of the educated middle class. For example, a 1971 survey of a sample of Consumers' Association (United Kingdon) members showed that 35 per cent had a terminal education age of 19+ compared with 6 per cent of the general population (personal communication from Consumers' Association). Inevitably, they scarcely begin to touch the consumer problems of the poorer sections of the community who are not aware of their own information needs and whose education does not equip them to deal with such information as the consumer organizations provide.

Low-income consumers

A systematic analysis of the problems of the low-income consumer was reported by David Caplowitz in *The Poor Pay More*.[9] This study was based on a survey of 464 households in low-cost public-housing projects in East Harlem and on the lower East Side, in New York City. One of the most interesting findings was that low-income consumers were just as likely to be engaged in the purchase of major durables as more wealthy citizens.

The cultural pressures to buy major durables reach low- as well as middle-income families. In some ways, consumption may take on even more significance for low-income families than for those in higher classes. Since many have small prospect of greatly improving their low social standing through occupational mobility, they are apt to turn to consumption as at least one sphere in which they can make some progress towards the American dream of success. If the upper strata that were observed by Veblen engaged in conspicuous consumption to symbolize their social superiority, it might be said that the lower classes today are apt to engage in compensatory consumption. *Appliances, automobiles, and the dream of a home of their own can become compensations for blocked social mobility.*[9]

For this compensatory consumption, it was noted that the poor paid a heavy price. Their small cash funds and poor credit rating exposed them to a variety of situations in which they could be considered consumers 'at risk'. The goods they were sold tended to be low quality, but carried high retail profit margins. They were exposed to fraudulent or misleading sales practices: the 'new' appliances they were sold, for instance, might in reality be reconditioned.

In general, these low-income consumers had a low awareness of consumer information services and of the professional or semi-professional help they could turn to when they found themselves in difficult situations. Information, even when available, was unlikely to be translated into action. Although just over one-third of the sample could name a source of help (e.g. in the form of a Better Business Bureau, Legal Aid Society, Small Claims Court, lawyer) only 9 per cent of those in difficulty over consumer goods purchases had actually turned to such a source for advice or support.

Caplowitz's study is supported by other studies of the disadvantaged consumer in the United States. Sturdivant reports that in Watts, the Negro section in south central Los Angeles which was the focus of bitter rioting in 1965, consumers. '. . . can expect to pay from 7 per cent to 21 per cent more for a market basket of 30 items if they shop for groceries in one of the small local stores than would a family shopping in a supermarket in affluent Beverly Hills.'[10] The absence of comparable studies of low-income consumers in other countries should make one wary of generalizing from these examples drawn from the United States. Nevertheless, they do suggest that the existing range of consumer organizations, which have so effectively helped to redress the balance of information for the educated middle class, are unlikely to be able to fulfil the same role for low-income consumers. A new range of social institutions may need to be developed, and it is significant that in the United Kingdom the Consumers' Association has persuaded a number of local authorities to finance shopping advice centres. These are 'information shops' situated in high-street shopping centres, whose services are directed primarily (but not exclusively) at the low-income consumer.

Influence of consumer organizations

Consumer organizations may have closed the information gap for the educated middle-class consumer, but what has been their effect either on the market situation or on technical progress in consumer goods and services? There is a serious shortage of anything other than anecdotal information. Strickling found that in the United States most manufacturers of household durables disparaged Consumers Union as an influence to be reckoned with. 'None of the major appliance manufacturers make it a policy to get high Consumers Union ratings, although a few say they consider CU in the design of products . . .'[11]

On the other hand 'One manufacturer found that its market share of a certain appliance had risen from 6.0 per cent the previous year to 13.7 per cent in the year it got a top rating for that appliance' and a number of retailers testified to the importance of CU ratings in influencing consumer choice.

What seems to be incontestable is that the main influence of consumer organizations has been in determining consumer choice within the confines of the existing market and the existing (and developing) state of technology. In the field of information, in particular, it has acted as a countervailing power to the 'administered' information of producers and distributors. If consumer organizations are to have a more substantial effect on the system within which they operate, they will almost certainly have to become more political in character. A number of organizations are already in an interactive relationship with government, in the sense that they either receive support from or make representations to government, or both. As yet, none have the kind of influence on government that producers' organizations – trade unions and employers' federations are able to exert. We may still be some time from the day when consumers' interests weigh as heavily with government as those of producers.

In spite of this lack of political influence, there are indications that some progress is being made. A recent example is the anti-trust case brought by the United States Consumers Union, in which the Secretary of State and foreign steel companies were sued on the basis that United States consumers had had to pay higher prices for steel because of the agreement between the United States Government and the foreign steel companies that their sales in the United States would be voluntarily restricted. Although the court decided that no injunction should be made against the foreign producers, because they had acted in good faith, Consumers Union gained an important victory in that it was ruled that the government did not have the power to give assurances that anti-trust legislation was not being violated.

The case was unusual, in terms of its being a legal action taken by a consumer organization against a national government. This particular mode of influencing governments may remain rarely used outside the United States, but the idea that consumer organizations should play a more significant part in determining economic and technological policies may well be adopted more widely.

A better-known example from the United States is the extraordinary success achieved by Ralph Nader, who has challenged both the government and producers on a number of issues, notably, in the field of automobile safety.[12] The distinctive feature of Nader's campaigns is that they are not launched from any firm organizational base. There is no mass or élite consumer organization behind him, no lengthy list of members or subscribers to legitimate his right to speak in the interests of consumers. In an increasingly complex pluralistic society, in which the interests of different groups within the society are promoted and defended by organizations, Nader has shown that it is possible for a single individual to challenge, on equal terms, some of the major institutional forces. It is too early to say whether Nader's example will remain an isolated one. Possibly, the combination of legal and publicity techniques that he uses is particularly culturebound, and would not have the same results if transplanted to other countries. However, even if this proves to be true, there is no doubt that Nader has significantly broadened the horizons of the consumer movement, in the sense he has demonstrated the possibilities and opportunities that exist for influencing national policies.

This 'demonstration effect' could not be more opportune, coming as it does at a time when discussion of the need for technology assessment is being publicly debated. So far, consumer organizations have operated mainly within the framework of existing technologies. Their primary function has been to help the consumer to make rational choices in the context of current technologies markets and prices. To what extent are they capable of developing so that they can play a part in the process by which the potential drawbacks and benefits of new technologies are assessed? The answer will depend on the outcome of the present debates about both the process of technology assessment and the structures that are necessary to give the process political substance.

So far as process is concerned, it is possible to maintain that technology assessment is itself a form of the scientific process. It can be seen as the objective and analytical study of the possible economic, social and environmental consequences of new technological developments, or of changes in existing technology. The facts themselves must be neutral. The decisions about what weight should be given to the facts in determining decisions about technological development are, however, essentially political in character and lie outside the process of technology assessment itself.

This 'objective' conception of technology assessment can be contrasted with the view that the process itself is a political one. In the words of Harvey Brooks: '. . . the choices between alternative technologies and their effects are essentially political choices; that is, they involve choices between competing and conflicting interests and scales of value, and, therefore, can only be resolved as part of the political process'.[13] This view of technology assessment as an integral part of the political process has important implications for the structures that are needed.

Technical expertise and professional judgment are important in predicting the social and environmental consequences of various alternative courses of action, or at least in pointing out possibilities and probabilities, but the final process of choice is one among consequences, and among consequences that can only be predicted with a certain limited degree of probability. It is this weighing of imponderables that is the function of the political forum, and it is important that a forum be developed in which the widest possible spectrum of interest and values can be brought forward and defended.

This is an argument which implies that technology assessment should be diffused throughout society, involving a wide variety of social and economic interests, rather than being confined to central government. It is an argument which is gaining ground. Indeed, the establishment in the United States of the Office of Technology Assessment as a creature of the legislature, quite independent of the executive, means that, in one very pluralistic society, at any rate, the battle for a centralized technology assessment process under the control of the executive has already been lost.

If this pattern of diffused technology assessment, in which different interests play their part, is followed in other countries, there are two implications for the possible role that consumer organizations might play. First, consumer organizations should concentrate on the consequences of technological change for consumers. For example, suppose the change involved the development of a new source of energy which could be used for domestic heating. It would be the consumer organization's responsibility to assess the change (or potential change) in terms of its economic and other consequences for consumers. How would it compare for cost with existing fuels? How would it compare for convenience? What would it mean in terms of the conversion or replacement of existing domestic appliances? What would be the effects on the social organization of the household?

Providing the consumer organization made its values explicit, it should not involve itself in assessing the effects of the change on, for example, the producers of other fuels, except in so far as they might affect consumers. Consequential changes in the price or availability of other fuels to the consumer would be relevant, but plant closure or increased unemployment among the work force would not. Responsibility for assessing effects of this kind would be the responsibility of the producer interests concerned. Government, too, would have its own part to play – for example, in assessing the consequences for the balance of payments or economic growth.

It may seem somewhat shocking to suggest that consumer organizations should largely ignore such matters as unemployment or the balance of payments when carrying out technology assessment, but this is inherent in a pluralistic system in which the contributions of different interest groups are introduced into public debate and weighed as part of the political process.

The second implication for consumer organizations lies in the part they might play in identifying consumers' unsatisfied technological needs. The idea of technological development as an autonomous variable has taken a long time to die, but it is now finally buried. Increasingly, technology is seen in context, subject to social control and – potentially, at any rate – responsive to social needs. What new technological changes would help to improve both the standard of living, in economic terms, and the quality of life of consumers? This kind of question is more difficult to answer than the questions that consumer organizations currently set themselves, but it is one that will have to be put with increasing urgency if consumer organizations are to adapt themselves to the needs of the last quarter of the twentieth century.

References

1. Mrs Sidney Webb, *The Discovery of the Consumer*, Benn, 1928.
2. John Kenneth Galbraith, *The New Industrial State*, Hamish Hamilton, 1967.

3. Martin Meyer, *Madison Avenue U.S.A.*, Bodley Head, 1958.
4. John Pearson and Graham Turner, *The Persuasion Industry*, Eyre and Spottiswoode, 1965.
5. C. Kennedy and A. P. Thirlwall, 'Technical progress: a survey', *Economic Journal*, Vol. 82, No. 325, 1972, pp. 11–72.
6. D. S. Ironmonger, *New Commodities and Consumer Behaviour*, Cambridge UP, 1972.
7. Stuart Chase and F. J. Schlink, *Your Money's Worth*, Macmillan, 1928.
8. Eirlys Roberts, *Consumers*, Watts, 1966.
9. David Caplowitz, *The Poor Pay More*, Free Press of Glencoe, 1963.
10. Frederick D. Sturdivant, 'Better deal for ghetto shoppers', *Harvard Business Review*, March–April 1968, pp. 130–9.
11. Harry L. Strickling, 'Implications of the existence of Consumers union for marketers of major appliances and related consumer durables', 1965 (mimeo.).
12. Ralph Nader, *Unsafe at Any Speed*, Grossman, 1972 (rev. edn).
13. *Technology Assessment.* Hearings before the Subcommittee on Science Research and Development of the Committee on Science and Astronautics, United States House of Representatives, 1969.

Technology and trade union control

David Elliott and Ruth Elliott

[. . .] Organizations of workers are in a potentially strong position to exert some control over technology, since they interact with technology *collectively* and have developed strong collective organizations over time. Historically they have used their collective organization both to rouse public sympathy and to pressurize Governments to enact legislation which would redress somewhat the imbalance of power in industry, by ensuring workers' rights to organize in trade unions and engage in industrial action, and by making the employer more 'accountable' towards his employees in crucial areas such as health and safety.

Indeed the fundamental motivation behind the formation of the independent Labour Party, at the end of the last century, was this pressing need to have a representative base within Parliament from which to urge new legislation that would protect organized workers from all the abuses – economic and technological – to which they were subject within industry.

However, despite the tremendous advances that have been made, this legislative framework provides little more than a minimum level of protection for workers. Workers still rely largely on their organized strength within factories to enforce a due consideration of their interests, and workers who lack this organized strength are in a very weak position. Government agencies such as the factory inspectorate are important, but they scarcely have the resources to tackle the huge field of technology abuse in factories[1] and their impact is seriously weakened by the fact that they usually need the permission of the employer before they can enter a factory and carry out an inquiry, whatever the desires of the employees may be.

One major factor limiting the power of workers within industry is the fact that the employers' overall legal accountability is still fundamentally to the shareholders,[2] and this must inevitably inhibit any moves towards 'social control' of technology within industry, particularly in relation to top-level policy decisions.

Extracts from Chapter 5, 'Social control of technology' in David Elliott and Ruth Elliott, *The Control of Technology*, Wykeham, 1976.

Some pressures do exist at the present time for *extending* the legal accountability of employers through changes in company law.

For example the British Labour MP Michael Meacher has argued that:

A pre-requisite must be the restriction of the legal right of property, particularly equity capital. This must mean ending the shareholders' prerogative to control the direction of companies, the maximisation of shareholders' wealth as the main company objective, and the unilateral power to dispose of industrial assets to others. Risk-bearing capital would retain a place, but only after commitments to the community and the firm's employees had first been met.

He also suggests that the new industrial rights contract should 'focus on extending the role of organized workers and the community in the government of large-scale enterprise. . . . Furthermore the area and forward scope of collective bargaining should be extended and legal rights to scrutinise plans made under company law should be established.'[3]

Also relevant in this area are two draft proposals of the Commission of the European Communities: the draft 5th directive on the harmonization of company law, and the draft Statute for a European Company, both of which support the establishment of a Supervisory Board with certain rights of veto over the Management Board of a company, and which would be composed both of shareholders and employees representatives. Clearly, unless there were at least equal numbers of employee and shareholder representatives, such a scheme could do little to redress the existing supremacy of shareholder rights and interests. Consequently, the British Trades Union Congress has insisted in its own proposals[4] that half the members of the supervisory boards should be drawn from the workers, and that the boards should be able to overrule boards of management, shareholders' meetings and owners of a company on all major decisions, including those on technological changes, investment plans, mergers and takeovers. Such a structure could potentially offer trade unions a new 'lever' for exerting control over technological developments within industry, should they wish to take advantage of it. Not surprisingly, however, employers' organizations are not enthusiastic about such proposals.[5] The British Engineering Employers' Federation has reported that 'they find the concept of a two-tier board, and therefore the EEC proposals in their present form, totally unacceptable';[6] while the Confederation of British Industry has announced its preference for a form of empoyee participation which 'in no way takes over from a board its duty and legal responsibility to manage the company efficiently in the interests of the shareholders'. It proposes 'not co-determination or a veto by employees . . . but the process of bringing the employees into the consultative process in order that their ideas can be taken account of before a decision is reached'.[7]

The employers thus prefer a limited amount of purely discretionary 'accountability' where they are free to accept or reject employees' opinions and viewpoints as they see fit.

It becomes clear, in employers' comments on these EEC and TUC proposals, that they will only accept participation in decision-making by employees' representatives as valid if these representatives are prepared to commit themselves to pursuing existing company goals and promoting long-term company interests. They are thus able to argue that in the present industrial climate of conflicting interests, supervisory boards are, in their terms, a logical impossibility. As the Engineering Employers' Federation (EEF) argues:

It has long been established practice in the UK that the members of a Board of Directors are collectively responsible for the prosperity of the company as a whole. If worker representatives on Boards are to be nominated by trade unions and responsible to them they would be unable to acknowledge such responsibility. . . . If on the other hand worker representatives are to acknowledge their responsibility to the company first and foremost and only secondarily to the workers they represent, they will gradually tend, as their interests widen, to become more and more 'company men' and less and less worker representatives'.[8]

And indeed, as long as the aim of participation is defined in this way as the development of 'a spirit of co-responsibility' for existing company goals, the logic of the EEF is irrefutable. Few unions would in fact *want* participation on these terms.

The employers tend to see 'participation' *not* as a way of ensuring that conflicting interests are adequately represented; but rather as something that can only exist when conflicting interests have been set aside in favour of 'co-responsibility' and 'until that sense exists, the presence of employee representatives on the Board could not only be detrimental to the interests of the company as a whole, but also to the case of participation.'[8]

The very terms, therefore, on which employee representatives would be *accepted* by employers on a supervisory board would ensure that their presence was virtually irrelevant in terms of affecting the existing values and priorities on which policy decisions are made. The representatives would be constrained to press for 'marginal adjustments' to policy which did not seriously threaten the prevailing definition of company interests, and would find it virtually impossible to initiate fundamental changes in policy.

This highlights the basic problem underlying *any* attempts by trade unions to act as a countervailing force for increased social control within industry. The same limitations apply to all forms of participation and joint regulation within industry. Although collective bargaining, for example, has considerably circumscribed arbitrary managerial authority, it has not been able to fundamentally alter the fact that 'basic policy decisions . . . continue to be determined by the criterion of the economic interests of the employer'.[9]

As Fox has commented, the sufferance extended to organized interest groups like trade unions 'is heavily conditional upon the interest groups concerned being prepared to accept as given those major structural features which are crucial for the power, status and rewards of the owners and controllers'.[10]

Certainly collective bargaining has not led to any fundamental changes in the nature and application of technology in the production processes. For example, it is only comparatively recently that workers have managed to make 'the speed of the line' a legitimate bargaining issue in certain factories – and most workers are far from being able to bargain over whether or not minute division of labour and assembly line production methods should in fact be used, or whether or not a particular process has enough safeguards against health hazards, accidents, etc.

Consequently, what control workers do exert over technology tends to be of a defensive and negative kind; they resist work study, they resist the introduction of new machinery or processes that seem to threaten their jobs and their skills.

Job enlargement has been advocated as a technique which gives workers some positive control over the production process, but this technique has its limitations. In many instances it means simply that a worker performs a variety of fragmented unskilled jobs instead of one fragmented unskilled job, and although in some cases it may considerably increase the need for skill and responsibility, such experiments are as yet limited. More important, such experiments tend to be introduced on the initiative of management, when management judge that such action is in their overall economic interests; and by implication, they could equally be withdrawn at management's initiative.

Even if job enlargement does give workers a little more control over technology in the immediate context of their job, it gives them no real control over future technological developments. These remain as an ever-present threat looming over the workers' economic well-being, his skill, and his security. It is still usually up to employers to decide, according to their own values and priorities, what new technologies should be developed and how they should be applied and manned. Frequently all workers can do to safeguard their own interests, if these appear to conflict with those of management, is to stubbornly resist the changes when they are finally confronted with them; a response which is not particularly helpful to either side, but which seems to be the only response available under the existing system. A typical outcome of this process is the containerization dispute in the London docks, during which a container ban operated by the unions resulted in most berths at the brand-new £30 million Tilbury container extension being kept empty for virtually two years.[11] When such deadlocks can occur, technology is hardly under social control.

One proposed solution for preventing such deadlocks is to move towards a system of 'management by agreement',[12] in which workers can negotiate over *all* levels of management decisions and policies. Much of this bargaining would be concerned with the future and hence it has been labelled 'predictive bargaining'. At present it is suggested 'far too much of the atmosphere around the bargaining table is rooted in the past. This is largely because most negotiation arises out of attempts to redress and adjust past grievances and complaints by one side or the other'.

Clearly if the issue at stake is some costly innovation, it is madness to wait until problems occur before they are discussed and negotiated. Consequently some industrial relations theorists have suggested that 'one way in which a more productive atmosphere might be generated would be if a link could be established between collective bargaining and corporate planning.'[13]

The British Labour Party's recent proposals for 'planning agreements' are one practical suggestion for establishing just such a link. All important firms in private ownership would be invited to sign such agreements with the Government and their own workers. The agreements would not be legal contracts but would indicate forecasts and plans for three years ahead on topics such as investment, prices, productivity, jobs, product development, regional developments, exports, import saving, industrial relations proposals and the interests of consumers and the community at large. As the White Paper on 'The Regeneration of British Industry' (Cmnd. 5710, August 1974) commented:

Employees and their representatives will have a major interest in the issues covered by Planning Agreements. The Government intends that the plans to be covered by an Agreement will be drawn up by management in close consultation with trade union representatives from the firm. The framing and updating of agreements will thus involve a continuing discussion between management and unions and will constitute an important advance in the part to be played by industrial democracy in the planning of company strategy.

Similarly, Michael Meacher[14] has suggested that the Labour Party's new industrial rights contract must lead to

real sharing in the planning of development, whether investment in physical assets, manpower planning, or the finance of development. Where employees lack confidence in the direction being given to the firm, they should be empowered, either through direct electoral means based on their trade union structure or through a social audit by an independent state agency, to effect the necessary change of policy.

He argues that 'the future technology of work process should be planned so as to (embrace) wider consideration of such problems as location, pollution and safety as effect local communities as well as ensuring improvements in shop floor conditions and work organisation'.

Clearly such an extension of collective bargaining could be very relevant to the social control of technological development, by admitting the possibility of conflict and disagreement at a much earlier stage of policy formation, before choices and investments have been finally made.

Coupled with the kind of national level consultations between Government and union representatives which are presently being advocated by the British Minister of Trade and Industry, Mr Tony Benn, this might lead to a much more balanced development of technology in the industrial sphere, geared towards social needs. Mr Benn has indicated that his department

wants to open up and maintain the same kind of relationship which exists at present between Mr Michael Foot's department [the Department of Employment] and the unions . . . Mr Benn says that the exact nature of consultation needs to be defined, but it should include consultation on all major policy initiatives; the on-going industrial and regional policy of the department; individual industrial problems affecting major firms, including threatened redundancies; and development of industrial democracy and corporate strategies.' [15]

However, even assuming such an unprecedented extension of collective bargaining *did* take place, the preceding discussion of employers' attitudes to 'participation' should alert us to certain of its limitations. Some of these limitations are in fact implicit in the nature of McCarthy's proposals for management by agreement. For example, he casts the union, doubtless realistically, in their traditional role of 'protest' or 'appeal'; management draws up the corporate plan, and the unions would be allowed to 'appeal' against parts they disagreed with.

They would be free to suggest ways in which the plan might be altered, or adapted, to help gain their agreement on its industrial relations aspects. Thus they might suggest that the pace of proposed innovation was too fast, or that its impact was too uncertain. Modification might be proposed in production targets, or future manpower plans. Unions could take the view that their position would be made easier if only management would agree to revise its marketing objectives, or pricing policy, or diversify its products in a more labour intensive way. Objections could even be lodged against proposals to appoint industrial managers to carry out certain parts of the corporate plan, or to the salaries they would be paid. [16]

The very fact that management initially draws up the plan means that unions are inevitably placed in the position of negotiating over marginal adjustments to a plan whose fundamentals are already determined. If the union and management disagreed over fundamentals, the likely outcome would be, in the event of a failure to agree, that management would unilaterally impose its own approved plan, for McCarthy suggests that 'a management which cannot get unions to agree on a proposed change should be free to impose this change unilaterally once the joint arrangements for seeking agreements have failed to produce a solution'.

Hence the whole procedure would only really work where divergencies of interest were slight and unions were broadly prepared to accept managerial objectives. When divergencies widen the most likely outcome is a return to unilateral management control. In this sense it is an unreliable mechanism of social control. The crucial role of the government as a 'third party' to the bargain in the Labour party's proposed planning agreements might alter this situation somewhat, but these have yet to be put to the test.

Other factors within the present socio-economic system also tend to limit the likelihood of such mechanisms acting as effective means of social control, particularly in the field of product control. For most workers identify their economic security with the product of their industry, and hence it could be suicidal for them to make fundamental criticisms of this product or to suggest that it might be abolished. For example, many Concorde workers might feel that Concorde is a waste of resources that could better be applied in other fields; yet they would hesitate to campaign for the scrapping of the Concorde. For the scrapping of Concorde spells to them the dole queue. Moreover, they are aircraft workers and have a pride in their specific skills, skills which might not be transferable to other fields of activity. Similar pressures can lead to a situation where workers occupy their factory and campaign for the 'right to work' to make, or contribute to military equipment such as torpedoes (as happened at Plessey Alexandria).

In their search for security and prosperity, workers are in many respects constrained to uphold and perpetuate the priorities of the system which in many ways engenders their insecurity and their relative deprivation.

However, to acknowledge these limitations of the trade unions' role is not to dismiss them as totally impotent in influencing the direction of technology. They still represent a tremendously powerful and well-organized pressure group, and questions are increasingly being asked about the nature of work, its social relevance, its organization, the type of technology used, the pollution produced, and other environmental issues.

One example of unions moving towards a more positive approach to technological developments, as opposed to a purely *defensive* approach, is presented by the recent establishment by one group of workers of their own Science and Technology Advisory Service.[17] The function of the service is to provide an early warning about the difficulties likely to be associated with the introduction of a new technology or process, and it is being set up 'by the Lucas Aerospace Combine Shop Stewards' Committee, itself a remarkable group representing all workers – ranging from senior technologists to the semi-skilled – at 11 Lucas Aerospace sites in the United Kingdom'.[18] Ernie Scarbrow, the secretary of the body, envisages that the new Service 'will represent a cross-fertilisation of the expertise of the technologists with the great common sense and trade union understanding of those on the shop floor'.[18] The Service will act in a consultative capacity to the autonomous shop stewards' committees at each of the 11 sites. 'It will advise on skill fragmentation, increased work tempo, job security, dangers of shift working, and possible hazards in the use of new processes and materials'.[18] There are also many instances where pressure from the workforce in specific factories has led to modifications and changes in both production technology and product design. An example of quite wide-ranging influence is presented by the Builders Labourers Federation of New South Wales, Australia, which has been involved in a number of major environmental protection confrontations, in the face of pressure from land speculators. They effectively vetoed the development of a vast $A2 million car park for Sydney Opera House, in the interests of the environment, and received much public support. They blocked a major billion-dollar project in a working class housing area of Sydney, with the active support of the residents. Another $A70 million project is currently being held up by the Unions fight to preserve a famous local hotel, used by dockers, writers and artists. They have also fought with local residents to defend areas of cheap housing against redevelopment.[19]

As their secretary, Jack Munday, puts it:

As far as we're concerned, we believe that a union in this day and age must be concerned about things other than just bread and butter issues . . . all that we've done is to support residents or progressive architects, engineers and other people, town planners, in trying to slow down the destruction, to slow down the erection of a concrete jungle, and make cities a place where people should live . . .

As this suggests, it is quite possible for trade unions to exert influence on technological developments that goes far beyond defensive self-protection and seeks to establish links between industrial issues and community issues such as town planning.

References

1. See Patrick Kinnersley, *The Hazards of Work*, Pluto Press, 1974. (Also *Science for People*, No. 27, 1974.)
2. There is also a strong normative commitment to the shareholders. For example *The Times* Survey of Directors of Britain's 500 largest companies published in January 1973, reported 'that 60 per cent regarded management's first responsibility as being to the shareholder, and 18 per cent to the rest of the Board, and only 12 percent saw their prime commitment as being to their employees and 9 per cent to their customer'. Michael Meacher, 'Chronic boom', *The Guardian*, 5.6.1973.
3. Ibid.
4. Interim Report by the TUC General Council, *Industrial Democracy*, 1973.
5. Critics of the proposals also exist among trade unionists. Some trade unionists see the proposals leading to a dangerous form of 'collaboration' between unions and management and the idea that such supervisory boards should be made mandatory was rejected by the Trades Union Congress of 1974.

6. *EEC Proposals on Company Law and Two-Tier Boards*, a report by the Engineering Employers Federation, June 1973.
7. *The Responsibilities of the British Public Company*, final report of the Company Affairs Committee, CBI, 1973.
8. EEF, op. cit.
9. R. Hyman, *Strikes*, op. cit.
10. Alan Fox, 'Industrial relations: a social critique of pluralist ideology', in John Child (ed.), *Man and Organisation*, 1973.
11. David F. Wilson, *Dockers, The Impact of Industrial Change*, Fontana/Collins, 1972, Chapter 13.
12. W. McCarthy and N. D. Ellis, *Management by Agreement*, Hutchinson, 1973.
13. W. McCarthy and N. D. Ellis, *Management by Agreement*, Hutchinson, 1973.
14. M. Meacher, op. cit.
15. 'Benn plans on open ministry', *The Guardian*, 22.5.1974.
16. W. McCarthy and N. D. Ellis, op. cit.
17. 'Technological self-help', *New Scientist*, 21.3.1974. See also *Science for People*, No. 27, March, 1974.
18. 'Technological Self-Help', *New Scientist*, 21.3.1974. For more recent developments see *New Scientist*, 3.7.1975, and *Undercurrents*, Vol. 12, 1975.
19. Reported in *IWC Bulletin*, Oct. 1973.

Is greater citizen participation in planning possible and desirable?

Stuart A. Umpleby

Introduction

In recent years a body of literature has emerged which proposes that participation in planning can be enlarged by means of new communica-cations technologies. Since this is one case where physical scientists and engineers come to tread on the turf of social scientists, humanists, and those presently engaged in planning, it may be well to review the various proposals that have been made, the justifications given for changing the status quo and the counter arguments that these proposals are likely to encounter. Although other technologies will be discussed, the focus of attention here is on computer-based communications media and their use for involving the public in planning.

Present activities

[. . .] A large number of activities have been undertaken over the years to increase the information available to the public about social and political issues using electronic media. In addition to radio and tele-vision news programs and documentaries there have been radio talk shows with questions and comments phoned in by listeners. Some stations even broadcast city council and school board meetings.

[. . .] In Germany Helmut Krauch has used a combination of television documentary, discussion, phone-in, and electronic opinion polling to review priorities for dealing with pollution. In early 1971 three programs were broadcast on successive evenings on an education channel based in Cologne and capable of reaching about a third of the West German population. The series began with a cartoon criticizing the gap between government and the public and then showed a film reminding people of the problems presented by pollution. The viewers were told that during the rest of the evening questions would be asked from time to time to which they could phone in their answers. Thirty lines were

Extracts from Stuart A. Umpleby, 'Is greater citizen participation in planning possible and desirable?', *Technological Forecasting and Social Change*, Vol. 4, 1972.

available. Callers were asked to answer the latest question on a five-point scale (strongly agree, agree, don't know, disagree, strongly disagree) and were also asked their sex, age, income, educational level and post code. No names were requested. Cards were punched and processed looking for patterns in the replies.

The phone-in sessions alternated with 'organized conflicts' between representatives of industry, government, doctors, consumers, and other interested groups. The participants were encouraged to be aggressive rather than conciliatory. A panel of experts in attendance could supply factual information and interrupt if one of the participants in the discussion made a false statement or an unjustified generalization. A second, smaller sample of the public – a representative panel of 30 people – could phone in and intervene in the discussion to make a point or ask a question. The results of the large-scale phone-in were introduced into the discussion. Some 3,000 phone calls were received in all and there would have been more if the lines had not been jammed for part of the time.[1]

Recent proposals

Going beyond periodic public discussions, Vincent Campbell has suggested a move toward direct democracy. His system would use newspapers to present and summarize issues and suggest references for background reading. Voting would be done by dialing in the telephone code numbers listed in the newspaper. Campbell suggests using the system for day-to-day politics and to replace legislators at least in part.[2]

David Loye has advanced a plan for using computers, television and the Delphi method to enable a very large number of people to participate in reordering national priorities at intervals of approximately each year. Small groups would discuss a list of issues for about two hours and then each person would cast a ballot. The returns would be processed by computer and the results broadcast on television as is done with Presidential elections.[3]

Mike McManus is the director of a project for the Regional Plan Association of New York City that will use a series of local telecasts to focus public attention on critical social issues and explain alternatives proposed by public and private agencies. Viewers, organized into small groups, will discuss the issues and mark ballots coded for computer processing. The results would go to government and private decision-makers, or eventually to a special advocacy group set up to push for public wishes. The first stage of the project, called Choices for '76, is scheduled for the spring of 1973.[4]

Amitai Etzioni and others have proposed a series of experiments in community participation named after Minerva, the Roman goddess of political wisdom. His system would use existing technology of radio, television, telephones, and some additional equipment to link members of a community to one another and communities to each other.[5]

The various activities and proposals cited above, clearly indicate that citizen participation in public discussions and perhaps also planning and decision-making are possible in the next few decades. Computer-based communications equipment will not be widely distributed for at least 15 to 20 years. However, the other proposals are more nearly realizable with existing technology. How the various technologies can be used in the political process is now beginning to be investigated in a variety of communities. Experiments with computer-based communications media could be enhanced by the fact that the teaching computer can also be thought of as a gaming laboratory.[6] Thus the same equipment which people may be using in the future for part of the actual political process will be readily available in the classroom for gaming simulations of political processes including a computer-based communications medium.

Will people participate?

Despite the growing number of new media for political participation, there is some doubt whether people will actually use them after the novelty has worn off. The idea of an accurate sample, essential for a poll, may be dropped in computer-based exercises due to the somewhat time-consuming nature of the programs and the level of concentration required. Consequently a kind of voluntary participation to the extent of the individual's time and interest might develop. Such exercises could provide a theatre of activity for those who would like to be more politically involved than simply reading the newspaper and voting but who are not actually decision-makers and who may be less interested in group organizing than the present political process requires.

The teaching computer might evolve into a communications medium used by the various active groups in a community. Groups interested in ecology could prepare the programs on ecology, and those interested in educational reforms could prepare the programs on education, etc. Then that part of the citizenry interested in discussing a particular issue and registering an opinion and influencing others could work through the appropriate computer program. Thus a nucleus group would prepare a preliminary program which would be expanded and modified by later participants. If used in this way the computer would not be acting as a communications medium between planners and the public but rather as a communications device linking up the more active citizenry.

One factor that could contribute to the intensive use of computer-based media for citizen participation is the possibility that these media might increase the productivity of political activity by groups with widely dispersed membership. Political scientists have repeatedly found that the bulk of the population is relatively uninformed and does not extensively use the means of participation now available. Recognizing that some people are simply not interested in politics, an additional factor is the marginal cost of participation in terms of a person's time and energy. Computer-based communications media might have the effect of lowering the operating costs of citizen lobbies and making them more competitive with the lobbies of wealthy interest groups.

The opposing arguments

Even if greater citizen participation is possible, there is likely to be little agreement on whether it is desirable. Opposition to these forms of participation has been expressed by both establishment and non-establishment sources. Those who identify with the establishment are usually concerned lest their power be somehow diminished. Non-establishment opponents argue that those in power will use the new technologies to protect and extend their influence at the expense of the already poor and disenfranchised. Those who identify with the establishment tend to divide into two groups – social scientists and technologists. Thus three separate groups have so far expressed serious reservations – the establishment social scientists or pluralists, the technologists, and the antiestablishment social scientists or radicals (see Table 1 and Fig. 6).[7]

The pluralists

The establishment social scientist will oppose increased citizen participation using concepts from a well-developed although recent school of political theory. This group, commonly called the pluralist school, maintains, contrary to classical democratic theory, that civil liberties and democratic rules of the game are more likely to endure in the hands of a wealthy, highly educated minority than if entrusted to the volatile, more easily misled masses.[8] As Peter Bachrach has explained: 'Widespread mass support of totalitarian movements in prewar Europe and the rise of powerful proletarian-based Communist parties in postwar France and Italy, of Peronism in Argentina and McCarthyism in the United States have badly shaken the confidence of liberals in the cause of democracy.'[9] A reverse trend resulting largely from growing disenchantment with the Viet Nam war has in turn diminished confidence in the liberal elites, led to severe rifts within the social science disciplines and contributed to the rise of 'radical' social science.

The pluralist position leads to a number of arguments against increased participation.

1. Their theory rests on an important assumption regarding *the limits of the possible*. Bachrach quotes Dahl, a leading pluralist spokesman, as having written, 'It goes without saying that except in exceedingly small groups, specific decisions must be made by a relatively few

Table 1. Synopsis of opposing arguments

	Establishment		Nonestablishment
	Pluralists	Technologists	Radicals
Basic position	Educated elites maintain political stability and basically liberal policies	More technical expertise is needed in decision-making	People should have control over their lives
View of the world	The current political system is as good as can be expected; the essence of politics is now as it has always been and ever will be	There is a long-term trend toward higher standards of living for everyone; we should work together and use expert advice	Life is a continuing struggle between the haves and the have-nots; 'experts' are in the employ of the haves
View of technology	It is useful in the economy but of little if any professional interest to political scientists	Technology is responsible for prosperity and happiness; it is man's greatest achievement	Technology is dehumanizing and a tool used by the establishment to further its ends
Reason for opposition	Reactionary policies will be more likely; political stability will decrease	Level of information on which decisions are based will decline	These methods will be used by the establishment to solidify its power and prevent needed basic change
Ultimate fear	Political instability will lead to authoritarian government as an instrument to preserve order	Uninformed decisions will lead to breakdown of effective government and reversal of progress	The existing repressive system will continue with the privileged rich exploiting the oppressed in this country and abroad

people acting in the name of the polity.[10] Further describing the position of the pluralist school Bachrach writes:

To continue to advocate (democratic) theory in today's world, it is argued, is bound to foster cynicism toward democracy as it becomes evident that the gap between the reality and the ideal cannot be closed. Thus it is said that there is no alternative but to recast democracy, emphasizing the stable, constitutional, and liberal nature of the system of elite pluralism; the competitiveness of political elites, their accountability to the electorate at periodic elections; and the open, multiple points of access to elite power for those who bother to organize to voice their grievances and demands.[11]

But as the activities and proposals cited earlier imply, alternatives *do* exist. Cable television and the probable future availability of

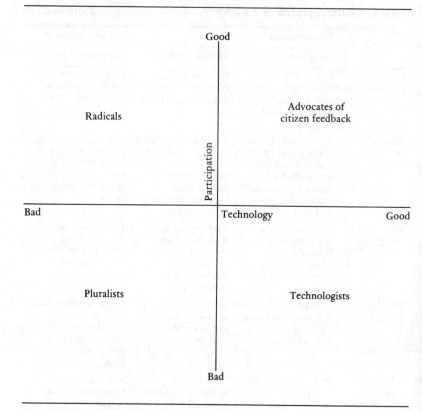

Fig. 6. Normative positions of the various groups.

computer-based communications media will certainly make broader participation possible.

2. The pluralists are also quite concerned about *the extent of public commitment to democratic rules* such as freedom of speech. It is useful to note that their fears of increased participation are based on historical examples that took place when radio and television were widespread. By comparison teaching computers tend to be cognitive rather than emotional media. The major difference between responses made using a teaching computer and votes or data from polls is that with a teaching computer instruction and background information can be provided and possibly a certain level of comprehension made mandatory before a person is allowed to render a judgment. We tend to forget that under present procedures, a person's information gathering on political issues and his voting, or answers to polls, are separated. This situation is not inevitable but results from what is practical with present technologies. Computer-based communications media will make possible both pro-

viding carefully prepared background information and opinions in the voting booth and public discussions of long-range community goals.

Thus democratic rules can be contained not only in people's minds, as the pluralists assume, but also as a part of the environment that people interact with, for example as a part of the constraints and background information provided by computer programs. Needless to say, a voter's information on the issues would not be limited to the information contained in the computer programs. The programs could simply guarantee a minimum level of understanding of the issues, somewhat like a mandatory reading of party platforms. Not incidentally the PLATO IV system includes audio equipment which could be used by illiterates or semi-literates. Information can be presented in as many languages or dialects as required.

3. In the pluralist's view of the world *apathy performs a support function* for the political system. If people were not apathetic, the demands on the political system would exceed its ability to respond. Apathy makes it difficult for opponents to organize support and thus tends to dampen shifts in policy. Furthermore, ignorance permits people to agree with others on short-range actions when they may have quite different goals. Increasing awareness of differences in views will increase hostility among groups and thus political instability. What the pluralists are less concerned with is that ignorance and apathy also permit manipulation of the public by elites. Increased public knowledge about how the system is operating would increase the public's power over the system.

4. A variation of the pluralist position is set forth by the Lindblom school of public administration.[12] Just as the pluralists have dominated the discipline of political science in recent years, the Lindblom school has dominated the field of public administration. Whereas the pluralists look askance at any development that might reduce political stability, those who are concerned with public administration point to *the value of maximizing consensus*. By looking at politics through the eyes of the public administrator this group comes to regard as 'functional' those things which make the public administrator's job easier.

By trying to create a consensus in favor of his policies the public administrator minimizes opposition and denies a following to those who would displace him. *Not* specifying long-range goals is considered desirable partly because of the difficulty of accurately anticipating consequences but primarily because specifying goals tends to alienate some groups which would be willing to agree on short-range actions. However, what is expedient for a public administrator is not necessarily in the best interests of either the public at large or other persons, for consensus is interpreted to mean consensus among the *active* interest groups. The pluralist theory implicitly assumes that the costs of political activity are essentially the same for all interest groups and are equally easily borne by all interest groups.

5. Social scientists of the pluralist school have one final reservation about increasing political participation. They generally see themselves as having greater than average influence on public policy and as favoring positions more liberal than those of the average American. Thus to increase the power or influence of the electorate would likely result in *the adoption of more conservative policies* than those they consider to be desirable. Granted that this assumption is probably true, there is nevertheless an alternative to continuing to limit popular participation. It is a well-known principle that people adapt their opinions and beliefs to fit their environments. A person introduced into a more conservative environment will tend to become more liberal. Consequently, a second way to ensure the adoption of relatively liberal policies would be to correct the conservative bias of the information environment of the American people. In his book *Don't Blame the People* Robert Cirino has presented abundant data to support his contention that the mass media in the United States quite adequately present information regarding the range of opinion in the establishment but tend not to report opposing news and points of view.[13] It would seem that considerably more attention could be focused on this latter strategy. Computer-based communications media, by moving information gathering and selection closer together, will probably help to call attention to the very important relationship which has always existed between the two.[14]

The technologists

Those with a technological background who oppose increasing public participation in decision-making generally use the argument that the amount of information or expertise going into public decisions would decrease. This group, consisting mostly of physical scientists and engineers, believes that the amount of expertise in decision-making should increase, not decrease. Thus the pluralists and the technologists share a belief in the wisdom of educated elites and the prudence of a social order in which these elites have inordinate influence. However, they differ both in the type of knowledge which is valued and in their justifications of the importance of using knowledge in decision-making. The social scientists focus on knowledge of law and government procedures; the technologists are believers in scientific expertise. With regard to rationale, the social scientists emphasize the importance of political stability; the technologists display a preoccupation with making 'better' decisions.

By 'better decisions' they usually mean that a forecast was made of relevant aspects of the future environment of the decision or policy, that as wide as possible a range of alternatives was drawn up and that possible secondary and tertiary effects of each alternative were considered.

What this point of view neglects is that there are basically two ways of improving the performance of a complex system. One can either improve the forecasting capability of a system, thus reducing the need to take quick corrective action to compensate for errors or change in the environment. Or one can improve the responsiveness of the system, thereby increasing the capability of the system to take corrective action and reducing the need for accurate forecasts.

It is no accident that people who favor the forecasting approach to dealing with social problems are usually high-ranking professionals who tend to identify with decision-makers and seek approval from them rather than blacks, students, or some other group. Advocates of rational decision-making processes rarely stipulate that all groups to be affected by decisions should be represented in making them or at the very least that their interests should be understood and seriously weighed.

The radicals

Whereas those who favor decision-making by elites are primarily interested in the quality of the policy results, those who support greater public involvement emphasize the educational function of participation in government. The nonestablishment opponents of this form of participation are, therefore, not opposed to increased political participation. Their reservations are first that technology is a tool of the establishment. They argue that vested interests, due to their superior resources, will come to own and operate the new media and will use it for their purposes – presenting the issues that they think are important and in the way they see them.[15]

A second objection is that the power of minorities will be reduced in two ways – those presently disenfranchised can be expected to have the greatest difficulty in making use of the sophisticated technology, and 'instant plebiscites' would increase the power of majorities at the expense of minorities.[16] No doubt less-educated adults may be deterred by anxiety from using this technology. However, experiments have shown that second-grade school children can easily use the PLATO equipment. Since teaching computers are likely to be used in education prior to their use for public involvement in planning the disadvantage to minorities may not be of long duration.

It may be well to emphasize that I am not suggesting either direct democracy or instant plebiscites but rather an ongoing discussion in which the choice of issues and phrasing of questions is continually being modified by the participants themselves. The criticism that electronic media would vastly increase the power of majorities over minorities does not necessarily follow. Such a situation would result only if questions were decided by the rule of majority vote. However, alternative systems are quite easily constructed. For example, in a community discussion on a computer-based communications medium, a rule might be formulated that any suggestion or comment could be eliminated from the program for reasons of economy if 20 per cent of the participants rated it as irrelevant (assuming that other participants did not bother to rate it). However, the issue could be reintroduced by a single individual and rendered impossible to delete if 10 per cent or more favored its remaining in.

One further variety of opinion criticizes the notion that certain technologies 'by their very nature' will bring about ecological harmony, decentralization of power, or increased political participation. More realistically, it is noted, technology serves the interests of the people who use it.[17]

Conclusion

This short presentation cannot do justice to the complex systems of thought sketched above. Nevertheless the record clearly indicates that present social theories have been based upon the examination of present and past social systems with little effort given to imagining possible future social systems and thus to constructing more comprehensive theories. Specifically the present theories do not deal well with a social system that would include computer-based communications media – a social system in which a citizen's information gathering and decision-making on public issues could be more nearly combined, in which the information environment would therefore receive rigorous scrutiny and in which democratic rules of the game could be incorporated into environmental constraints thereby relieving pressures on the school system to supply most of the public's education about democratic methods.

The present deficiencies of political theories give reason to believe that significant opportunities for improving the performance of the political system and reducing alienation may be lost due either to the new media being absorbed into the existing structure of interests or to opponents of the present structure being unwilling to compete for control of technological resources or both.

References

1. Bryan Silcock, 'You too can govern the nation's future', *The Times*, 18.7.1971, reprinted in *Presseberichte über das System ORAKEL*, Studiengruppe für Systemforschung, Oct. 1971.
2. Vincent Campbell, 'Democracy by telephone: an alternative to revolution', *Avant Garde*, Jan. 1970.
3. David Loye, *The Healing of a Nation*, Norton 1971, last chapter.
4. *Behavior Today*, 1.11.1971.
5. Eugene Leonard, Amitai Etzioni, Harvey A. Hornstein, Peter Abrams, Thomas Stephen and Noel Tichy, 'MINERVA: a participatory technology system', *Bulletin of the Atomic Scientists*, Nov. 1971, p. 4.

6. Stuart Umpleby, 'The teaching computer as a gaming laboratory', *Simulation & Games*, March 1971, pp. 5–25.

7. The classification of groups into pluralists, technologists, and radicals parallels Arthur Waskow's grouping of the attendants at the First International Future Research Conference into humanist-social democrats, technocratic planners, and participatory futurists; 'A three-way report on an international future research meeting', *The Futurist*, April, 1968, p. 28.

8. Robert Dahl, *Who Governs?* Yale University Press, 1961, pp. 314–15.

9. Peter Bachrach, *The Theory of Democratic Elitism: A Critique*, Little-Brown, 1967, p. 8.

10. Ibid., p. 86.

11. Ibid., p. 8.

12. Charles E. Lindblom, *The Intelligence of Democracy*, Macmillan, 1965. For a comparison of the Lindblom view of the policy-making process with the problem-solving approach used in Program Budgeting see Charles L. Schultze, *The Politics and Economics of Public Spending*, Brookings Institute, 1968.

13. Robert Cirino, *Don't Blame the People: How the News Media Use Bias, Distortion, and Censorship to Manipulate Public Opinion*, Diversity Press, 1971.

14. A quantitative relationship between information and selection has been suggested by Ashby in his 'law of requisite variety': appropriate selection can be based only on information in the requisite quantity. W. Ross Ashby, *An Introduction to Cybernetics*, John Wiley, 1956, pp. 202–218.

15. For a persuasive treatment of this position see Herbert I. Schiller, *Mass Communications and American Empire*, Augustus M. Kelley, 1969, particularly the last chapter. Also Herbert I. Schiller, 'Madison Avenue imperialism', *Transaction*, March/April 1971, pp. 52–8, 64.

16. In their book *Participatory Democracy*, Cranfield Press, 1971, p. 18, Terrence E. Cook and Patrick M. Morgan deal with the use of electronic media only briefly in a refutation of instantaneous plebiscites. They refer to articles by Robert H. Cushman 'Real-time, two-way communications between citizens and leaders', *EDN Magazine*, 1.6.1969, pp. 28, 112–113) and Martin Shubik ('Information, rationality, and free choice in a future democratic society', *Daedalus*, Summer 1967, p. 777).

17. James W. Carey and John J. Quirk, 'The mythos of the electronic revolution', *The American Scholar*, Spring and Summer, 1970.

A ladder of citizen participation

Sherry R. Arnstein

The heated controversy over 'citizen participation', 'citizen control', and 'maximum feasible involvement of the poor', has been waged largely in terms of exacerbated rhetoric and misleading euphemisms. To encourage a more enlightened dialogue, a typology of citizen participation is offered using examples from three federal social programmes: urban renewal, anti-poverty, and Model Cities. The typology, which is designed to be provocative, is arranged in a ladder pattern with each rung corresponding to the extent of citizens' power in determining the plan and/or programme.

The idea of citizen participation is a little like eating spinach: no one is against it in principle because it is good for you. Participation of the governed in their government is, in theory, the corner-stone of democracy – a revered idea that is vigorously applauded by virtually everyone. The applause is reduced to polite handclaps, however, when this principle is advocated by the have-not blacks, Mexican-Americans, Puerto Ricans, Indians, Eskimos, and whites. And when the have-nots define participation as redistribution of power, the American consensus on the fundamental principle explodes into many shades of outright racial, ethnic, ideological, and political opposition.

There have been many recent speeches, articles, and books[1] which explore in detail *who* are the have-nots of our time. There has been much recent documentation of *why* the have-nots have become so offended and embittered by their powerlessness to deal with the profound inequities and injustices pervading their daily lives. But there has been very little analysis of the content of the current controversial slogan: 'citizen participation' or 'maximum feasible participation'. In short: *What* is citizen participation and what is its relationship to the social imperatives of our time?

Citizen participation is citizen power

Because the question has been a bone of political contention, most of the answers have been purposely buried in innocuous euphemisms like

Extracts from Sherry R. Arnstein, 'A ladder of citizen participation', *Journal of the Royal Town Planning Institute*, April 1971.

'self help' or 'citizen involvement', Still others have been embellished with misleading rhetoric like 'absolute control' which is something no one – including the President of the United States – has or can have. Between understated euphemisms and exacerbated rhetoric, even scholars have found it difficult to follow the controversy. To the headline reading public, it is simply bewildering.

My answer to the critical *what* question is simply that citizen participation is a categorical term for citizen power. It is the redistribution of power that enables the have-not citizens, presently excluded from the political and economic processes, to be deliberately included in the future. It is the strategy by which the have-nots join in determining how information is shared, goals and policies are set, tax resources are allocated, programmes are operated, and benefits like contracts and patronage are parcelled out. In short, it is the means by which they can induce significant social reform which enables them to share in the benefits of the affluent society.

Empty ritual versus benefit

There is a critical difference between going through the empty ritual of participation and having the real power needed to affect the outcome of the process. This difference is brilliantly capsulized in a poster painted in May 1968 by the French students to explain the student-worker rebellion.[2] (see Fig. 7). The poster highlights the fundamental point that participation without redistribution of power is an empty

Fig. 7. French student poster. In English: I participate; you participate; he participates; we participate; you participate . . . *They profit.*

and frustrating process for the powerless. It allows the power-holders to claim that all sides were considered, but makes it possible for only some of those sides to benefit. It maintains the *status quo*. Essentially, it is what has been happening in most of the 1,000 Community Action Programmes, and what promises to be repeated in the vast majority of the 150 Model Cities programmes.

Types of participation and 'non-participation'

A typology of eight *levels* of participation may help in analysis of this confused issue. For illustrative purposes the eight types are arranged in a ladder pattern with each rung corresponding to the extent of citizens' power in determining the end product[3] (see Fig. 8).

The bottom rungs of the ladder are (1) *Manipulation* and (2) *Therapy*. These two rungs describe levels of 'non-participation' that have been contrived by some to substitute for genuine participation. Their real

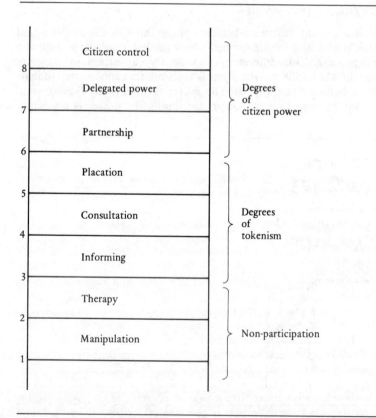

Fig. 8. Eight rungs on a ladder of citizen participation.

objective is not to enable people to participate in planning or conducting programmes, but to enable powerholders to 'educate' or 'cure' the participants. Rungs 3 and 4 progress to levels of 'tokenism' that allow the have-nots to hear and to have a voice: (3) *Informing* and (4) *Consultation*. When they are proffered by powerholders as the total extent of participation, citizens may indeed hear and be heard. But under these conditions they lack the power to insure that their views will be *heeded* by the powerful. When participation is restricted to these levels, there is no follow through, no 'muscle', hence no assurance of changing the *status quo*. Rung (5) *Placation*, is simply a higher level tokenism because the ground rules allow have-nots to advise, but retain for the powerholders the continued right to decide.

Further up the ladder are levels of citizen power with increasing degrees of decision-making clout. Citizens can enter into a (6) *Partnership* that enables them to negotiate and engage in trade-offs with traditional powerholders. At the topmost rungs, (7) *Delegated Power* and (8) *Citizen Control*, have-not citizens obtain the majority of decision-making seats, or full managerial power.

Obviously, the eight-rung ladder is a simplification, but it helps to illustrate the point that so many have missed – that there are significant gradations of citizen participation. Knowing these gradations makes it possible to cut through the hyperbole to understand the increasingly strident demands for participation from the have-nots as well as the gamut of confusing responses from the powerholders.

Limitations of the typology

[. . .] The ladder juxtaposes powerless citizens with the powerful in order to highlight the fundamental divisions between them. In reality, neither the have-nots nor the powerholders are homogeneous blocs. Each group encompasses a host of divergent points of view, significant cleavages, competing vested interests, and splintered subgroups. The justification for using such simplistic abstractions is that in most cases the have-nots really do perceive the powerful as a monolithic 'system', and powerholders actually do view the have-nots as a sea of 'those people', with little comprehension of the class and caste differences among them.

It should be noted that the typology does not include an analysis of the most significant roadblocks to achieving genuine levels of participation. These roadblocks lie on both sides of the simplistic fence. On the powerholders' side, they include racism, paternalism, and resistance to power redistribution. On the have-nots' side, they include inadequacies of the poor community's political socio-economic infrastructure and knowledge-base, plus difficulties of organizing a representative and accountable citizens' group in the face of futility, alienation, and distrust.

Another caution about the eight separate rungs on the ladder: In the real world of people and programmes, there might be 150 rungs with less sharp and 'pure' distinctions among them. Furthermore, some of the characteristics used to illustrate each of the eight types might be applicable to other rungs. For example, employment of the have-nots in a programme or on a planning staff could occur at any of the eight rungs and could represent either a legitimate or illegitimate characteristic of citizen participation. Depending on their motives, powerholders can hire poor people to co-opt them, to placate them, or to utilize the have-nots' special skills and insights.[4]
[. . .] It is in this context of power and powerlessness that the characteristics of the eight rungs are illustrated by examples from current federal social programmes.

1. Manipulation
In the name of citizen participation, people are placed on rubber stamp advisory committees or advisory boards for the express purpose of 'educating' them or engineering their support. Instead of genuine citizen participation, the bottom rung of the ladder signifies the distortion of participation into a public relations vehicle by powerholders.
[. . .] This sham lies at the heart of the deep-seated exasperation and hostility of the have-nots toward the powerholders.

One hopeful note is that, having been so grossly affronted, some citizens have learned the Mickey Mouse game, and now they too know how to play. As a result of this knowledge, they are demanding genuine levels of participation to assure them that public programmes are relevant to their needs and responsive to their priorities.

2. Therapy
In some respects group therapy, masked as citizen participation, should be on the lowest rung of the ladder because it is both dishonest and arrogant. Its administrators – mental health experts from social workers to psychiatrists – assume that powerlessness is synonymous with mental illness. On this assumption, under a masquerade of involving citizens in planning, the experts subject the citizens to clinical group therapy. What makes this form of 'participation' so invidious is that citizens are engaged in extensive activity, but the focus of it is on curing them of their 'pathology' rather than changing the racism and victimization that create their 'pathologies'.

3. Informing
[. . .] Informing citizens of their rights, responsibilities, and options can be the most important first step toward legitimate citizen participation. However, too frequently the emphasis is placed on a one-way flow of information – from officials to citizens – with no channel provided for feedback and no power for negotiation. Under these conditions, particularly when information is provided at a late stage in planning,

people have little opportunity to influence the programme designed 'for their benefit'. The most frequent tools used for such one-way communication are the news media, pamphlets, posters, and responses to inquiries.

4. Consultation

[. . .] Inviting citizens' opinions, like informing them, can be a legitimate step toward their full participation. But if consulting them is not combined with other modes of participation, this rung of the ladder is still a sham since it offers no assurance that citizen concerns and ideas will be taken into account. The most frequent methods used for consulting people are attitude surveys, neighbourhood meetings, and public hearings.

When powerholders restrict the input of citizens' ideas solely to this level, participation remains just a window-dressing ritual. People are primarily perceived as statistical abstractions, and participation is measured by how many come to meetings, take brochures home or answer a questionnaire. What citizens achieve in all this activity is that they have 'participated in participation'. And what powerholders achieve is the evidence that they have gone through the required motions of involving 'those people'.

Attitude surveys have become a particular bone of contention in ghetto neighbourhoods. Residents are increasingly unhappy about the number of times per week they are surveyed about their problems and hopes. As one woman put it: 'Nothing ever happens with those damned questions, except the surveyor gets $3 an hour, and my washing doesn't get done that day'. In some communities, residents are so annoyed that they are demanding a fee for research interviews.

Attitude surveys are not very valid indicators of community opinion when used without other input from citizens. Survey after survey (paid for out of antipoverty funds) has 'documented' that poor housewives most want tot-lots in their neighbourhood where young children can play safely. But most of the women answered these questionnaires without knowing what their options were. They assumed that if they asked for something small, they might just get something useful in the neighbourhood. Had the mothers known that a free prepaid health insurance plan was a possible option, they might not have put tot-lots so high on their wish lists.

5. Placation

[. . .] It is at this level that citizens begin to have some degree of influence though tokenism is still apparent. An example of placation strategy is to place a few handpicked 'worthy' poor on boards of Community Action Agencies or on public bodies like the board of education, police commission, or housing authority. If they are not accountable to a constituency in the community and if the traditional power elite hold the majority of seats, the have-nots can be easily outvoted and outfoxed. Another example is the Model Cities advisory and planning committees. They allow citizens to advise or plan *ad infinitum* but retain for powerholders the right to judge the legitimacy or feasibility of the advice. The degree to which citizens are actually placated, of course, depends largely on two factors: the quality of technical assistance they have in articulating their priorities; and the extent to which the community has been organized to press for those priorities.

6. Partnership

[. . .] At this rung of the ladder, power is in fact redistributed through negotiation between citizens and powerholders. They agree to share planning and decision-making responsibilities through such structures as joint policy boards, planning committees and mechanisms for resolving impasses. After the ground rules have been established through some form of give-and-take they are not subject to unilateral change.

Partnership can work most effectively when there is an organized power-base in the community to which the citizen leaders are accountable; when the citizens group has the financial resources to pay its leaders reasonable honoraria for their time-consuming efforts; and when the group has the resources to hire (and fire) its own technicians, lawyers, and community organizers. With these ingredients, citizens have some genuine bargaining influence over the outcome of the plan (as long as both parties find it useful to maintain the partnership). One community leader described it 'like coming to city hall with hat on head instead of in hand'.

7. Delegated power

[. . .] Negotiations between citizens and public officials can also result in citizens achieving dominant decision-making authority over a particular plan or programme. Model City policy boards or CAA delegate agencies on which citizens have a clear majority of seats and genuine specified powers are typical examples. At this level, the ladder has been scaled to the point where citizens hold the significant cards to assure accountability of the programme to them. To resolve differences, powerholders need to start the bargaining process rather than respond to pressure from the other end.

8. Citizen control

Demands for community-controlled schools, black control and neighbourhood control are on the increase. Though no-one in the nation has absolute control, it is very important that the rhetoric is not confused with intent. People are simply demanding that the degree of power (or control) which guarantees that participants or residents can govern a programme or an institution, be in full charge of policy and managerial aspects, and be able to negotiate the conditions under which 'outsiders' may change them.

A neighbourhood corporation with no intermediaries between it and the source of funds is the model most frequently advocated. A small number of such experimental corporations are already producing goods and/or social services. Several others are reportedly in the development stage, and new models for control will undoubtedly emerge as the have-nots continue to press for greater degrees of power over their lives. [. . .] Among the arguments against community control are: it supports separatism; it creates balkanization of public services; it is more costly and less efficient; it enables minority group 'hustlers' to be just as opportunistic and disdainful of the have-nots as their white predecessors; it is incompatible with merit systems and professionalism; and ironically enough, it can turn out to be a new Mickey Mouse game for the have-nots by allowing them to gain control but not allowing them sufficient dollar resources to succeed.[5] These arguments are not to be taken lightly. But neither can we take lightly the arguments of embittered advocates of community control – that every other means of trying to end their victimization has failed!

References

1. The literature on poverty and discrimination and their effects on people is extensive. As an introduction, the following will be helpful: B. H. Bagdikian, *In the Midst of Plenty: The Poor in America*, Beacon, 1964; Paul Jacobs, 'The brutalizing of America, *Dissent*, Vol. 11, Autumn 1964. Stokely Carmichael and Charles V. Hamilton, *Black Power: The Politics of Liberation in America*, Random House 1967; Eldridge Cleaver, *Soul on Ice*, McGraw-Hill, 1968; L. J. Duhl, *The Urban Condition; People and Policy in the Metropolis*, Basic Books, 1963; William H. Grier and P. M. Cobbs, *Black Rage*, Basic Books, 1968; Michael Harrington, *The Other America: Poverty in the United States*, Macmillan, 1962; Peter Marris and Martin Rein, *Dilemmas of Social Reform: Poverty and Community Action in the United States*, Atherton Press, 1967; Mollie Orshansky, 'Who's who among the poor: a demographic view of poverty', *Social Security Bulletin*, Vol. 27, July 1965, pp. 3–32; and Richard T. Titmuss, *Essays on the Welfare State*, Yale UP, 1968.
2. The poster is one of about 350 produced in May or June 1968 at Atélier Populaire, a graphics centre launched by students from the Sorbonne's Ecole des Beaux Arts and Ecole des Arts Decoratifs.
3. This typology is an outgrowth of a more crude typology I circulated in March 1967 in a HOD staff discussion paper titled 'Rhetoric and reality'. The earlier typology consisted of eight levels that were less discrete types and did not necessarily suggest a chronological progression: Inform, Consult, Joint Planning, Negotiate, Decide, Delegate, Advocate Planning and Neighbourhood Control.
4. For an article of some possible employment strategies see, Edmund M. Burke, 'Citizen participation strategies' *Journal of the American Institute of Planners*, Vol. 34, No. 5, Sept. 1968, pp. 290–1.
5. For thoughtful academic analyses of some of the potentials and pitfalls of emerging neighbourhood control models, see, Alan Altshuler, 'The demand for participation in large American cities', An unpublished paper prepared for the Urban Institute, December 1968; and Hans B. C. Spiegel and Stephen D. Mittenthal, *Neighbourhood Power and Control, Implications for Urban Planning*, A report prepared for the Department of Housing and Urban Development, Nov. 1968.

Decentralisation and community technology

Neighborhood technology

David Morris and Karl Hess

Independence is as popular today in America as it was 200 years ago. People are quick to accept the notion that their lives should not be dominated by distant bureaucracies or immense corporations. But constructing alternatives is difficult. Part of what is needed is political: communities must organize themselves to run their own affairs. Another part of what's needed is economic. Independence, whether of neighborhoods, cities, or nations, requires a material base. Local communities in particular can realistically attain a measure of autonomy only when they can begin to sustain it economically.

Not surprisingly, the notion of neighborhood 'independence' raises a lot of questions. Even if people were well organized – and prepared to set up a locally controlled economy – would it conceivably be practical? Can a neighborhood of, say, 30,000 people generate its own energy, grow its own food, manufacture its basic necessities? What are the limits of local self-sufficiency?

Grappling with these questions means exploring the alternatives now available. The answers are necessarily tentative. But the new technologies that have come to prominence since the Second World War are promising. In the past, many of our institutions were built when technological innovations, distorted by war, produced ever-larger concentrations of economic power. Now these institutions are like over-armored dinosaurs, standing in the way of more local and flexible technologies. When steel, for instance, replaced wood as a major structural material in the last century, it required a much greater capital investment in factories, not simply for technological reasons but also for reasons of profit efficiency. Plastics, reinforced concrete, and other materials, which are rapidly replacing steel, require less technological capital and have so far avoided the concentrations of ownership that have characterized the steel industry. Even within the steel industry innovations are pointing to decentralization. No less an authority than *Fortune* magazine declared recently:

From David Morris and Karl Hess, 'Neighborhood Technology', *Working Papers for a New Society*, Vol. 3, No. 1, Spring 1975.

The famous old economies of scale which demanded gigantic equipment and blocked the entry of small would-be competitors are greatly diminishing in importance. Small companies, emboldened by steel's 'new economies', are streaming into the industry, setting up regional, even local plants, splintering the business into smaller pieces – and making money.

John Blair, former chief economist for the Senate Subcommittee on Antitrust and Monopoly, argues that the same process is happening throughout the economy. The new technological advances are neither labor intensive nor capital intensive, he says, they are knowledge intensive. In his textbook, *Economic Concentration*, he writes[1]:

With plastics, fiberglass, and high performance composites providing high strength and easily processed materials suitable for an infinite variety of applications; with energy provided by such simple and efficient devices as high-energy batteries, fuel cells, turbine engines, and rotary piston engines; with computers providing a means of instantaneously retrieving, sorting, and aggregating vast bodies of information; and with other new electronic devices harnessing the flow of electrons for other uses, there appears to be aborning a second industrial revolution which, among its other features, contains within itself the seeds of destruction for concentrated industrial structures.

What does all this mean for neighborhood development and the future of cities? It could mean, quite simply, that we may now be able to choose which way we want to go: whether we want to rely on outside forces and their dense concentrations of power and capital, or strike out for ourselves locally.

The most dramatic example of what's possible on the neighborhood level is the direct conversion of sunlight into electricity. It is commonly written that we are at least 50 years away from the time when photovoltaic cells will become competitive with fossil-fuel-powered generators as efficient sources of electricity. Recent events, however, belie this pessimism. A small corporation in Maryland, for example, has managed to lower the cost ratio of photovoltaic cells to fossil-fuel electrical generation from 100:1 to 7:1. The president of this corporation thinks that the figure can be lowered to 5:1 within a couple of years, and that the cells should be competitive with fossil-fuel-generated electricity by the end of the 1980s. These projections assume that the cost of fossil fuels will remain relatively steady during the next ten years, a conservative assumption. The advances achieved by this corporation have required investment capital of around $750,000 and a labor force recruited virtually right off the streets. The firm not only does research and development, but also markets its solar cells, testing them in the field.

Solar cells could be made in small neighborhood facilities. They would last almost indefinitely, and they could be placed on roofs to supply a major part of residential electrical needs. It seems probable that they will become available within the next 15 years. Right now, however, the largest corporations and the federal government are subsidizing and pushing for the introduction of nuclear energy plants all over the country. These plants will be located outside cities. They will generate enormous amounts of radioactive wastes and thermal pollution, and they will be far removed from any effective public control.

Like a solar-cell system, a complete nuclear system will take at least 15 years to establish. Given the cost and adverse effects of nuclear energy technology, neighborhoods interested in future planning could reasonably demand that their tax money be spent in subsidizing solar-cell development. An organized community could even undertake a contractual arrangement with research-and-development companies, and later manufacture its own solar cells with the experience and expertise gained through the R & D period. This is less fanciful than it sounds. As mentioned, one corporation produced its breakthroughs with less than a million dollars in venture capital, and it is making a profit.

Washington DC is currently building a subway system. At the height of its operation, according to the planners, the system will carry only 15 per cent of the commuter traffic coming into the city. It will be completed in the mid-1980s and will cost anywhere from $4 billion to $8 billion. This amounts to between $1,500 and $3,000 for very man, woman, and child in the metropolitan area. If such an expenditure were brought down to the neighborhood level, between $50 million and $100 million would be available for transportation research and development in a community of 30,000. This is a fantastic sum for only one neighborhood. It could be multiplied if the research were not limited to transportation, and if neighborhoods began to specialize. One neighborhood could work with solar collectors, another with windmills, another with plastics production, another with computers, another with inhouse toilet systems, another with electric-vehicle production. The point here is that the money is available; it is the ingenuity to diversify its use that is missing.

The new technologies are knowledge intensive. They need personnel trained in the new sciences who are competent to keep up with advances in the field. They need people with special knowledge about new equipment coming on the market. This kind of expertise, of course, is not found in every neighborhood. This, however, does not mean that it couldn't be nurtured. Our urban educational systems are massive, with thousands of trained scientists at work in them, millions of dollars worth of equipment, and hundreds of thousands of technicians in the classrooms. Some of these educational personnel could be diverted into useful community technology programs. Also, although we noted that the new technologies are knowledge intensive, we also noted that they are not labor intensive. Only a few highly trained professionals are needed. Production forces would not have to be more than semiskilled; in some cases they could be unskilled.

Since this is a new area for most people we would like to explore other examples of how cities could save money by using small-scale technology. Currently, sewage is a major problem in our cities. Most municipal sewage systems were designed and constructed during the early part of this century. They never were expected to handle current loads or to last this long. Many are in dire need of repair, yet this would require literally billions of dollars in municipal outlays. Also, only one-half of our municipal sewage treatment plants, according to the Federal Water Quality Control Board, are adequate. Drinking-water supplies now require a huge amount of chlorine to keep them purified, yet chlorine itself is in short supply. Coastal cities are finding that even the ocean cannot absorb the continuing deluge of billions of gallons of human waste. In New York City, raw sewage is now within two miles of the shoreline, and many experts predict that within two years it will be up on shore.

Yet there are simple, low-cost alternatives. In Washington DC, the authorities are spending hundreds of millions of dollars to modernize their treatment plant. By the time the new system is operational it will be overloaded, by the planners' own admission. The city still has not spent the money to separate the sanitary and storm-sewer systems. Whenever it rains, raw sewage is shunted directly into the Potomac River. However, a preliminary study indicates that, given the amount of money the city is willing to spend on modernizing treatment facilities, in-house, non-water-carrying disposal systems could be installed in almost every house in the District. Such a system would conserve water, capture wastes to be used as fertilizer, and lead to the cleaning up of the Potomac River (which has major recreational potential).

One more example. The internal combustion car, with its steel body and 5,000 pounds of weight, requires large factories and enormous capital expenditures. The pollution from cars requires pollution-control boards, and devices on the mufflers of cars which in turn lead to less efficient gasoline utilization. The cars consume huge quantities of petroleum. The thousands of moving parts require frequent repairs, increasing the cost of the vehicle to its owners. The cars are noisy, bulky, and smelly. They are large, in size and horsepower, even though the average urban trip is less than two and a half miles and the average urban auto carries less than two people per trip.

Electric vehicles with lightweight plastic bodies, on the other hand, can be manufactured in small factories, possibly located within a city. Electric motors can be made in very small shops. Plastic-injection molding techniques considerably reduce the amount of capital needed to produce car bodies. The cars are quiet and small. They require less energy to operate because when the accelerator is not depressed, the electrical connection is broken, thereby cutting off electricity from the batteries (whereas the fuel consumed by idling internal combustion vehicles represents a significant amount of the petroleum consumed in inner-city driving). Electric cars also have few movable parts to go wrong and therefore save money on repairs.

So we have a choice. Nuclear power plants, metropolitan sewage-treatment plants, internal combustion engines – or solar cells, inhouse waste-cycling systems, and electric cars. It is not only an ecological and economic choice, it is a deeply political one. It asks whether we want to move our productive facilities back into our communities, or remain at the mercy of isolated forces operating on criteria that give human concerns a low priority.

Doing it: food

There are steps that can be taken right now to develop neighborhood production, if this is the choice we decide to make. Consider the example of food production. There's no reason that a neighborhood, even a densely populated urban neighborhood, cannot grow a good part of the food it needs. A first approach might be to take a survey of what space is available in the neighborhood – rooftops, vacant lots, and the like – and how much sunlight falls on it. The next step is to figure out what kinds of food are needed and how they can be produced.

This step gets us into the murky area of human nutrition and basic needs. It is not enough to examine how much of each food item could be raised in a given geographic area. It must be seen how far the neighborhood can go in producing a balanced diet: protein, minerals, vitamins, fats, carbohydrates, and fibers. (Frances Moore Lappé's *Diet for a Small Planet* is a complete, popular work on the subject, with charts breaking down basic needs and the kinds of foods that will provide those needs.[2])

The content of the food we eat can vary markedly, depending on whether the vegetable or grain has been grown in good or bad soil, whether it has been harvested at the right time, and whether it has been prepared properly. Any analysis of a neighborhood's potential thus has to take into account a number of factors.

Department of Agriculture technicians use the rough rule of thumb that to feed one American one acre of land is needed. Other studies indicate that we might get by with less. One researcher in California has preliminary figures indicating that one-eighth of an acre might be enough to feed one person a vegetarian diet for a year. Whatever the projections are, there are some hard data available on current yields of various crops. The local extension agent can give you yields for your area of the country. These yields may be conservative, for there have been numerous advances in small-scale intensive agriculture. In Palo Alto and Santa Cruz, California, people are investigating a technique of labor-intensive gardening called biodynamic gardening. In some areas, scientific advances in cross-planting various vegetables for space-saving purposes are being integrated into family plots. Finally, and maybe most exciting for inner-city areas, it is possible to utilize greenhouse techniques with soil or other media as the base.

Hydroponics, for example, is a method by which plants are grown in media other than soil. Nutrients are provided periodically in solution. It is not a new technique. Some 40 per cent of the tomatoes sold in Phoenix, Arizona, for example, come from hydroponic greenhouses. This technique has three advantages. First, yields seem to be higher than with soil gardening. Second, hydroponics prevents the depletion of soil, which is scarce in the city. Third, soil might well be too heavy on residential rooftops. But soilless media, such as a combination of perlite and vermiculite or small clay pellets, are quite light.

Of course, people don't live by vegetables alone. Although we can get some protein from vegetables (some say all we need), it is not clear that people will forsake meat or fish unless they are on the verge of starvation. The average person needs 0.9 gram of protein per kilogram of weight. This means that a 150-pound person would need three ounces. Get a census for your neighborhood. It breaks down the population into age groups. Then get a weight chart for each age group. This will give you a method for roughly estimating how much protein your neighborhood needs to survive.

Meat is not the only source of protein. Other foods compare favorably with meat; partly because the quality of our protein intake is as important as the quantity. Protein needs certain combinations of amino acids if it is to be utilized efficiently by the body. In other words, one food might have more protein quantity, but because of its combination of amino acids, less of it is used in the body per weight than another food.

Some of the best sources of protein are fish, eggs, meat, and soybeans. Although there may be municipal ordinances that prohibit the raising of some fowl and animals within city limits, it is a good idea to estimate what kind of production you can get in any case. Some sources of protein, like cattle, are ruled out in the beginning. In the absence of land for grazing, it takes more than 20 pounds of cereal protein to produce one pound of beef protein. This is an inefficiency Americans have lived with for many years – much to the detriment of the rest of the world, where human-use cereal production has been reduced while large numbers of beef cattle are raised for export. It takes six pounds of cereal protein to get one pound of hog meat, and two and a half pounds of vegetable protein fed to chickens to get one pound of animal protein in return.

There are interesting compromises possible for those who eat meat. Chickens, for example, can survive on a diet of flies, and some people in Palo Alto are currently devising an effective fly trap for just this purpose. Rabbits can survive on scraps, and, of course, their rate of reproduction is legendary.

Fish are good converters of protein. Rainbow trout, for example, produce 16 ounces of fish flesh for every 24 ounces of feed they eat. What is more, they can be raised intensively in very small areas, even in urban basements. Experiments are now in progress around the country involving lobster cultivation and shrimp, salmon, catfish, and trout rearing. Lobster and shrimp research is still in the preliminary stages. Lobster research, in any event, is being done because of the high cost per pound, with a view to the commercial market, rather than as a low-cost way to raise food. Recent investigations in California with shrimp, however, have tentatively found that this omnivorous animal can be fed a diet of vegetables and scraps, rather than meat, and still thrive. Rapid advances are being made in salmon research in Providence, Rhode Island, and in closed-loop catfish farming in Woods Hole, Massachusetts ('closing the loop' means recycling external inputs so that the system becomes ecologically stable – e.g. wastes are used to feed single-celled creatures which are fed to fish which are then eaten, producing waste). In Providence, salmon reportedly grow to 2 pounds in 18 months in fresh-water tanks, and then grow rapidly to 8 pounds in salt-water facilities. In Washington DC, Dr Fern Wood Mitchell has raised eggs to maturity in his basement with a simple tank and filter system that uses city water in very small quantities (25 gallons a day compared with 25 gallons a minute in traditional commercial trout farming). In Milheim, Pennsylvania, the Marine Protein Company has now begun to raise one million pounds of trout per surface acre, more than ten times the average figure in outdoor 'raceways'. The fish are raised in 12-by-17-foot food silos.

There are possible interlocks between these systems. For example, rainbow trout are especially good for urban areas because they can be raised intensively. But they have two drawbacks. They require high-grade protein (usually fish meal) as a diet, and they require cold water. Energy must be used to keep their space air-conditioned. It may be possible to use windmills to generate the electricity for the air conditioning. Or one can look to other types of fish. One group in Woods Hole, Massachusetts, is working with tilapia, a kind of catfish, which is a warm-water fish and herbivorous. Several people around the world are currently experimenting with systems by which human waste can be used to raise algae, a simple-celled plant organism, which can in turn be fed to fish in indoor tanks. The more ways that the system of food production, consumption, and waste can be closed, the more a neighborhood can become independent of outside sources of energy and food.

The research into the carrying capacity of the neighborhood will not inevitably be transformed into community action. No matter how much information you compile about community resources, it is only when residents can see the results of such labors – can eat the tomatoes, taste the fish, see the gardens growing, watch the windmills spinning, feel the hot water heated by a solar collector – that they can get interested in the visions that the research projects. Therefore, the next stage is to construct demonstration projects. Make a fish tank and stock it; put up several greenhouses and invite people to see how vegetables grow during the colder months; raise some vegetables hydroponically and sell them in community stores, with signs telling how they were grown;

erect a windmill or two and show people how it generates electricity; buy a couple of solar cells and show residents how they can be used to power a transistor radio.

Demonstration projects are an ideal way to create a link with those interested in these projects as a hobby and those interested in the economic possibilities. It is a way to attract the attention of different kinds of skilled people, from plumbers to bankers. It is a way to get publicity from citywide news media. And it is a way to get in touch with people in the area who may have vital information or demonstration models of their own.

Only when people begin to talk about what 'we did' can they begin to discuss and explore what 'we can do'. And once that process is initiated neighborhoods will explore the limits of their own self-sufficiency in increasingly creative ways.

References

1. John Blair, *Economic Concentration*, Harcourt Brace, 1974.
2. Frances Moore Lappé, *Diet for a small planet*, Ballantine, 1975.

The changing market place

Barry A. Stein

Smaller-scale alternatives

[. . .] What are the alternatives available, at least in principle, for establishing efficient industrial units on a scale smaller than that now conceived as optimum? Clearly, the details for any given industry or product orientation would differ and would have to be analyzed more carefully. No attempt will be made to solve those particular problems in this paper, even if it were possible. What is possible instead is the presentation of an outline of broad approach that can be used as a framework for further work and that takes advantage of the general conclusions reached so far. From the present perspective, although a case has been made against increasing or even constant returns to scale, several categories can be distinguished.

Some preliminary remarks are, however, necessary. First, it should be noted that conventional (not unuseful, merely accepted) approaches to economic development and industrial location use certain basic parameters which are as important in the present context as anywhere else. To some degree, labor intensity, capital requirements, access to and size of markets, competitive environment, and the need for specialized technology are obviously relevant, although the significance of some of these depends, as will be seen, on the context.[1] Again, however, this paper is primarily concerned with other areas, less widely addressed, and will deal with the conventional issues only to the extent that they are particularly relevant.

Second, it should be clear that the present discussion is not limited to enterprises that are typically regarded as 'small' (unless, perhaps, one sets the definition so as to include all but the largest industrial enterprises). One conventional definition sets the upper size limit at a point 'which, considering the nature of the business, permits personalized management in the hands of one or a few executives, as opposed to institutionalized management characteristic of larger enterprises'.[2] This definition, although it describes a type of organization which will often or generally exist in early stages of development, is entirely too limiting

Extracts from Chapter 3 of Barry A. Stein, *Size, Efficiency and Community Enterprise*, Center for Community Economic Development, 1974.

for several reasons. For one thing, such firms may or may not be efficient producers; this distinction is in that sense somewhat arbitrary. Also, it assumes an entrepeneurial or narrow control model for firms that is in distinct contrast to the collective alternatives, which may never be actually organized that way, even if it were possible given the size. Finally, it does not offer in any case an effective training/development opportunity for other workers nor the potential to take maximum advantage of shared resources available throughout the organization. And if the latter does not occur, the organization will be inherently less efficient in its use of resources.

Most critically, what is needed are ventures that have the potential of becoming substantial enough to make a significant economic impact on the community or area in question, and while some of these may be considered small, if measured by the above definition, others will not be. A useful concept for comparative purposes here is a dual economy, in which there co-exist two rather independent economic spheres; one, the core economy, composed of entities sufficiently large and effective to accumulate resources, to take risks, and to plan for the future; and the other, the peripheral economy, composed of firms that exist marginally, largely depend on core institutions, and are forced to minimize costs and risks absolutely. In a general way, firms in the peripheral economy are much likelier to meet the definition of small business offered above.[3]

Scale and efficiency are not, of course, the only critical parameters: at first glance, it would appear that a given product could be efficiently produced in the same size plant for the same nominal market, independent of its ownership or control structure. However, closer examination shows this conclusion to be false, particularly in certain substantial and definable sectors of industry. To put it more directly, efficiency in social – even in economic – terms is not independent of the nature of ownership and control. Since these issues are critical to this discussion of true productive efficiency, they are dealt with in what follows.

In particular, we wish also to differentiate between the conventional entrepreneurial firms, which are controlled and owned individually, and those based on some form of collective action. In the latter case, two polar types exist, although, as indicated below, these are not necessarily incompatible. One can consider control by either workers (those whose primary work is within the enterprise) or by the community (a larger and much more encompassing social unit with, perhaps, many such enterprises). Both forms of collective control are, however, quite different from individual control, and the implications for action are correspondingly different. The terminology is not entirely satisfactory, since it could be argued, for example, that a conventional publicly held corporation is collectively owned. What is meant by 'collective' in the present connotation, however, is a social unit having a collective identity, rather than a cluster of otherwise unrelated individuals. In this sense, shareholder-owned firms are still individually owned, since the stock-holders perceive a commonality of interest only with regard to the sucess of the firm and act as individuals, in any case.

We can now reformulate the basic issues posed here. In the institutional and normative framework of the American economic system, firms existing in the peripheral economy can have no long-term impact, even if in the short run they produce desirable goods and services or involve people in satisfying and productive effort. What is necessary is to focus on those sectors where there exists opportunity for acquiring at least the *characteristics* of core economic institutions, even if the enterprise is small by typical core standards. What then are the important distinctions as to the potential for collective entities as against individually controlled ones? In what way can the overall productive system be broken down so as to make those distinctions concrete. And finally, in either case, what is the expected effect of size and scale on those redefined sectoral boundaries? To move toward answers to those questions, it is appropriate to consider first the nature of collective economic activities.

Collective enterprise

Economic institutions in any society are of course ultimately justified by the prevailing ideology in terms of their substantive contribution to the well-being of that society and its members. Such institutions are no more to be viewed as ends in and of themselves than are the products or services they generate. In the United States, or for that matter, in capitalist-type economies anywhere, it is asserted that these broader social purposes are optimally achieved through the separate decisions of individually controlled firms interacting through the market mechanism. The defects and limitations of this view are by now well known and have been written about extensively. What is less clear however is the impact of other, quite different, alternatives on the social fabric.

In the present context, these things are mentioned only because the very idea of collective enterprises, whether that means worker or community control, is inherently incompatible with that ideology. It is not merely a matter of a market now composed of firms differently organized, but a fundamentally different ideological and value structure that incorporates a set of different assumptions about the relationship of economic institutions to society and to its members alike. The notion of collective economic units sees business as rooted in the community in particular ways, and it is organized around principles which strongly differentiate such ventures from those of a more conventional character.[4]

Clearly, this does not mean that a market would not exist, but rather that the basis on which decisions are made and the goals directly internalized in collective entities would be of a different sort. This follows directly from the fact that participation of the workers in the broader community, which controls the enterprise and benefits from its presence, removes the workers from the position of mere 'labor' and offers, at least in principle, a broader role, a different self-image, and an altered sense of identity with others. It is clear that community enterprises, if they aim to achieve the human and social purposes enunciated earlier, cannot merely replicate industry as is, conventional bureaucracy and all, but must operate by different processes, more attuned to the individual and social needs of those who are involved. To do otherwise will not only inevitably fail to produce the expected benefits but will, instead, create the same kinds of dysfunctional distinctions among participants as are seen in conventional enterprises. Andre Gorz, for example, has written that: 'The demand for self-management . . . cannot be contained within the factory walls, the laboratories and research bureaus. Men who cannot be ordered around in their work cannot be ordered around in their life as citizens, nor can they submit to the rigid decisions of central administrators.'[5]

We can now distinguish between enterprises that are strictly worker controlled and those that are more broadly community controlled. The workers are, of course, a part of the community, but it is apparent that the latter type of control would involve more people in decisions affecting the venture than would the former. In particular, use of accumulated resources or economic surplus would presumably be determined by community priorities, as against those related merely to the firm itself and the workers composing it. Thus, one of the key distinctions has to do with whose interests are internalized into the firm's decision-making apparatus.[6]

Vanek, in a major study of the economic and social values to be gained from the worker-controlled economy, has concluded that such an economy 'appears in a very favorable light, both in comparison to an absolute standard of efficiency and in comparison with other economic systems. . . . It has a definite advantage in generating full employment, long-range price stability, and growth.'[7] Vanek also concludes that such a system has important advantages in social terms. For example, it automatically takes into account such things as pollution, which are ordinarily externalities, and it offers a genuine opportunity for people to integrate their personal goals, interests and capacities with organizational aims. Since workers' control offers, by definition, the opportunity for the most direct and meaningful form of participation, the remarks made earlier on its value apply here in full force.

In any case, it is clear that those directly engaged in an organization, whether economic or not, are the most informed about its operational characteristics, are in the best position to implement internal options, and are the most directly (in many cases, the only ones) affected by the organizations' structure, roles, work arrangements, and styles. There is thus an overwhelming case to be made for workers' control, at least in such matters, whether or not the enterprise is organized on a broad community base. This conclusion, further, is supported by the extensive evidence and arguments that have been widely reported elsewhere.[8]

It is also evident that the *absence* of worker control in a nominally community controlled firm would constitute a basic contradiction of the elementary principles involved. The basic requirement in both cases is simple and straightforward; those affected by the activities of the organization should have the controlling influence in its decisions, the more so when they affect interests that are primary and central to those involved. Robert Dahl has called this 'the principle of affected interests'. In one way or another, then, a true measure of community control will be the extent to which workers are involved in the decision-making processes of the enterprise and offered options for growth and learning different from those typically encountered, thereby changing, very substantially, the alienated response to routinized labor referred to by Blauner.[9]

It would be excessively naive to imagine that these desirable ends will automatically spring into existence from the beginning. Certainly, they will not. But the direction is clearly desirable, the benefits are evident, and to the extent that the community, or any meaningful segment of it, is involved in the control and operation of the enterprise, such ends will be the natural trend. The issue thus revolves about the means of achieving these desirable features of workers' control in the broader context of community enterprises. It would seem that such a goal is possible, probably by retaining for workers control over internal decisions, while retaining for the larger community (perhaps through a board of directors or a community assembly which will, of course, include both workers and nonworkers) control of certain key decisions such as allocation of surplus resources and strategic directions for the enterprise. Assuming, then, that community enterprises will also be characterized by worker control, it is possible to look more deeply into the nature of economic opportunities for such firms.[10]

Industrial sectors and scale

As has been noted earlier, the marketplace is changing so as to shift demand increasingly towards goods and services meeting individualized needs and desires. Within this context two classes of goods can be distinguished in principle. In the first class are the tailored products, those that may be significantly modified to meet specific needs or interests. Such products, for example, include clothing, food, and furniture. Clothing can vary as to style, size, color, and fabric; furniture, as to material and design; food, as to flavor and cut, even without a consequent price difference.

The second class of individualized products are those inherently incapable of supporting significant differences (call them commodities), but which nonetheless are often artificially distinguished for purposes of sales, marketing, and promotion. This category includes such items as common pharmaceuticals, glass products, many foods, and cleaning materials. The artificial differentiations applied to such products are typically based on elaborate packaging, misleading advertising, imputed qualities, and brand names. Clearly, to rigorously apply this distinction between the two classes of products is difficult, if not impossible. For present purposes, however, it may be noted that these two categories suggest distinctively different conclusions as to the relevance of the scale of production and the consequent efficiency.[11]

The class of tailored products clearly includes those to which true mass production is inapplicable and which, moreover, ought to be produced in conformity to the wishes of individual consumers. However the individual characteristics of these goods are often disregarded in order to permit economies of scale to be realized, thus permitting firms producing such goods the possibility of centralizing operations, gaining substantial markets, increasing sales and assets, and producing greater profits for the owners. This disregard, however, is largely the result of the vertical integration of the operations required to form relatively basic materials into those tailored products. The visible industrial structure, in other words, is determined neither by technological nor scale considerations, but instead by choosing one of a wide range of options for producing such goods. Thus, Dean and Smith have made this point with vigor.

We now recognize that important kinds of flexibility exist at many points in the process that determines the size of a firm. . . . Great advantages of specialization do not always require firms large enough to use the entire output of a specialist. . . . In general, firms can obtain any resource under a variety of arrangements, of which ownership is only one.[12]

As an example, consider clothing, say shirts. In the ideal case, each shirt produced would uniquely suit the customer for whom it is intended. Its color, fabric, shape, style, and quality would reflect personal attention. Even so, the manufacture of the tailored product will need large quantities of a commodity – basic fabrics, undyed and uncut – to produce the individualized shirts. Such commodities can be efficiently produced by large scale mass production methods. And although the scale required for their efficient production will not be as great as the present industrial structure suggests, it is clear that a substantial enterprise is needed.

At each successive step required to convert those commodities to tailored product, the market becomes progressively smaller and the opportunities for mass production correspondingly less. Thus, the required quantities needed for a given fabric dyed to a specific color will obviously be much less than the total amount of material needed; and, similarly, when the dyed fabrics are cut into different patterns, each combination of pattern and color will be still smaller in quantity, until finally only one shirt with a given set of features will be produced. At each such step, alternatives exist for separate firms to purchase intermediate goods for modification to a stage closer to final consumption.

Truly efficient production of such products will be maximized, other things being equal, when finished products correspond precisely to consumer preferences (of course, at the least price). Several conclusions follow from the preceding.[13]

First, since even approaching that precise matching of products and preferences requires detailed interaction between customer and supplier, there is a positive benefit to be gained from close relationships. Although this closeness is attainable to some degree by entrepreneurial firms, there is a clear advantage accruing to collective enterprises, at least to those whose members are also potential users of the goods. Second, it follows that production of such goods for export is less efficient than similar production for local use, since the desired interaction with consumers is less available. However, there is a trade-off calculation to consider; since there is a real and significant increase in efficiency gained by production at a size above the technical minimum, consumers will often prefer somewhat less specific tailoring if there is a cost saving involved.

Industries producing tailored goods are also likely to be characterized by substantial competition, including that based on price, since the real capacity of such products to be differentiated and the consequent lessening of scale and aggregation advantages permit more differentiation among producers. Finally, it should be stressed that the minimizing of final cost to consumers calls for different scales of production and different forms of organization at each step in the transformation of raw materials to commodities to tailored goods. Summing up these considerations concerning tailored products, we may conclude, first, that there are less likely to be large unnecessary costs associated with their production; second, that since these tailored goods are capable of being efficiently produced at a scale whose market size is relatively small (both geographically and numerically), they offer preferential opportunities for collective (as against private) enterprise; and third, that the production of final rather than intermediate goods is more desirable for collectives.

By contrast, production of commodities suggests a different set of conclusions. To start, we may note that even though there are needed, as with tailored products, a series of more-or-less discrete operations to transform the raw materials into final consumer products, there exists no corresponding possibility of modifying these products to meet individual needs, except at a very gross level of aggregation. But the potential to utilize mass production techniques and to gain all possible economies of scale does exist in its fullest sense. The 'decay' of efficient scale, characteristic of tailored goods, does not appear in the case of commodities. It is therefore to be expected that such industries would tend to be composed of a relatively few large plants, which would be subject only to the constraints introduced by the process of physical distribution.

Now if commodity products were available in the market in the undifferentiated form that their nature suggests, competition, even of an oligopolistic kind, would not only tend to reduce consumers' costs to a level consonant with the costs of production and distribution, but would provide strong incentives for producers to minimize their own costs by constructing just such factories. Instead, attention has been focused on the strategy of attempting to convert true commodities to apparent tailored goods, so as to avoid direct price competition in the marketplace. The distinctions introduced – elaborate packaging, exhortative advertising and promotion that asserts the presence of unmeasurable values, and irrelevant physical modification (colored toothpaste) – do not, in fact, render these competing products 'different' in any substantive sense, but to the extent that consumers are convinced by these distinctions and treat them as if they were different, product loyalty is generated.

From the point of view of the firms in question, this process is profoundly beneficial. Not only does it minimize the requirement for price competition with its attendant low margins, risk, and hard work, but by generating a new type of expenditure the process offers the possibility of greater growth in sales, and a consequent increase in status and influence. From the consumer's point of view and, still more, with regard to a productive use of society's resources, this process is sheer waste.[14]

Here then is a case where very substantial cost savings are available in principle, should a firm produce commodities without the artificial means of differentiation noted. The counter-argument, that such expenditures are in fact useful since they are necessary to assure a scale of production in which the final costs are lower, does not accord with the facts on scale efficiency. In particular, these are the goods most typically sold as private brands by local retailers, at the very great savings (up to 50 per cent) referred to earlier. It is, of course, true that efficient production scale for commodities in general will be greater than that for tailored goods, but, at the same time, the local market for such goods will be also greater since these goods are not differentiable in character.

There is a further feature of such commodities that requires attention. They are, by no accident, faced with a nearly static market or at least one whose size will only increase with the population itself. These goods, which may be called mature, are well known, have become routine elements in most people's lives, and in a highly developed economic society, such as the US, have virtually saturated the total present market. The production of such commodities is no longer seen as presenting opportunities for growth in the same sense as do the new products. Mature commodity goods effectively define the material level of a society; they are the components of the 'market-basket' that must be available to every consumption unit, if it is to regard itself as a minimum participant in society's prosperity.[15]

As economic growth continues, more and more goods become mature in this sense; that is, they become nominal necessities for an adequate level of material existence. The increase in disposable income, noted earlier, therefore tends to be consumed by increased expenditure on just these sorts of items. This is the essential meaning of 'the revolution of rising expectations'. In this process, the opportunities for private entrepreneurial firms diverge sharply from those available to the collective enterprises with which we are here concerned.

To the extent that producers of mature commodities in particular industrial sectors of the economy utilize techniques of artificial differentiation, such sectors tend to become more concentrated (that is, produced increasingly by relatively few large-scale units). Since the market is effectively saturated, by definition, these promotional activities are designed to maintain market share, for there is no significant possibility of increasing market save at the expense of another firm which is attempting to do precisely the same thing. Since, as many economists have pointed out, no single firm can afford to reduce its expenditures on differentiation unless others will follow the same pattern (the prisoner's dilemma model) an assumption that cannot be made, the result is for such expenditures to increase. This in turn results in both higher prices (relative to costs) for the consumer and increased barriers to entry for new firms. As Bain has written: 'product differentiation is of at least the same general order of importance as an impediment to entry as are economies of large-scale production and distribution. ... Second, great entry barriers are more frequently attributed to product differentiation than to scale economies in production and distribution.'[16]

There is no strong incentive for private firms to enter such a market, characterized as they are by substantial and capital-intensive barriers to entry, well-entrenched competitors, considerable risk, and a saturated market which permits acquiring customers only at another firm's expense. When new competitors do arise in such industries, they are drawn by the potentially high returns that accrue to a well-established figure in the field. Such new entrants will generally be those whose promotion and differentiation strategy is thought to be powerful – as, for example, the recent successful entrant in the women's hosiery field, L'Eggs, whose strategy was clever packaging and a name that would 'stick'. In any case, it is clearly more likely for firms to enter growth markets where opportunities are less risky.

For enterprises rooted in the community, however, the situation is reversed. The very purpose that brand-name based promotion serves is to forge links between the producers of a good and the consumers and, through that mechanism, to bypass both wholesalers and retailers whose connection to the market is closer in principle. In fact, the history of American industrial development has been characterized by a shift in focus from retail outlets, to wholesale merchant, to the manufacturers themselves. One of the key strategies that has been recommended for community-based enterprises and for Community Development

Corporations, specifically, is to obtain some means to secure a captive market; for example, contractual relationship with other firms.[17]

However, there is a more powerful and *unique* opportunity available to community-based ventures, due to the very fact of community control and participation. To the extent that people perceive the new venture(s) as operating for their express benefit, responsive to their needs, controlled by their decisions, and providing them with desirable goods and opportunities, they will tend to support and maintain it. This is in contrast to the usual case in which customers and producers are related only through the impersonal medium of the market. Customers' interests here are concerned solely with the product or service; if these are inadequate or unsatisfying, another source will be found. There exists neither the commitment nor the means to maintain or build a relationship to the producer of those goods.[18]

[. . .] This, again, is related to the fact that large national corporations must expect to spend even more to maintain the value of their brand name, thereby adding to the final consumer cost. There is, however, a great opportunity for community-based ventures to [. . .] *build on the commitment of community members to enterprises operating in their interest.* This advantage is *not* available to either larger, more remote, entities lacking the same ties to the community, or to private entrepreneurs who, though resident in the community, are operating in their own private interests and who, over time, are certain to diverge from the interests of the community at large and, in any case, are unable to truly tap the community's self-interest.[19]

We may sum up this argument about commodity products as follows. First, although such goods, in fact, require some reasonable scale for technically efficient production, that size need not be outside the capacity of modest-sized communities. In many cases (e.g. compounded products like aspirin and cleaning materials) that size is small. Moreover, consideration of total cost to consumers suggests that even if there is an optimum production scale, operation below it would be more than compensated by other, larger, economies derived from savings in distribution and promotion.

Second, since these are mature commodities, a modest community would constitute a sufficient market for production of such goods. And, if we focus particularly on relatively poor or deprived communities or regions, we find that here also these goods make up the bulk of local consumption expenditures. Accordingly, the production of such goods by a community-based enterprise for the use of that same resident group would, in the aggregate, significantly reduce the flow of funds out of the community itself and thus improve both its economic position vis-à-vis other wealthier areas and provide a degree of local autonomy, without which community development must remain a vain hope.

Since advertising and promotional costs are passed on, willy-nilly, to each purchaser of the product being advertised, there exists the possibility that these costs produce a highly regressive income redistribution scheme. That is, to the extent that a particular product category is more important to the lower rather than the higher-income group, then the former are subsidizing both those with higher incomes and the firms in question. There are, in fact, data suggesting that urban blacks, for example, preferentially purchase national instead of local brands because these brands are important to the maintenance of an adequate self-image. Wealthier consumers, not confronted with their problem, therefore benefit from the availability of equal quality products at lower prices.[20]

Third, the savings to be gained by purchase of local products, so far as consumers are concerned, in principle are very great, as the earlier figures have indicated. Thus, people will purchase such goods initially because the products are of lower cost and represent more value per dollar. Only as that fact becomes clearer will the more important long-term source of support for such enterprises come into play. That support lies in the very community focus itself; such enterprises, controlled by community members, will become perceived as an integral and important aspect of the community. Workers, owners, managers, and others depending on those ventures will be known more personally to customers and identified as members of their community. People will thus buy because it is psychologically and socially meaningful for them to do so. And that, in the long run, is what is needed.[21]

Consumer vs. producer goods

A natural conclusion of the foregoing argument is that community enterprises should focus on consumer goods rather than on intermediate or producer goods. This is so for several reasons. The first is related to the opportunity to serve directly the needs of community members (making available to them the goods and services they need). The production of producer goods, even if based on a contractual or legal arrangement that guarantees a market for a certain volume and time, is not equivalent. If focus is on producer goods, it will not be possible to develop the same commitment of community residents to the venture, since only with consumer goods can they directly experience the fact that the enterprise is actually providing them with useful and meaningful products.

Second, with regard to the changing market place and the differentiated needs of the people in the community, only a consumer-oriented venture can actually fill those particular needs. Such ventures are required to take advantage directly of the feedback from the community; through that means the community can begin to exercise autonomous decisions and assure that its wishes/desires are being heard and attended to. Community-based ventures of this sort would make evident the value of the enterprise to the residents; would make more difficult the invasion of that market by external firms; and would add measurably to the credibility of the community to act on its own behalf. The provision of producer goods, in contrast, is ultimately dependent on other firms over which the community has little control and takes away the broad base of production related *to the consumer*, which alone will gurantee future success.

Third, as has been noted, it is precisely consumer goods' prices, specifically mature goods, that are most inflated. Because of the need for large external producers to maintain strong brand images and to occupy large production facilities serving extensive areas (thus requiring high costs of physical distribution), it is in the production of simple and routine consumer goods where the best opportunity is found to reduce final costs. As national labels lose ground, manufacturers' unit costs go up, greater expenditure on brand promotion is needed, and the competitive balance tips still further. Community enterprises, on the other hand, offer the same goods, promote their value, and increase their market loyalty as a direct result of the very nature of the enterprise. Its unit costs over time, accordingly, can be expected to show a relative decrease, as both learning and growth (at least up to a point) take place.

It is also in this area of consumer goods that smaller scale enterprises make best sense, since it is here that one can take advantage of the basic materials and products produced by large firms as commodities, which are more nearly cost-efficient than differentiated final products. These, in turn, can be modified or finished in whatever way is appropriate to the local market: bulk industrial chemicals can be mixed and packaged for household and/or agricultural needs; steel strip can be cut, painted, and assembled into venetian blinds; or bolts of fabric can be cut, dyed and sewn for a multitude of purposes. This is not a matter of cottage industries; significant enterprises can be generated in these and similar areas, employing anywhere up to a hundred or so, taking full advantage of modern technology and industrial organization, and producing for the community's needs.

One benefit of such goods as a focus for community enterprises lies precisely in their prosaic nature. The need for these goods or services is generally long-standing, predictable, basic, and not subject to rapid change. They are not, in short, glamorous products out of which new growth industries will develop, although there will always be exceptions. This approach assures minimum risk that the expected/needed market will not develop. It follows that the advantage that large firms have in financing extensive development programs or in taking a series of new product risks is of small consequence here. Moreover, since such goods are, by and large, relatively easy for the consumer to test and evaluate, the impact of large-scale promotional campaigns aimed at convincing consumers that 'Brand A' has special features that differentiate it from all others is less likely to be successful. The great increase in 'consumerism', as indicated by the large sales volume of private or off brands, clearly suggests a more sophisticated and knowledgeable consumer;

a development which community ventures should support and on which they can build.

Finally, it should be noted that products or services meeting direct consumer needs offer a significant option for the members of the community to participate in novel ways in those enterprises. Victor Fuchs has pointed out that the 'study of productivity in the service industries [demonstrates] . . . the importance of the consumer as a cooperating agent in the production process . . . this point, is neglected in the analysis of productivity in goods-producing industries . . .' And, as he also has indicated, this is understandable in the case of such industries as automobile production. The consumer is effectively isolated from the production process in these areas. However, it is arguable that it is this isolation that is *precisely* at the heart of the failures of many industries to effectively meet individual and social needs.[22]

In the final analysis, all goods are useful and desirable only to the extent that they offer a service to the consumer. No material product is produced or used as an end in itself. As Alfred Marshall pointed out: 'Man cannot create material things . . . when he is said to produce material things, he really only produces utilities; or in other words, his efforts and sacrifices result in changing the form or arrangement of matter to adapt it better for the satisfaction of wants.'[23] Industry and enterprise thus exist only to carry out those satisfying adaptations or, to put it another way, to provide the services desired through whatever intermediary physical or social arrangements are required. One of the major benefits to be gained from smaller enterprises oriented to the satisfaction of directly perceived consumer needs is that it makes the value of the *service* more clear, while providing the real opportunity for members of the community to influence the production of the goods required for those services. Education of the potential consumers to this possibility is thus of great importance. The focus of community enterprises on the provision of those goods and services that the members of the community themselves desire and can use directly, ultimately makes of the economic system something more consistent with its basic social purposes.

The productive community

[. . .] Given, then, that efficient operation is not restricted to large-scale enterprises, it would seem possible for community-based enterprises to develop some of the strength of the core economy. Community enterprises, even on a modest scale, can achieve the influence over their environment that is needed to permit investment for future growth and development. Of course, the details, such as the relation between size and efficiency, will depend on the specific industry or enterprise in question. Also the potential for community enterprises to develop desirable characteristics will vary enormously with the particular situation. For example, it is not likely that production of basic industrial raw materials (e.g. steel, sulfuric acid, plastic resins) will be as efficiently carried out in small, highly decentralized plants, although as has been shown, the present scale is certainly not justifiable on grounds of efficiency, technical or social. However, the *conversion, combination* and *modification* of such products to meet final market demand does offer significant and immediate opportunity.

Community-based enterprises can serve as a source of pride to citizens as well as a source of economic power for the community. The very fact that such an enterprise produces goods and services of significant value to local consumers, competes effectively with distant and previously invincible powers, and generates a flow of capital that the community can use in its own interests, can transform the attitudes of members of the community (as well as those in the larger community of the nation). If, as has been stated, an economic development strategy requires that the social system also be changed and, further, that individuals be enabled to combine and act as *collectivities*, then the demonstration that such possibilities are real, and can be seized on the community level, is of central importance.

Such an enterprise will *not* on its own replace the need to offer goods and services at a price equal to or below that demanded for similar goods available from other sources. Although people are often willing to pay more for products because of perceived noneconomic or quantifiable value (as in the case of national brands vis-à-vis unknown but less expensive equivalents), such a choice is not likely to be a permanent one. In any case, competition on the basis of price alone is neither typical of large producers (as noted earlier) nor adequate assurance of permanence and opportunity for growth and resource development. Larger firms with greater resources can, if they choose, always underbid much smaller firms in the interests of maintaining or extending their markets.[24] What is necessary is that the products of the community enterprise be differentiated from all other similar products, but by a social process rather than by the expensive promotion, advertising, and branding incorporated in products of more conventional enterprise.

The need for strong social links between the enterprise and the community is thus great. Two criteria can be laid down if such links are to be effective. First, it is necessary to provide as much feeling of and opportunity for involvement of community members in the enterprise as possible. This follows from the great importance of shaping the venture into an instrument of *perceived* opportunity for the citizens whose interest it is intended to serve. The community's involvement will largely determine the enterprise's real impact. Moreover, such an approach helps to build the sense of community. Second, the priorities that determine the relationship of the enterprise with the community and the region, and which in turn shape the use of profits or retained earnings, must be set by the 'community' itself. No other arrangement can build the commitment of community members to the organization or accurately respond to their wishes, no matter how 'reasonable' or 'appropriate' the other arrangements seem to an outside agency and *regardless of the similarity of the end result*. It is the *process* which builds commitment.[25]

Above and beyond the technical advantages that would derive from community-based enterprises of this sort is the fact that they would be socially efficient as well as economically efficient (in the narrow sense). Community ventures, in principle, come closer to the more stringent meaning of 'efficient' discussed earlier. It has long been recognized that a productive and fruitful economic system rests, among other things, on the widespread ability of citizens to afford the output of the productive apparatus. Walter Hoving, ex-chairman of Tiffany and Co., referred to this as the principle of self-consumption: 'The man who makes the product must be one of its major consumers.'[26]

There is more to his statement than general rhetoric. In the sense that consumers in the aggregate are able to use the productive output in the aggregate, his observation is merely an obvious statement of overall system requirements. However, its greater significance lies in the personalized application to specific individuals and the efforts in which they are specifically engaged. One of the important virtues of community-based enterprises is related to their potential for involving people in work that has meaning and whose value is clear. There are many ways to achieve this involvement. However, if one aim of community ventures is to reduce dependence on others, then the value of ventures producing goods which not only the producers (in this instance, workers) but members of the general community may routinely utilize in their own affairs, becomes clear. Again, this type of venture is not suggested merely as a social desideratum, but as a direct response to the low efficiency and destructive (to human growth) aspects of large-scale, impersonal enterprises in which work is purely instrumental. Where that is the case, people work because otherwise they could not eat (at least, above some minimum threshold).

One of the important advantages of community-based enterprises in the sense of *social* efficiency, is that they convert what are ordinarily externalities into internalities of the firm. That is, by virtue of the community control of and participation in a venture, the firms' decision-making process is able to take into account factors that previously had not been involved. Such factors include, for example, pollution, the effect of the firm on other local businesses, and the impact of work on other aspects of life. Kapp, in stressing the need for a reformulation of basic economic concepts to include social costs and benefits, has concluded that: 'Instead of conceiving wealth and production merely in terms of exchangeable utilities, the new concepts of wealth and production will have to be defined in such a manner as to include also nonmarket values ... Similarly, the principle of economy (that is, 'economizing') will have to ... take account of social costs and returns.'[27]

By their very nature, true community enterprises operate on concepts redefined in this way. The social virtue of such a system is evident, since to the extent that individual enterprises operate on the basis of these broadened concepts, more formal and inherently less flexible regulatory measures are unnecessary. However, by the same token, concern for such other factors is likely to *increase* the narrowly defined economic costs of doing business, as contrasted to more conventional organizations. The very special problem of community enterprises, then, is to balance these two conflicting (at least in the short run) tendencies. It means, in essence, that community ventures must be either efficient enough to maintain their products' prices at or below other equivalents and, at the same time, absorb the additional social costs, or that the customers must be willing to pay a premium because of the nature of the enterprise and their relationship to it, or both.

For reasons already described, there is every possibility that a strong commitment of community citizens to their ventures/institutions can be developed, but this takes time. It is, therefore, all the more important that the initial enterprises be selected from those that maximize immediate visibility and connection to the community, as well as afford *direct savings* to customers at the scales appropriate to the community in question. In the long run, if federal, state, and local governments move toward techniques forcing private enterprises to account for present externalities, these start-up problems will disappear, or at least, become markedly reduced in importance. It would be a tragedy indeed if community ventures, which are equal in efficiency to or more efficient than private larger enterprises – all things considered – were unable to survive because of temporary defects in the cost system.

It is the conclusion of this analysis that in certain selected industrial sectors, the potential cost saving is sufficiently great to minimize or eliminate the theoretical risk of apparent short-term cost inefficiency. To do otherwise would be to run the risk of placing technical efficiency and bureaucratic modes of organization above the social purpose of the enterprise, thus recreating the very system being challenged.

References

1. The present argument does, however, strongly dissent from the view that these considerations determine, in effect, the shape of industrial structures and economic organizations at any point. If anything seems clear, it is that more real options and choices exist in this realm than are usually assumed.
2. Edward D. Hollander et al., *The Future of Small Business*, Praeger, 1968, p. 5.
3. The terminology and the basic notion derive from Robert L. Averitt, *The Dual Economy*, Norton, 1968.
4. This is, of course, more than an assertion. It is also a straightforward recognition of experiences in other settings that involve collective enterprises, such as in the Israeli kibbutzim, the workers' management in Yugoslavia, and in the Chinese communal or brigade industries. A few related remarks on this subject can be found in Barry Stein's 'The internal economics

of communes', in Rosabeth Moss Kanter (ed.). *Communes: Social Organization of the Collective Life*, Harper and Row, 1973.

5. Andre Gorz, *Strategy for Labor*, Beacon Press, 1967, p. 126.

6. One of the key points is that only when the firm is seen as a part of the community and as having a substantial influence over its economic (and therefore social) well-being will attention to community priorities assure that the firm's future remains connected to that of the community (Barry Stein. *The Community Context of Economic Conversion*, OCED, 1971). But, of course, this need for continuity and association must be balanced by some attention to efficiency and use of resources. There is therefore necessarily some political process involved that balances one consideration against another. This shows up particularly well in the Yugoslavian case. See, for example, Gerry Hunnius, 'Workers' self-management in Yugoslavia', in Gerry Hunnius, David Garson, and John Case (eds.), *Workers' Control*, Vintage Books, 1973.

7. Jaroslov Vanek, *The Participatory Economy*, Cornell UP, 1971, p. 39.

8. The basic point here is, of course, widely agreed to in principle if not in practice. Decentralizing decision-making to include those who possess the most relevant information and who are in the most direct position to implement decisions and gain feedback as to their effect is standard operating ideology, even though the practice is rarely applied as consistently as it could and should be. The literature on participation (industrial democracy) is replete with examples indicating the benefits from such a strategy. It is equally clear that the reason more such ideas are not implemented has to do with control preferences and power issues rather than operating efficiency. The 1973–74 Watergate hearings have had one most interesting result in this regard. Robert G. Cox, 'The open-door boss and the other kind: Watergate symbolizes managerial deficiency', *New York Times*, 1.7.1973, has noted that many corporate chief executives have begun to wonder if they, like President Nixon, are actually as uninformed about the reality of matters below as he claims to be.

9. Robert Dahl's remarks on this subject are available in *After the Revolution?* Yale UP, 1970; the (Robert) Blauner reference is to *Alienation and Freedom*, University of Chicago Press, 1964.

10. See Hunnius, op. cit., and Gar Alperovitz, 'Toward a pluralist American commonwealth', in Alperovitz and Staughton Lynd (eds.), *Strategy and Program*, Beacon Press, 1973.

11. The concept of differentiated products was developed to great lengths by Edward H. Chamberlin who, in his pioneering work, *The Theory of Monopolistic Competition*, 8th edn., Harvard UP, 1962), went so far as to suggest that virtually all products were in fact virtual monopolies in some sense, always being differentiated to a degree from other products (hence the expression 'monopolistic competition'). But this categorica! statement washes out crucial distinctions about the nature of such differentiation. Similarly, Paul Samuelson (*Economics*, 8th edn, McGraw-Hill, 1970, p. 489) uses a simple typology distinguishing products and markets on the basis of product differentiation strategies.

12. Joel Dean and Winfield Smith, 'The relationship between profitability and size', in William W. Alberts and Joel E. Segall (eds.). *The Corporate Merger*, University of Chicago Press, 1966, p. 11.

13. This is a difficult point to formulate precisely, because of an ongoing debate as to whether the nature of consumers' 'preferences' is endogenous or exogenous; also about how preferences can be changed and their stability over time. However, the point can be made more narrowly: whatever the structure of preferences existing at a given moment, perfect efficiency implies an exact matching of these preferences with goods at the lowest prices associated with the set of existing preferences.

There is also a radical critique possible in this regard to the effect that there is such a thing as pseudo-individuality, whose hallmark is the attempt to suggest, by such devices as different shirts or colors, a difference that does not actually exist. It is, therefore, still a form of artificial product differentiation, whose real purpose is to create continually expanding markets for the benefit of capitalists, but whose real effect is to waste resources.

This seems a matter of degree; artificial and dysfunctional distinctions certainly are wasteful. On the other hand, the ability of persons to differentiate themselves, in part by personal property, seems a requisite for healthy human development, although the extent is some reflection of the historical situation.

14. Elsewhere in this paper is a discussion about whether or not large firms compete in price and, related to that, the issue of consumers sovereignty (see pp. 55 ff.). The conclusion to the former is 'not enough' and to the latter, 'not generally present'. Whatever it is that firms attempt to maximize (if anything), whether profit, growth, assets, or managerial utility, the effect noted here assures their ability to do so at the expense of the consumer.

15. See, for example, Lee Rainwater, 'Economic inequality and the credit income tax', *Working Papers*, Vol. 1, Spring 1973, p. 50–9.

16. Joe S. Bain, *Barriers to New Competition*, Harvard UP, 1962, p. 142.

17. This conclusion has been drawn, for instance, by Abt Associates, Inc. in a large-scale evaluation of the Special Impact Program of OEO and of the Community Development Corporations (CDCs) it has funded. As to the comment on industrial development, see Alfred D. Chandler, Jr., *Strategy and Structure*, MIT Press, 1969, or Nicholas Kaldor, 'The Economic Aspects of Advertising', *Review of Economic Studies*, **18**, 1.1949–50.

18. The very essence of the market system is its impersonality; as soon as personal relationships develop among participants in the marketplace, the system's theoretical virtues disappear. However, the advantages of such relationships to particular participants has always been clear, which is the explanation for much observed behavior. In effect, the relationship offers one (possibly meaningful) method for differentiating among otherwise indistinguishable supplies and suppliers of a given good.

19. See Stein op. cit. This notion in particular assumes the idea of a collective unit, to which people can be committed, as against individual self-interest alone. It does not assume, however, that community ventures, or co-operatives, necessarily promote that commitment. They can be just as bureaucratic, impersonal, and privatized as conventional entities.

20. The finding about urban blacks was contained in a study by the Lee Sturzberg Research Co., New York City, and reported in 'Blacks favor national brands', *Bay State Banner*, 14.9.1972. Credit for the comments about the possibly regressive nature of advertising costs belongs to Mark Hodax, CCED. This proposition requires detailed work for proof.

21. This principle has been spelled out in detail in a related proposal by Charles Hampden-Turner. See his 'A proposal for political marketing', *Yale Review of Law and Social Action*, Winter 1970, pp. 93–100.

22. Victor R. Fuchs, *The Service Economy*, National Bureau of Economic Research, 1968, p. 194.

23. Alfred Marshall, *Principles of Economics*, 9th (variorum) edn, Macmillan Co., 1961, p. 63.

24. Whether and under what circumstances firms actually do underbid (sell below cost) is a subject of much dispute. It is clear that the practice of selling products below average (but not marginal) cost, which is called dumping, is widespread, as witness all the laws preventing it. Similarly, it is obvious that firms will bid low for an initial piece of work if it appears that the profits or other returns can be recouped later by being locked-in (having

market power) to that situation. Indeed, from the perspective of individual firms, all these and related strategies (e.g., complex transfer pricing) are rational. From the standpoint of social welfare, they are pernicious, but very difficult to control precisely because of their individual rationality.

25. See, for example, Rosabeth Moss Kanter, *Commitment and Community*, Harvard UP, 1972; and 'Some social issues in the Community Development Corporation', in C. G. Benello and D. Roussopolos (eds.), *The Case For Participatory Democracy*, Grossman, 1971.
26. Walter Hoving, *The Distribution Revolution*, Ives Washburn, Inc., 1960, p. 12.
27. K. William Kapp, *The Social Costs of Private Enterprise*, Schocken Books, 1971, p. 254. See also, in this regard, Ezra J. Mishan, *Technology and Growth: The Price We Pay*, Praeger, 1970.

Small industries and industrial villages

Colin Ward

Kropotkin, whom one imagines was never without his notebook when visiting a field, factory or workshop (which he did more frequently than most economic theorists), felt a certain exasperation at the assumption, whether by capitalists or Marxists, that there was a necessary and inevitable process of industrial concentration which all right-thinking people took for granted. When the Chief Inspector of Factories began publishing statistics on the numbers of industrial undertakings of various sizes, Kropotkin was delighted because they so amply confirmed his observations, and entered into correspondence with the Chief Inspector on the further elucidation of the figures. His friend and fellow-exile, Cherkesov, wrote a pamphlet, *The Concentration of Capital: A Marxian Fallacy*,[1] which, in terms of the distribution of ownership, supported his point of view.

Today we would ask more complicated questions. Are we talking about the number of employees, the capital value of the undertaking, the value of the product, its profitability, or the ownership of the capital invested in its production? The economist's attempt to evaluate the significance of scale in industry is characterised by Michael Utton's *Industrial Concentration*[2] in which he concludes that 'the amount of evidence on the economies of scale that can be achieved by large *firms* (as opposed to large plants) is very sparse . . . and what evidence there is tends to suggest that such economies are not universal throughout manufacturing industry nor significant in reducing costs'. But the reader's dilemma, in considering the validity of Kropotkin's point of view, is most readily resolved by looking around the room he is sitting in. Will he not find that most of the artefacts it contains, from clothing to furniture, are in fact the output of industry on a minute scale? Even his transistor radio ('sophisticated product of advanced technology', etc.) was probably made from components produced in tiny factories and assembled by women and children on the very pavements of Hong Kong.[3]

The worship of bigness in industry makes us exaggerate its actual extent, as Kropotkin found. My own experience, confined to the build-

From Colin Ward, Editor's Appendix to Chapter 3 of Peter Kropotkin, *Fields, Factories and Workshops Tomorrow*, Allen and Unwin, 1974.

ing industry, predisposes me towards his point of view. I remember working on a building designed from industrialised components where it was said to be essential (to reap the benefits of industrialisation) that the structure should be confined to standardised parts. When I actually went to the factory where they were made, I found that these lattice beams were being made by a single old man, using a Staffa bending machine by hand, and could be varied simply by telling him to make the next one longer or shorter. We just assume that industry *ought* to be big.

We are in fact hypnotised by the cult of bigness in industry, even though the actual size of the industrial unit relates neither to technical complexity nor to functional efficiency, but rather to the cult of sheer size and of power and profit: the inevitable by-products of authoritarian society. This used to be reflected in the building of uneconomically over-sized ships like the giant Cunarders, and, since their demise, has been expressed in the building of grotesquely uneconomical planes, of which Concorde is simply the last of a long line. (Remember the Brabazon – whole villages were swept away to make a runway for it; then it rusted in its million-pound hanger until it was finally broken up for scrap.)

In the 1950s, Professor S. R. Dennison made the same discovery, declaring that the belief that modern industry *inevitably* leads to larger units of production was a Marxist fallacy:

Over a wide range of industry the productive efficiency of small units was at least equal to, and in some cases surpassed that of the industrial giants. About 92 per cent of the businesses in the United Kingdom employed fewer than 250 people and were responsible for by far the greater part of the total national production. The position in the United States was about the same.[4]

Again, those who think of industry as one great assembly line would be surprised by Dr Mark Abrams's observation that:

In spite of nationalisation and the growth of large private firms, the proportion of the total working population employed by large organisations (i.e. concerns with over 1,000 employees) is still comparatively small. Such people constitute only 36 per cent of the working population and are far outnumbered by those who hold jobs as members of comparatively small organisations where direct personal contact throughout the group is a practical everyday possibility.'[5]

It is also revealing to study the nature of the industrial giants and to reflect on how few of them owe their size to considerations of industrial efficiency. H. P. Barker distinguished between two essentially different types of motive: the industrial and the non-industrial. By the industrial motive he meant,

the normal commercial development of a product or a service which the public wants; for instance the motor-car industry or the chain store. There is also the vertical type of growth in which a seller expands downwards towards his raw materials, or a primary producer expands upwards towards the end products of his primary material. The soap and oil industries are such cases. Then there is the kind of expansion in which a successful firm seeks to diversify its business and its opportunities and to carry its financial eggs in several baskets – and lastly there is the type of expansion by which whole industries are aggregated under a single control because they cannot effectively be operated in any other way. Electricity and railways are an example.[6]

But the very examples that he chose as cases of industrially necessary concentration, are ones which not only anarchists would query. I am not alone in thinking he is wrong about electricity. For example, an editorial in *New Scientist* commenting on the appalling complexity of the present system, prophesied that 'in future there will be a tendency to return to more or less local generation of electricity' and a correspondent of *The Guardian* castigates the Central Electricity Generating Board for 'spinning a web of electrical transmission lines without much reference to any other interests than its own' thus 'prejudicing the development of a more flexible and useful power system'. I know he is wrong about railways, where the history ever since the nationalisation of railways in Britain has pointed to the desirability of regional autonomy rather than of central control. The international co-ordination, without central control, of railways was one of Kropotkin's standard arguments for the success of non-hierarchical federation. Paul Goodman noted that: 'It is just such a situation that Kropotkin points to as an argument for anarchism – the example he uses is the railroad network of Europe, laid down and run to perfection with no plan imposed from above.' I suspect that he is wrong about the motor industry. We know, from the much-publicised experience of Volvo, that manufacturers in the interests of 'job-enlargement' find it perfectly feasible to abandon the giant assembly-line in favour of small working groups. We know too that, in Colin Buchanan's words,

two-thirds of the factory value of a car is represented by components bought by the actual manufacturer from outside suppliers. *Brake drums, water pumps, oil seals, fuses, gaskets, connection rods, dynamos, petrol tanks, shock absorbers, carburettors, ball bearings, axles, cam-shafts, road springs and a couple of hundred other items in car assembly are in fact made by a very large number of specialist firms scattered all over the country.[7]*

When Mr Barker turned to what he called the non-industrial and less healthy types of growth, he was describing familiar territory.

Among these there is the type which starts and ends in the Stock Exchange and where the sole reason is the prospect of making a profitable flotation. Then there is the type of adiposity which often occurs when a successful company becomes possessed of large resources from past profits. The

*directors then look round for ways of investing the surplus fat merely
because they have it. Then there is the type of large business born only
out of doctrinaire or political considerations. Last of all there is the
industrial giant created primarily to satisfy the megalomania of one man.*[8]

He was writing before the wave of take-over bids and government-
supported mergers of the late 1960s, for which the usual explanation
was that of the economies of scale that would result and the argument
that larger units would enable British industry to compete effectively
in international markets. But since then, a study by the Industrial
Policy Group itself has stressed the importance of small-scale enterprise
and has dismissed the theory that Britain's industrial weakness stems
from an inadequate number of large firms,[9] while Gerald Newbould
concludes in his book, *Management and Merger Activity*, that while the
declared aims of mergers and take-overs was industrial efficiency, the
real objects were the creation or reinforcement of market dominance
or defence against competitors.[10]

A growing number of such mergers are, of course, sheer financial
piracy: the activity known as asset-stripping, when a company is
acquired with the intention of making a profit, not from its productive
activities, but by closing it down and selling off its assets – real property
and capital goods. This certainly affects any attempt to draw contemporary conclusions from Kropotkin's analysis. In a debate in the
House of Commons on the subject, Mr Arthur Blenkinsop said: 'In
1960, 100 of our largest firms were responsible for 22 per cent of the
nation's net industrial assets. By 1970 there had been a dramatic change,
and the 100 largest firms were responsible for 50 per cent of our industrial assets. That is a much heavier concentration than that in the
United States of America.' In the same debate, Mr T. H. Skeet remarked:

*In 1949 the top ten companies accounted for 25 per cent of the pre-taxed
profits of all British industrial and commercial companies. By 1969 the
figure was about 50 per cent. Therefore, the concentration had doubled
in twenty years. . . . The Bolton Report also indicated that small firms, as
a share of manufacturing output, accounted in 1924 for 42 per cent and in
1951 for 32 per cent, and that in 1968 the figure had gone down to 25
per cent.*[11]

The figures are different, of course, if you argue, like Kropotkin, in
terms of the number of workers: 'Small firms – with 500 employees or
less – still constitute more than 90 per cent of Britain's manufacturing
industry, for instance. In the United States there are more than 300,000
companies with 500,000 factories, employing 16 million people and
producing half the world's manufactured goods. The majority are
quite small.'[12]

The confusion about definitions which arises in any discussion of the
issue can be seen by comparing these conclusions with those of Jonathan
Boswell, who says:

there may be around 45,000 private and independent manufacturing firms employing fewer than 500 – responsible for about 20 per cent of total manufacturing employment, and a rather lower percentage of net manufacturing output. For practical purposes, therefore, small firms as I define them can be said to be responsible for around one-fifth of economic activity in British manufacturing: by any standards an appreciable share.[13]

The Bolton Report, referred to by Mr Skeet, was the report of a government inquiry, which concluded: 'In manufacturing the share of small firms in employment and output has fallen substantially and almost continuously since the mid-1920s. There was also a dramatic fall in the number of small manufacturing firms up to 1948 and a slower but continual decline has been going on since then.'[14]

The Bolton Report saw the small-firm sector as 'the traditional breeding-ground for new industries – that is for innovation writ large' – and noted that technological changes could make small-scale operation highly economic. But what about automation? The word itself is simply the current jargon for a more intensive application of machines, particularly transfer machines, but it is seen as yet another factor which makes greater industrial concentration inevitable. This is simply another expression of the centralist mentality, for as Dr J. Langdon Goodman says:

Automation can be a force either for concentration or dispersion. There is a tendency today for automation to develop along with larger and larger production units, but this may only be a phase through which the present technological advance is passing. The comparatively large sums of money which are needed to develop automation techniques, together with the amount of technological knowledge and unique quality of management, are possibly found more in the large units than in the smaller ones. Thus the larger units will proceed more quickly towards automation. When this knowledge is dispersed more widely and the small units take up automation, the pattern may be quite different. Automation, being a large employer of plant and a relatively small employer of labour, allows plants to be taken away from large centres of population. Thus one aspect of the British scene may change.

And he goes on in a truly Kropotkinian vein:

Rural factories, clean, small, concentrated units will be dotted about the countryside. The effects of this may be far-reaching. The Industrial Revolution caused a separation of large numbers of people from the land and concentrated them in towns. The result has been a certain standardisation of personality, ignorance of nature, and lack of imaginative power. Now we may soon see some factory-workers moving back into the country and becoming part of a rural community.[15]

The very technological developments which, in the hands of people with statist, centralising, authoritarian habits of mind, as well as in the hands of mere exploiters, demand greater concentration of industry, are also those which could make possible a local, intimate, decentralised society. When tractors were first made, they were giants, suitable only for prairie-farming. Now you can get them scaled down to a Rotivator for a smallholding. Power tools, which were going to make all industry one big Dagenham, are commonplace for every do-it-yourself enthusiast.

The most striking evidence, within industry as we know it today, in favour of reducing the scale of industrial organisation, comes from the experiments conducted by industrial psychologists, sociologists, and so on, who in the interests of morale, health or increased productivity, have sought to break down large units into small groups. Thus Professor Norman C. Hunt remarked that the problems arising from the growth of industrial enterprises were such that:

A number of larger companies have recently decentralised their organisations and established smaller, largely autonomous units, each to some extent a managerial entity in itself. A few years ago the President of the General Electric Company of America, one of the companies which has followed such a policy, said: 'With fewer people we find that management can do a better job of organising facilities and personnel. This results in lower management costs and better production control.' It may be that the current interest in and apparent tendency towards the decentralisation of large undertakings is a somewhat belated recognition of the importance of people in organisations. One can only hope that at long last we are beginning to think about the pressures which traditional forms of organisation put upon the people who are required to work in them.[16]

He concluded by reflecting on the possibility of reversing the trend of so-called scientific management:

decentralising rather than centralising; increasing the significant content of jobs rather than subdividing them further; harnessing group solidarity rather than trying to break it up; putting more satisfaction into the work situation rather than expecting workers to find it outside their jobs; in short, making it possible for workers to utilise their capacities more fully and thus truly earning their keep.

Notice his last phrase, which tells us why the industrialists employ the psychologists.

And how have Kropotkin's decentralist and regionalist ideas fared? Once again the evidence is equivocal. On one side, we have a stream of advocates of decentralist planning: Ebenezer Howard, Patrick Geddes and Lewis Mumford, who have had some influence on official policy. But on the other, we have the 'natural' movements of capital and labour which have contradicted the trends which he predicted. Howard's immensely inventive and influential book was first published under the title *Tomorrow: A Peaceful Path to Real Reform* in the same year as Kropotkin's book. When it was re-issued as *Garden Cities of Tomorrow* in 1902, Howard made use of Kropotkin's findings.[17] His disciples, from Thomas Adams,[18] first Secretary of the Garden Cities Association (later the TCPA), through Lewis Mumford,[19] to Paul and Percival Goodman,[20] have acknowledged the fertile influence of Kropotkin's work. Howard's book was a creative synthesis of decentralist ideas which, as Mumford declared, lay the foundation 'for a new cycle in urban civilisation: one in which the means of life will be subservient to the purposes of living, and in which the pattern needed for biological survival and economic efficiency will likewise lead to social and personal fulfilment'. Kropotkin's similar vision can be traced in an American,[21] a Russian,[22] or a Chinese[23] context. In Israel the importance of Kropotkin's ideas on the decentralisation of industry (in a context which has nothing to do with Zionist nationalism) can be seen in the work of a variety of thinkers from Martin Buber to Haim Halperin.[24]

But at the same time we can see a world-wide tendency towards urbanisation. 'In 1850 there were four cities of the world with more than one million people. In 1950 there were about a hundred cities with a million or more population. By 2000 – less than three decades away – there will be over 1,000 cities of this magnitude.'[25] In the British context, there has been a *decline* in the population of the big cities, due partly to the implementation in the New Towns of Howard's proposals for decentralising both residence and work, but more to the growth of commuting and the increase in secondary occupations.

In the context of the Third World countries, there is one significant exception:

The development of industry, education, health and cultural life has naturally tended to concentrate in cities all over the Third World. China's example is the reverse of this picture. The 'inevitable' drift of population to growing industrial centres was firmly countered in the late 1950s by a new policy of developing agriculture as the 'foundation' of the Chinese economy, with the commune its basic unit. The commune provides a variety of jobs, social services, education and cultural life – all the attractions which draw people away from 'backward' villages to 'advanced' city life. It offers the first real alternative to the usual pattern of industrialisation: the growth of huge, unmanageable cities which drain the countryside of its 'best' people and leave agriculture impoverished and stagnant.[26]

The urgency of the task of developing industry on a village scale has been stressed in India by Gandhi, Vinoba Bhave and Jayaprakash Narayan, and in Africa by Julius Nyerere.[27] It was the intention behind the experiments sponsored by Leonard and Dorothy Elmhirst of Dartington Hall,[28] and is brilliantly expressed in E. F. Schumacher's *Small is Beautiful*,[29] a book which marvellously complements Kropotkin's work.

References

1. W. Cherkesov, *The Concentration of Capital: A Marxian Fallacy*, Freedom Press, 1896.
2. Michael Utton, *Industrial Concentration*, Penguin, 1970.
3. Chuen-Yan Lai, 'Small industries in Hong Kong', *Town-Planning Review*, Vol. 44, No. 2, April 1973.
4. S. R. Dennison, addressing the conference of the British Institute of Management and the Institute of Industrial Administration, 14.2.1953.
5. Mark Abrams, 'Bigness in industry', *Socialist Commentary*, June 1956.
6. H. P. Barker, 'Have large firms an advantage in industry?', *The Listener*, 1957.
7. Colin Buchanan, *Mixed Blessing: The Motor in Britain*, Leonard Hill, 1958.
8. Barker, op. cit.
9. Industrial Policy Group, *Paper No. 6*, 1970.
10. Gerald Newbould, *Management and Merger Activity*, Guthstead, 1970.
11. House of Commons debate on 24.11.1972 on 'Take-overs and mergers', *Parliamentary Debates*, Vol. 846, No. 19.
12. David Hamilton, *Technology, Man and the Environment*, Faber, 1973.
13. Jonathan Boswell, *The Rise and Decline of Small Firms*, Allen & Unwin, 1972.
14. *Report of the Committee of Inquiry on Small Firms*, HMSO, 1971.
15. L. Langdon Goodman, *Man and Automation*, Penguin, 1957.
16. Norman C. Hunt in *The Listener*, 1958.
17. Ebenezer Howard, *Garden Cities of Tomorrow*, edited with a preface by Lewis Mumford, Faber, 1945.
18. Thomas Adams, *Garden City and Agriculture*, Simkin Marshall, 1905.
19. For example in *Technics and Civilisation*, Routledge, 1946; in *The Culture of Cities*, Secker & Warburg, 1938; and in *The City in History*, Secker & Warburg, 1961, Penguin, 1963.
20. Paul and Percival Goodman, *Communitas: Means of Livelihood and Ways of Life*, Chicago UP, 1947, Vintage Books, 1960, Wildwood House, 1973.
21. See, for example, Ralph Borsodi, *Flight from the City*, Harper, 1933, 1972; and Ralph L. Woods, *America Reborn: A Plan for Decentralisation of Agriculture and Industry*, Longmans, 1939.
22. See Paul Avrich, *The Russian Anarchists*, Princeton UP, 1967.
23. See, for example, Robert A. Scalapino and George T. Yu, *The Chinese Anarchist Movement*, Center for Chinese Studies, University of California, 1961.
24. See Martin Buber, *Paths in Utopia*, Routledge, 1949; Haim Halperin, *Agrindus: Integration of Agriculture and Industries*, Routledge, 1963.
25. Gwen Bell and Jaqueline Tyrwhitt, *Human Identity in the Urban Environment*, Penguin, 1973.
26. Harriet Ward, 'China and the Third World', notes for slide set *China – Another Way*, Voluntary Committee for Overseas Aid and Development, 1973. See Jerome Ch'en, *Mao and the Chinese Revolution*, OUP, 1965.
27. See G. Dhawan, *The Political Philosophy of Mahatma Gandhi*, Navajivan, 1957; Jayaprakash Narayan, *A Picture of Sarvodaya Social Order*, Sarvodaya Prachuralaya, 1961; Julius K. Nyerere, *Ujamaa – Essays on Socialism*, OUP 1968).
28. Victor Bonham-Carter, *Dartington Hall*, Phoenix House, 1958, Dulverton, Exmoor Press, 1970; John Saville, *Rural Depopulation in England and Wales, 1851–1951*, Routledge, 1957.
29. E. F. Schumacher, *Small is Beautiful: A Study of Economics as if People Mattered*, Blond and Briggs, 1973.

Autonomy

Peter Harper

[. . .] Autonomy is a vague and fruitful idea. It has many ambiguities –
it can too easily hide 'I'm all right, Jack' escapism and deliberate disregard of the public good – but something like it is necessary to counter-
balance the insensitive gigantism of modern societies and rekindle the
sense of ability to initiate, create, control, and participate.

How far can autonomy be taken? Perhaps if we could achieve the
kind of political autonomy implied in the phrase 'workers' self-
management', that would be enough to be getting on with? But this
may need to be complemented by some kind of economic autonomy,
such as that implied by the phrase, much used in China and Tanzania,
'Self-reliance'. For some, even this is not enough, and they seek to
underpin political and economic autonomy by seeking autonomy in the
basic resources needed for survival. That is to say, in 'self-sufficiency'.

The notion of self-sufficiency and the idea of resource-autonomous
economic units may seem naive, but it has had a special attraction for
critics of industrial technology, because it seems to solve a number of
problems at once. The use of local and renewable resources in a cyclical
rather than linear-flow economy reduces depletion of non-renewable
resources and environmental impact. There would be no need to exploit
others, nor would such a unit be susceptible to economic exploitation or
interference. The alienation caused by remote, fragmented, inhuman
production systems would be overcome by the involvement and direct
participation of both producers and consumers, using 'convivial',
human-scale technologies.

Unfortunately the very ambitiousness of such schemes leads to their
dilution. In the nineteenth century, the spirit of thoroughgoing autonomy aimed at networks of utopian communities, but in spite of occasional successes resolved itself ultimately in the homestead and 'five
acres and a cow'. Things have not changed much. While many dream
that sophisticated but responsive and humane technology could now
allow us to realise the ideal of collective autonomy, what is now taking

Extracts from Peter Harper, 'Autonomy', in Harper, P. and Boyle, G. (Eds.),
Radical Technology, Wildwood House, 1976.

shape on the drawing boards, in suburban backyards, Welsh valleys and the hills of New Mexico, is the autonomous house, 3 bedr., all mod. con., built to reduce dependency on external supplies of energy, utility services, and to a lesser extent, food.

Autonomous houses have become one of the most conspicuous symbols of 'alternative technology'. As virtual zoos of alternative gadgetry, they provide a convenient summary of the state of the art, and they show how different small-scale technologies can operate more-or-less elegantly together in an integrated system.

The limits of material autonomy

[. . .] Consider Fig. 9: a house which generates its own energy, collects its own water, treats its own wastes and grows its own food. The idea of such 'autonomous servicing' for houses first started in response to 'ecological' problems of resource depletion and environmental damage

Fig. 9. An archetype: a miniature ecosystem in the country, sustained by sun, wind, rain, muck and muscle.
1. Solar roof captures sunlight to heat water.
2. Rainwater collected for home use. Wind powers windmill.
3. Water purified and stored.
4. Decomposition of wastes produces methane gas for stove in house.
5. Water from treatment systems flows to fish pond and vegetable garden.
6. Vegetable garden.
7. Animals provide nourishment.

associated with providing household services in more conventional ways. But there were other implications too. For many people, autonomous houses represented the technical realisation of political or existential autonomy: not just having legal or social control over one's destiny but having one's hands directly on the hardware. Some went even further and embraced autonomous servicing as a means of total self-sufficiency that absolved them from any obligation to the rest of society. Such notions still persist, and it is important to make clear just how autonomous servicing fits into wider concepts of autonomy, and in which aspects of our daily lives autonomy is technically feasible, economically rational, and socially desirable.

Different levels of autonomy and collectivity must be distinguished. A group may be collective with respect to an individual yet autonomous with respect to a larger group. Autonomy does not necessarily mean *private*. What we really need is a new pattern of autonomy/collectivity that counters the separation of public production and private consumption into completely distinct aspects of life done at different times and in different places. Obviously there are many other preconditions for solving the problems of post-industrial capitalism, but of all the 57 varieties of socialism that might replace it, radical 'autonomists' (let us call them that) would aim for those in which collectivity incorporates involvement and control from the bottom up; and autonomy implies also responsibility, solidarity, and belonging. A crucial part of this new pattern would be the revival of economic activity at the level of the *local community*, which has been bled dry during the course of industrial development. Certain aspects of consumption would be made more collective, certain aspects of production would be made more autonomous, and a far greater economic role would be played by the community. The idea is one of *co-operative autonomy*.

How would this affect economic life? Which spheres of productive activity might be better autonomised, which collectivised, and which left as they are? Consider five categories of basic requirements:

1. **Communications services:** roads, mails, telephones, TV etc.
2. **Social services:** medicine, education, legal aid, repairs etc.
3. **Domestic goods:** (a) large capital kind: house, furniture, car, cooker, sewing machine, etc.; (b) smaller day-to-day kind: utensils, washing powder, clothes, books, plaster ducks, etc.
4. **Utility services:** fuels, electricity, gas, water, waste disposal.
5. **Food:** as basic stuffs or processed (bread, canned food, TV dinners, etc.).

Typically, these are all produced centrally. Could it be changed? Communications for a start are intrinsically shared, and make no sense at the private level, although community transport, information and entertainment media could meet a great part of the needs. Social services could be (and are) organised at the community level (e.g. free schools, crèches, libraries, medical centres, advice, repairs etc). In all these cases, equipment and supplies would come from the public sector. 'Private' autonomy here is out of the question.

Turning to domestic goods, there is considerable scope for community, or even household, autonomy in finishing or assembling, given the basic equipment and materials. Autonomy can be taken quite a long way back along the trail of added value, but the trail leads ultimately to the public sector. A community may, for example, do its own baking and become 'autonomous' with respect to bread. It could go further and grind its own flour, but could hardly produce its own wheat. It might do its own building, furniture-making, printing, weaving; have its own foundry, dairy, garage, kiln, tannery and glass workshop. These would permit autonomy with respect to *processing*, and hence to control of work, but even apart from the initial capital stock, would need continual supplies of sand, cement, wood, steel, non-ferrous metals, glass, inks, paper, clay, leather, fibres and so on. Furthermore there are certain basic consumer goods that it would be absurd to make by any other method than mass production. They are all around us:

pencil	screws
thermometer	paint
bottle teat	window glass
light bulb	polystyrene insulation
matches	clock
string	tampon
sewing machine	disinfectant
spectacles	preserving jar
needles	. . . etc

The pattern of demand made on centralised production might be very different, but basic dependency on it would remain.

Consider now utility services and food. Here the possibilities for household and community autonomy are stronger. It seems to be far easier to conjure them 'out of the air' (in some cases literally) than is the case with durable goods, once the initial capital is provided, which of course must again be brought in from outside at the beginning. The rationality of massive investment in alternative servicing and food obviously depends on opinions about future supplies – particularly in a vulnerable trading economy such as Britain's – but if the gloomier scenarios prove close to the truth, greater autonomy at various levels may be inevitable, and could have profound consequences for social life. The argument goes like this:

High food yields are maintained only by declining supplies of fossil fuels and fertilisers; by imported feedstuffs; and at some cost in environmental deterioration. Even then output does not meet the demand. But continued imports of food cannot be guaranteed indefinitely. In Britain at least, greater yields per acre need to be achieved, by methods which do not require high inputs of energy and artificial fertilisers. This can only be done by relatively labour-intensive methods, and favours a gradual redistribution of population into rural areas. Meanwhile, to meet long-term energy needs (unless the nuclear gamble comes off better than expected) we should plan to meet a growing proportion of our energy demands from renewable sources such as sun, wind and biofuels. These are diffuse and distribute themselves. On the whole it makes no sense to elaborately concentrate them and distribute them all over again. They are not much use for industrial purposes, or for domestic use in cities, but are ideal for rural dwellings. Once again a major shift to these alternative sources favours redistribution of population. Similar arguments apply to water supply, waste treatment, and nitrogen recycling.

This general conclusion about redistribution of population is reinforced by the possibilities of small-scale production and social services discussed earlier. There should be many more factories and workshops in the countryside, serving the needs of the local population and making use of agricultural by-products. Back in the cities, possibilities for increasing food production are considerable.

There are, then, severe limits to the possibilities of autonomy in basic material needs. Given post-neolithic habits of consumption, attempts to achieve total autonomy are misconceived. In many areas less rather than more autonomy is desirable. Yet the overwhelming dominance of centralised production can only be countered by extremely practical – as well as ideological – forms of autonomy. These are to be achieved, not just by defiant acts of individual DIY, but by the growth of community production wherever it is feasible. At the moment the growing-point in technical autonomy is in the utility services, and they constitute a case-study for basic autonomy which can later be expanded to other spheres.

Means of autonomy

[. . .] There are logically three ways of reducing dependency on external sources of supply. Perhaps the most obvious is simply reducing personal consumption, or lowering standards of comfort, convenience, amenity, etc. I shall call this *Making Do*. The second is to make better use of what is available, getting an equal benefit for less input, for example by using fluorescent instead of incandescent lamps. I shall call this category *Clever Ideas*. The third way is to find *Alternative Resources*, for example wind energy to drive a generator and produce electricity. Typically, autonomous units reduce dependency by a mixture of all three.

[. . .] Total autonomy in all services, food and energy is unusual. Units are usually supplied by a mixture of four types of source (or, in the case of waste disposal, sinks). These four, gradually approximating 'pure autonomy' are:

1. **Mains:** supplied more or less continuously from large-scale central plant (electricity, gas, water, sewerage)
2. **Stored:** supplied intermittently, ultimately again from central plant (fuel oil, paraffin, bottled gas, refuse collection, bought food)
3. **Local:** supplied from on-site or within walking distance of the unit using resources characteristic of the locality rather than universally available (wood, peat, small-scale hydropower; spring or well water; septic tank, earth closet, land drain, garden produce, wild foods)
4. **Ambient:** in principle universally available (sun, low-grade heat from air, soil or water, wind, precipitation, water vapour, greenhouse and hydroponic produce). [. . .]

Electricity
Electricity, unlike food or sanitation, is not a fundamental need, but it has become a kind of *lingua franca*, for energy, allowing one form to be conveniently converted into others. Many functions which are normally performed by electricity could be handled in other ways (lighting, refrigeration, tools, washing machines, mixers, sewing machines) or in many cases dispensed with altogether. Only certain rather small loads actually *need* electricity (radio, TV, record player) and these can be run off accumulators or dry cells if necessary. However, many of these appliances have become part of the standard way of life in industrial societies, and most of them are specifically built for electrical operation. For these reasons, designers of autonomous units rarely feel they can ignore electricity altogether. Either they make provision for generating it on-site, or else they specify (or assume) mains connection, especially where other parts of the system themselves depend on electricity.

Electricity can be generated by direct conversion of fuels via the fuel cell, or direct from sunlight by photoelectric devices, but these are not yet economic for use on a large scale. The only practical method at the moment is by kinetic energy driving a generator or alternator. This energy may in rare cases be derived from water power or from a stationary heat-engine, but the overwhelming choice in autonomous units is a wind-driven rotor.

[. . .] Output varies a great deal with different windspeeds, and a voltage regulator is used to make the best use of this variable supply. At average windspeeds, the loads are supplied directly from the generator. When output exceeds demand, the batteries are charged, or when it greatly exceeds demand and the batteries are full, it can be used for larger loads which are normally not feasible, the commonest being a resistance heater in the solar heat-storage tank. When the output of the generator falls below the level of demand, current is drawn from the batteries. 'Normal' domestic consumption would require an extremely large rotor and a great deal of storage capacity, which would be difficult and expensive on a domestic scale. Uses of electricity are therefore usually restricted in autonomous units to essentials such as lighting, small appliances and pumps: an annual demand of about 1,200 kWh, with a wind generator of under 2 kW capacity. Such a small system generally produces low-voltage direct current, and extra equipment is needed to convert to high-voltage AC.

Costs vary in different circumstances, but wind-generated electricity with battery storage is likely to cost over five times as much per kilowatt-hour as grid electricity. This may change as grid prices rise, or if rotor, generator or battery costs fall. Nevertheless an economical and reliable wind-electric system needs a good windy site, low demand, careful use, occasional maintenance, considerable storage capacity or some kind of back-up system. In a sheltered site, a high tower will be necessary. The cost of this may be reduced somewhat by building it on to the structure of the unit but there are potential problems of vibration and noise. These have yet to be properly assessed, as has the matter of rotor blades shattering in a storm and slicing through the lover and his lass in the bedroom below.

Space heating

In cold or temperate climates, space heating accounts for the largest amount of energy consumed over a year in a typical house, but the *density* of heat needed is low compared with other energy needs – about 100 watts per square metre. This is about the same density as solar energy, on average, so there is some logic in trying to bring the two together. A large solar collector and heat store are usually the core of the heating system in an autonomous unit, supplemented by heat pumps, excess wind energy, wood, or bought fuel as a back-up, together with very high standards of insulation.

Solar heating systems can be either *passive* or *active*. In the passive types the collector and the store are the same, usually a massive glazed wall. Essentially they even-out heat variations over short periods and are ideal for heating in climates with cold but clear winters. Elsewhere they are relatively ineffective. Active solar systems collect heat by passing water or air over a blackened, glazed surface, then store it in carefully insulated tanks, from which it can be withdrawn in controlled quantities. The size of the collector and store relative to the building to be heated naturally depends very much on the climate. Where there is plenty of winter sun, both can be modestly sized, but in climates like that of Britain which are exceptionally ill-favoured in this respect, very large collectors are needed to catch what little there is, and very large stores to bridge the long sunless periods. In fact, in such cases, either storage has to be large enough for summer sun to be used for the winter, or auxiliary systems must be used.

[. . .] Greenhouses attached to the building are also used to collect certain amounts of solar energy. They are relatively cheap enclosures to create, can be shut off by insulated shutters if necessary, and have a

number of other advantages that have made them common features of autonomous unit designs (see Fig. 10).
[. . .] Another ambient source of low-density heat is that contained in the air, soil, or in bodies of water. This can be collected by a heat pump, a device which, rather like a sponge might do with water, can mop up dilute external heat and squeeze it out in a more concentrated form inside, where it is needed. [. . .] However, if power for the compressor comes from mains electricity, since electricity is generated at only 30 per cent efficiency at the power station, from the overall energy-use point of view the output of a heat pump must exceed the input energy by at least three times if it is to be better than burning the fuel direct. This is a great disadvantage of current heat-pump schemes, and it would be

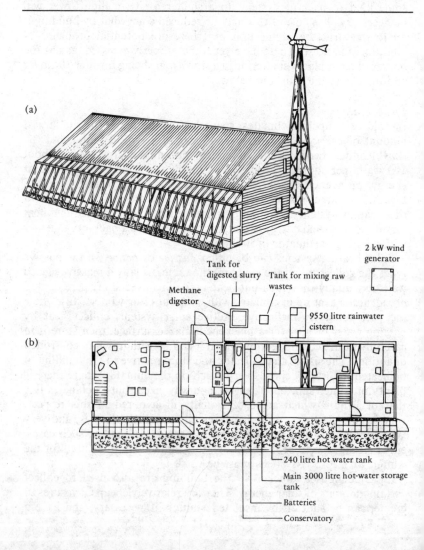

(a)

(b)

2 kW wind generator

Tank for digested slurry Tank for mixing raw wastes

Methane digestor

9550 litre rainwater cistern

240 litre hot water tank

Main 3000 litre hot-water storage tank

Batteries

Conservatory

(c)

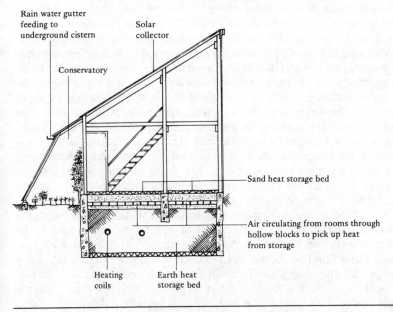

Rain water gutter
feeding to
underground cistern

Solar
collector

Conservatory

Sand heat storage bed

Air circulating from rooms through
hollow blocks to pick up heat
from storage

Heating
coils

Earth heat
storage bed

Fig. 10. Autonomous house design by Brenda Vale, awarded the British Institute Fund prize in Architecture. A long, wedge-shaped form with solar collector as roof, and light admitted via greenhouse on south side. First floor is smaller and can be shut off in the winter to conserve heat. Garden layouts are specified in the design. Occupancy 4. Materials cost £10,000.
  (*a*) General view of the exterior
  (*b*) Ground floor plan
  (*c*) Section

better to try and drive the compressors directly by wind. The braking effect of the compressor would help prevent the rotor over-revving in very high winds and allow the use of occasional high wind-energies which would otherwise be wasted because the rotor would have to be shut down to avoid damage. The main difficulty with this elegant scheme is that the compressor would not operate when the wind wasn't blowing, and the use of battery storage would be hopelessly uneconomic. Probably the best use for excess wind energy in space heating is to use a Callender friction device which converts fluid turbulence into heat.

[. . .] The chief *local* source for space heating is wood, which can be managed as a fuel crop. Trees are combined solar collectors and stores which work at lower average efficiencies than heat-collectors, but are relatively cheap and can be operated under very difficult conditions. On burning they provide heat at relatively high density that can serve for space-heating, water-heating or cooking. The work required to prepare them for burning can be an economic benefit or disbenefit, depending on how you look at it, but I am with Thoreau, who said, 'Wood warms you twice.'

Water heating

Over the year, less energy is needed for water than for space-heating, but water has to be hotter (over 40°C). In many autonomous unit designs, solar space and water heating are combined, the hot-water tank being fed from the heat-store and boosted to higher temperatures if necessary by immersion heater, methane gas, etc. In many schemes, particularly the low-cost ones, water-heating is the sole function of the solar collector. Since there is no need for enormous storage tanks or heat-distribution systems, these systems can be quite inexpensive. The BRAD roof, for example, is a simple construction of anodised corrugated aluminium, covered with glass-reinforced plastic, with a total area of 60 square meters. It is optimised for summer hot water, and provides adequate amounts for at least eight months of the year. Its cost of about £8 per square metre, compares with about £20 a square metre for systems with adequate storage for space-heating.

Other hot-water systems are optimised for the winter, and are mounted vertically. A collector of 40 square metres is said to be adequate to provide for 'normal consumption' of hot water all year round in a family dwelling, but in climates such as Britain's it is risky to put all one's eggs in the solar basket. A more practical scheme would be to use the solar collector to preheat water to feed a stored-fuel boiler. This would save fuel and guarantee *hot* water.

Cooking

[. . .] Cooking requires relatively small quantities of high-density heat. In a large number of autonomous unit designs, methane gas is specified for cooking, produced by anaerobic fermentation of organic wastes (usually sewage, kitchen and garden waste, or manure from any animals kept on the site). Other units use wood, wind, electricity or solar cookers but in many designs no special provision is made for autonomous energy for cooking, and in these cases bottled gas or a solid-fuelled range is generally used.

Methane gas can be produced in an airtight container called a *digestor*. In many as-yet unbuilt designs, digestors are dutifully and hopefully incorporated, but on a family scale in cool climates their efficacy is rather doubtful. Unless supplemented by some (usually off-site) source of waste they will not produce enough for 'normal' cooking demands. In temperate climates they need to be kept at optimum temperatures for the methane-producing bacteria to function (about 40°C) and this can use as much energy as the digestor produces. Building the digestor inside the house would help to keep it warm, but this is rarely done because there are inevitably odour problems and a certain risk of explosion.

The kind of elaborate design needed is shown by Jaap 't Hooft's digestor (see Fig.3). This is a sealed tank of 3 cubic metres capacity, with a double brick skin, heavily insulated and with a heating coil. It is fed with manure from a neighbouring hog farm, and provides gas for cooking and washing, via a small geyser, for at most two people. Some designers have proposed trying to boost methane yields by first using the sewage to grow algae, which are themselves digested.

Waste treatment

[. . .] Several kinds of wastes are generated by households, and, in autonomous units, different methods may be called for to deal with them in the most effective way. Normal urban households dispose of all solid waste via refuse collection, and all liquid wastes via the mains sewers. In the country solid waste is usually burned and/or buried; sewage wastes are led to septic tanks or cesspits; and other liquid wastes to 'soakaway' land drains. The aim in an autonomous unit is not merely to get rid of the stuff, but to use it in the most efficient way possible.

There is little to be done with non-organic refuse such as tins and bottles except to use them as little as possible and recycle them. Organic solid waste from kitchen and garden is usually *composted* in order to return the nutrients to the soil whence they came. The same holds for sewage wastes, which are particularly rich in nitrogen. They constitute the most 'dangerous' wastes from the point of view of health risks and must receive some kind of treatment to render them harmless. In contrast, dirty water from washing and laundry is relatively safe and can be put to various other uses, or, where water is scarce, recycled. Although there are a large number of elaborate garbage and waste-disposal systems which in theory might find a place in autonomous units, most of them are costly, require chemicals or extra energy for operation, may need periodic removal of products for treatment else-where, and completely waste the valuable materials which an auton-omous unit should be carefully husbanding. One proprietary brand of sanitation hardware is called the 'Destroilet'. That says it all.

Composting of both liquid and solid organic wastes can be either aerobic or anaerobic. Aerobic composting of sewage wastes is usually accomplished indoors in large containers such as the 'Clivus' compost-ing toilet, which is, in effect, an indoor compost heap and yields a hygienic soil-like substance suitable for use as fertiliser. Sewage is mostly water, and what is left behind after the composting process is surprisingly little, so these devices need emptying only perhaps once or twice a year. It is sometimes a disadvantage of these systems that they do not deal with waste ('grey') water, which needs a separate system. Where there is a garden, this can be used there (unless it contains toxic wastes). Even if grey water is disposed of through the mains sewers, the reduction of contamination and the saving of nitrogen is, from the public point of view, a step in the right direction.

Anaerobic composting in methane digestors, apart from yielding a certain amount of energy, as discussed under 'Cooking', produces a rich effluent which can be used in hydroponic food-growing, or directly on to garden soil, where it makes an excellent conditioner. Methane

(a)

(b)

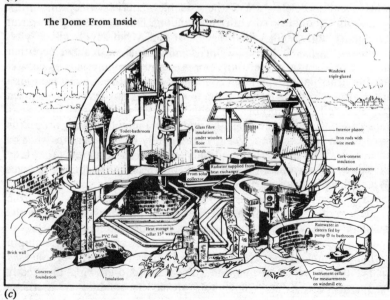

The Dome From Inside

Ventilator

Windows
triple-glazed

Toilet-bathroom

Glass fibre
insulation
under wooden
floor

Hatch

Interior plaster

Iron rods with
wire mesh

Cork-cement
insulation

Reinforced concrete

Radiator supplied from
heat exchanger

From solar
collector

Heat storage in
cellar 15³ water

Rainwater in
cistern fed by
pump ℗ to bathroom

PVC foil

Brick wall

Concrete
foundation

Insulation

Instrument cellar
for measurements
on windmill etc.

(c)

Fig. 11. Autonomous dome built by Jaap 't Hooft at the Small Earth Experimental farm, Boxtel, The Netherlands. A very compact geodesic frame insulated with cork-cement. Window area is very low (2 per cent), but the windows are carefully situated. The interior is a single room with a sunken lobby, and separate bathroom. Solar collector, wind-generator and methane digestor are all removed from the main structure.
Occupancy 1 or 2. Cost £3,000–£4,000. See also Fig. 12.

   (*a*). Layout of elements
   (*b*). The exterior
   (*c*). The interior

1. The house	7. Opening window
2. Methane digestor	8. Sunken doorway
3. Solar collector	9. Rain gutter
4. Wind generator	10. Methane digestor feed hatch
5. Vent	11. Stirrer handle
6. Nonopening windows	

digestors, even where gas production is not feasible, may often be cheaper to build than the more conventional septic tanks, because they do not need the 'absorption field' to handle overflow which is often the greater part of septic tank costs.

Water supply
[. . .] In rural areas where a supply of pure ground water is available from a spring or well, elaborate water systems are not necessary, although 'fancy' techniques such as wind-pumps might be used to bring the water to where it is needed. Otherwise an autonomous unit must rely on precipitation, and/or recycling.

Precipitation patterns vary greatly from one area to another and may require quite different systems of water supply. In very rainy areas roof-collection may alone be enough to meet the typical Euro-American demand of 100–200 litres per person per day. More usually, a very large collecting surface would be needed, and it is generally more expedient to recycle the water, even though technically speaking this can complicate the system quite a lot. Also, rain may arrive in large quantities in a short time, and large storage tanks are needed if this is not to be wasted, typically having a capacity of a quarter of the annual yield.

Mains water is usually purified uniformly up to drinking standards, but in a small unit it is slow and ultimately uneconomic to bring all water up to this level. It is usual to partition the water into 2, 3, or even 4 distinct levels of purity according to the job it has to do. These levels are: A, drinking water; B rainwater; C, 'grey' water (e.g. soapy water); D, 'black' water (sewage). A fairly simple application of this is in Jaap 't Hooft's house (Fig. 12, see also Fig. 11). Rainwater is collected from the surface of the dome via a gutter round the base, and is stored in an outside settling tank. Water is hand-pumped to a header tank inside the house, and used without further treatment for washing, laundry, etc. A small quantity is filtered to drinking and cooking standards. Waste water (purity C) is stored in a holding tank and used

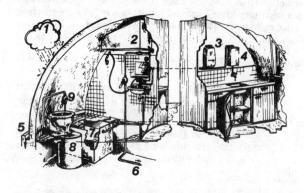

Fig. 12. Water collection and re-use system in Jaap 't Hooft's house.

1. Rainwater
2. Header tank
3. Geyser
4. Filter
5. Gutter to rainwater cistern
6. From rainwater cistern
7. Grey water store, for flushing
8. Septic tank
9. Hand pumps

for flushing the toilet. This is simple and effective. Strictly, there is no 'recycling', just sensible re-use.

Solar stills can be effective in certain climates, but for most of the year in climates like Britain's other means of purifying water are necessary if 'normal' demand is to be met from ambient sources. Slightly dirty rainwater can readily be treated in a slow sand filter, but water that has too much fatty material in it will quickly clog the filter. For recycling grey water it is usually necessary to precipitate the fats with agents such as sulphuric acid or ferrous sulphate. The scum of fatty acids produced can be fed to the methane digestor or aerobically composted.

Economics of Autonomy

Non-monetary costs

[. . .] Autonomous units are not generally built for short-term economic reasons. They may be built as an experiment to try out potential economies, or as an investment, or as a hedge against troubled times to come. But the rationales given are more commonly ideological, in the broad sense, usually to do with environmental impact and resource depletion. The claim is that in these respects autonomous systems offer a substantial improvement over mains services. Is this a reasonable claim?

Consider environmental costs. The kinds of techniques typically used in autonomous units are often referred to as 'Low Impact Technology', and one can hardly dispute that, say, a wind-generator emits less sulphur dioxide, carbon dioxide and particulate matter than, say, an oil-fired power station. Neither does it incur the inevitable side-effects of oil delivery, nor require transmission lines. The analysis is often left at this, QED.

But the operation of a wind-generator does have an environmental impact. It is not likely to be pretty; it can make a lot of noise; and there is some danger from broken blades and collapsing towers. And we cannot fairly compare the impact of a 2 kW wind generator with a power station producing perhaps a million times as much. Therefore we must consider the cumulative effect of a million such 2 kW machines or, if larger ones are constructed, tens of thousands – with transmission lines. This is merely to trade one set of environmental impacts for another, and who is to say which is preferable?

But even now, we have only considered the running environmental costs. A fair comparison must include the environmental costs of making the wind generators in the first place, as against those of building an equivalent central power station. This would involve comparing the environmental impacts of mining, refining and working the steel, copper, aluminium and lead; the impacts of producing the energy necessary for all this; and the transport. Given the economies of scale, far more material *must* be necessary to create a million 2 kW machines than a single 2 GW (2 million kilowatt) power station. Assuming that the environmental impact per unit of material is about the same in both cases, we can conclude fairly firmly that the *capital* environmental cost of small wind generators is higher, pro rata, than that of central power stations. Whether this extra 'investment' is 'paid off' by improved environmental impact during the life of the small machines depends on one's assessment of the relative running environmental costs. It is at best an open question.

A similar argument can be applied to other autonomous sub-systems, with the possible exception of garden produce. It is true that their running environmental costs are probably lower than those of wind generators (think for example of solar collectors, greenhouses, methane digestors, water towers) but they can hardly involve less sheer material than their mains equivalents and therefore almost certainly incur greater capital environmental costs. It is often argued that autonomous units would use less, and therefore mains-matching capacities of autonomous systems are not necessary: there would be fewer windmills, etc. But the same argument applies to central servicing: if households would use less, power stations could be shut down, tanker transits reduced, and flooded valleys restored, to exactly the same degree.

This general conclusion about materials inevitably raises the other 'ecological' issue: resource costs. Can autonomous units help to conserve scarce resources, given imminent shortages and the eventual exhaustion of a number of important industrial materials? Virtually by definition, the running costs of an autonomous unit are low. Some designers have attempted to use as far as possible abundant local materials in construction. Nevertheless many parts of any moderately 'fancy' autonomous unit must incorporate metals, that in many cases are scarce and non-renewable, and, further, require non-renewable sources of energy for extraction and processing – assuming that the ambient energy resources, apart from hydropower, have not the muscle for such big industrial jobs.

Take again the case of wind-generators. If every household had one, the demand for copper and lead would increase enormously. Alternatives to mechanical generation of electricity or lead-acid battery storage tend to be even less efficient and also require non-renewable materials (platinum, arsenic, gallium, nickel, cadmium, etc). While there is a lot of scope for scrap-technology here, fundamentally it seems that any kind of electricity-generating system involves non-renewable resources, and decentralised systems only seem to reduce the efficiency with which they are used. This is a conclusion which autonomists of every hue will be called upon to answer.

If this seems harsh, there is some comfort in turning to other sub-systems. Although they share the capital-resource inefficiencies of small-scale electricity, their construction usually involves more abundant materials such as aluminium, steel, glass, plastics, cement, sand, etc. The problem with all these is not that they are going to run out, but that they need a great deal of energy to make, energy of a kind which is itself non-renewable. So the next question to ask is, do typical autonomous systems repay their energy costs?

Thankfully, this is a bit more encouraging. Take the case of the BRAD solar roof. It is made of aluminium, glass-reinforced plastic, plastic plumbing and tanks, and a small amount of copper that could in principle be replaced by another material. The total energy cost can be generously estimated at 25,000 kWh (see Fig. 13), whereas the expected annual receipts are well over 10,000 kWh. It should therefore recover its energy outlay in three years. It is expected to last at least thirty. A similar brisk recovery seems to apply to most alternative energy systems.

Monetary costs

[. . .] A discussion of **non**-monetary costs is necessary because the mere price of goods and services does not reflect all the aspects on which we want to place value. Prices are also distorted by inflated profit-taking, monopolies, cartels, subsidies, and so on. But prices do reflect many things we want to take account of: material costs, labour costs, capital costs, scarcities and current social values. And since in practice they deeply condition every choice that has to be made in the design of autonomous units, money costs assume a central place (as usual) in this analysis.

1. Energy cost

Component	Energy of manufacture (kilowatt-hours per kilogram)	Weight used (kg)	Total (kWh)
Aluminium (plate and glazing bars)	85	176	15,000
Glass-reinforced plastic (covers, tank)	29	204	6,000
Copper (header pipe)	23	8	1,700
Other (electrical components, gutters, transport, etc)			(say) 2,000
			Total 25,000

2. Energy Receipts (annual)

	kWh
Daily incident energy per sq. metre, summer average	3
Useful heat, at 30 per cent efficiency	1
Total for 60 sq. metres (area of roof)	60
Total over 8 summer months (250 days)	15,000
Less energy for 180W pump operating 5 h/day, over 250 days (say 500 W thermal)	1,000
Net energy yield per year	14,000

These calculations do not allow for the entropic differences between energy of manufacture (high grade) and the relatively low-temperature heat collected. But 'pessimistic' figures have been chosen consistently. For example, published estimates for the manufacturing energy of aluminium range from 16 to 85 kWh(t), and the latter has been chosen for these calculations. The 'payback' period seems to be between two and three years.

Fig. 13. 'Energy cost' of BRAD solar roof.

A few numbers will illustrate the typical cost comparisons between autonomous and central servicing. A 'typical 3-bedroom detached house' cost about £3,000 for materials alone in 1973. The Bill of Quantities for Brenda Vale's house (Fig. 10), which is about the same size, came to £10,000. Mains servicing in electricity, gas, water and waste treatment for the typical house in 1973 cost about £80 a year (national average – it would be lot more now). Comparable supplies would be much cheaper in the autonomous house if the capital were provided free, but the average annual cost including interest on capital and maintenance costs would be at least twice as much and probably more. And this is not even quite as good as mains servicing. There are limits to the demands that can be made, and a certain level of daily or periodic maintenance is required. To mimic mains performance absolutely, for example to be able to run all electrical loads at once, flush noxious chemicals down the toilet, use sprinklers on the lawn, etc, raises the capital cost of autonomy (and hence its average annual cost) from high to astronomical. The point is, how near to mains standards of performance do we want to get?

The curious relationship between cost and standards of autonomy is reflected in the following remark of Ian Hogan's: 'Spend £1,000 or so on AT gadgets, and any house can become about 60 per cent self-sufficient in energy. Spend more, say £3,000, on heat-pumps and wind-mills, and you may achieve 80 per cent autonomy. The last 20 per cent will be hardest and costliest to achieve.' What he is saying is that these are the kind of costs needed to achieve 'normal' standards of consumption at 'normal' standards of performance. It costs less if you have lower than normal consumption, put up with lower standards of performance, or mix mains and autonomous supplies. More of this anon. What is important is the general form of the curve, which crops up over and over again, and is illustrated in Fig. 14. I shall call this **Hogan's Law.**

Figure 14 is a heroic generalisation of Hogan's remark, assuming the pattern applies to other services as well as energy, lumping all services together, and converting to average annual costs. What is implied is that, for a given level of consumption and standard of performance, the replacement of existing mains services with autonomous ones tends

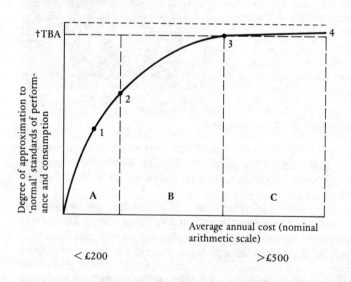

† TBA (threshold of bourgeois amenity)

Fig. 14. Hogan's Law. For explanation see text.

to get more and more expensive as 'total autonomy' is approached. On the graph, point 1 would represent a few autonomous systems grafted on to existing mains services, for example as fuel or food savers; 2 would represent autonomous systems making a substantial contribution to total demand, but with mains backup; 3 would represent almost complete autonomy, but with 'emergency' stored supplies; 4 would be a hypothetical complete state of autonomy with exactly mains standards.

But what if there is no mains supply to begin with, and you are starting from scratch? This gives a different interpretation to the same curve, one that is more useful for our purposes. Here the different cases are all independent of the mains, and hence equally 'autonomous' in formal terms, but they give different levels of consumption and performance. 1 now represents the minimum survival level: simple systems that yield very little and behave erratically; 2 represents an austere but not gruelling standard, with systems of modest performance; 3 represents 'as near as dammit' approximation to mains standards less than which most people, Building Societies and Local Authorities would find unacceptable; 4 as before represents a hypothetical perfect mimicry of mains standards; 3 is an important case because it sits at what I shall call 'the threshold of bourgeois amenity'.

A number of interesting features of autonomous servicing are reflected in this curve. One, which I shall discuss in more detail later, is the hiatus between the spartan autonomy of the *nouveaux pauvres* and the autonomy of 'bourgeois amenity'. The average annual costs represented by cases 2 and 3 divide the graph's area in three parts. Zone A is cheap – perhaps under £200 a year. Zone B is intermediate – perhaps up to £500 a year. Zone C is expensive – over £500 (all these are for dwellings of 3–4 people). In zone C we find designs restricted by the threshold of bourgeois amenity. Zone A is inhabited by designs restricted by finance. Zone B is a kind of no-man's land where few venture, but which is probably where the future lies.

It seems to me that the curve will always have the same general shape, although the actual values will change in different circumstances. In Fig. 15, curve A might represent costs in (for example) a sunny climate with mild winters, regular winds and well-distributed rainfall; curve B costs in a correspondingly unfavourable climate. Many families of such curves could be generated by taking into account all the factors which influence costs.

In contrast to these curves, mains service costs – at least to the consumer – are pretty well linear with consumption (the performance being virtually fixed), but again will vary under different circumstances, giving different slopes. Curve c in Fig. 15 could represent true mains costs in ideal circumstances of settlement density, cheap fuels and labour, etc; curve d costs for sparse population where raw materials and labour costs are very high. Figure 15 indicates how, under 'normal circumstances' (c and b) autonomy of any kind is hopelessly uneconomic.

But under conditions favourable to autonomy and unfavourable to mains servicing, cost advantage passes first to the cheap-and-simple systems, then through the intermediate range, and finally to the dear-and-fancy ones.

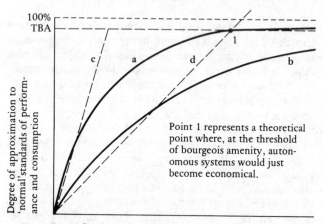

Point 1 represents a theoretical point where, at the threshold of bourgeois amenity, autonomous systems would just become economical.

Costs of mains and autonomous systems at different levels of consumption and performance, under relatively favourable and unfavourable circumstances.

Fig. 15. Costs of mains and autonomous systems at different levels of consumption and performance, under relatively favourable and unfavourable circumstances.

Mains v. autonomy: narrowing the differential
[. . .] Under what circumstances are mains services more costly, and autonomous services cheaper? In terms of Fig. 15, what might move curve c to curve d, and curve b to curve a? Some of these circumstances (e.g. location) have to be *found* or *chosen*. Others (such as fuel costs) are social or economic trends that have to be *anticipated*. Yet others (e.g. new designs or life-styles) must be *experienced* or *created*.

In remote areas transmission and distribution costs of mains services are already so high that autonomous systems may already be cheaper, even in capital costs. An isolated dwelling 1 km from central plant would cost about £6,000 to provide with mains electricity, gas, water and sewerage. The advantage of living in such a situation is that land is much cheaper, but this in itself favours autonomous units which make intensive use of their land for food and wood production. The relationship between location and the economics of servicing is succinctly summarised in Fig. 16, borrowed from Simon Longland. Running costs of central services will certainly increase as a result of higher fuel costs, labour and overheads, and probably social measures such

Service	Location			
	Sub-urban	Semi-rural	Rural	Remote
Hot water	Partially by solar collector	100 per cent solar	100 per cent solar	Full solar collector and storage – hydro or wind power to 100 per cent nominal design load.
Space heating	Central service but well insulated shell reduces energy demand.	Full solar collector and storage to about 60 per cent of normal design load		
Water supply	Central service	Central	From well or surface water course or by roof collection and storage	
Electricity supply	Central service	Central	Central – hydro – wind	Hydro – wind
Gas/sewage	Central service	Digestor	Digestor	Digestor
	Overshadowing problems reduce solar heating potential but 60 per cent load factor may be possible on some sites	Solar heat collection maximised to reduce load to central system. but complexity of on site electricity generation not yet justified, central services except gas and sewage still within 'economic' threshold distance.	Some sites – otherwise remote – may be close to 11 kV grid transmission lines (i.e. within 1 km) in this case 'economics' favours connection as before.	Full autonomy plant alternatives listed in descending order of preference.

Fig. 16. Notional selection of plant at various distances from central supplies. (From Longland.)

as stricter pollution standards. Not much more can be said about these, because of the uncertainties involved: it is merely a question of waiting. The scope for action lies mainly in the other limb of the pincer: reducing the costs of autonomous systems, and I shall deal with this at greater length.

Cheaper autonomous systems. First I will consider those 'social trends' which, although largely beyond our control, may reduce the costs of autonomous units: technological improvements; mass production; and general recognition of the social costs of conventional servicing.

Technological breakthroughs are something we can always dream about – although, considering where all the research money is, they are far more likely to apply to centralised systems and end up reducing *their* costs. But research into alternative systems is increasing. In the wind field alone, recent innovations include the Canadian National Research Council catenary rotor; 'Windworks' octahedral tower; and mass-producible teflon bearings for Savonius rotors. Other improvements and reduced unit costs are eagerly awaited in: selective absorbers for solar panels; photoelectric panels; simple and safe electrolytic hydrogen generation and storage; long-life batteries; fuel cells; insulation materials. And soya beans that really work in high latitudes.

Mass-production of components for autonomous systems, could affect costs quite a lot, although most of the materials are already standard (batteries, dynamos, corrugated aluminium, glass-fibre, panel radiators, insulation, pumps, tanks, pipework, etc). It would need to be determined exactly when and where mass-production of total systems with formal labour would be more economical than self-assembly from basic materials and parts on a more informal, co-operative basis, more exactly tailored to the needs of the users.

[. . .] A final social trend that may affect the relative economics of mains and autonomous servicing is the recognition of the *social* costs of central servicing, for example certain kinds of environmental damage, resource depletion, balance of payments, political dependencies arising from resource needs and so on. This recognition might be reflected in extra charges for mains services (or reduction of various subsidies) or financial assistance for alternatives. Financial assistance might be to manufacturers, or to householders, possibly in the form of low-interest loans that could allow rational whole-life costing without an exaggerated burden of interest payments.

Quite a different approach to reducing the costs of autonomous units lies in exploring the category of Clever Ideas and taking more care to find exactly the best patterns of autonomy for particular circumstances. For example, designers should consider carefully for each sub-system whether Leak-Plugging, overdesign or back-up systems are going to be the cheapest, and in what combinations. In the case of back-up systems, designers must find the optimum balance between the autonomous system and the back-up. This can in favourable circumstances be cheaper than either system alone, as indicated once again by Hogan's Law (Fig. 17).

Economy may lie therefore in *partial* autonomy for certain sub-systems, and even more in *selective* autonomy: attempting it only for those services where it is most economic. This is pretty obvious really. BRAD's house shows some examples. The solar roof is limited to summer hot-water heating, and for this needs no store and can be very cheap. Winter water heating is provided by wood and mains electricity. No attempt was made to achieve autonomy in electricity as a mains supply was already installed, the site is very sheltered, and reliable performance is essential for driving the heat-pump and solar collector pump. In a similar way most of the units described in this article have a mixed pattern of autonomous servicing and external supplies. This is what practicality dictates at the moment, and I see no reason why this should change.

Finally we reach a category of cost reductions which in my opinion are the nub of the whole matter: the social rather than technical adaptations and innovations. Hogan's Law indicates that the initial basic measure of autonomy is relatively cheap, and if its deficiencies can be tolerated, adapted to, softened, or compensated for in inexpensive ways, the lower end of the curve could hold all the best bargains. I shall consider two broad topics. One is the more-or-less systematic sacrifice of consumption/performance/reliability/comfort/convenience. This necessarily violates the canons of bourgeois amenity, and splits autonomous designs into two broad classes which I shall try and define more closely. The other topic is that of economies of scale, which raises the

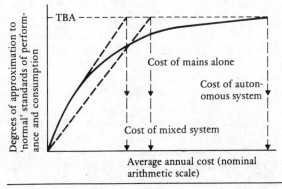

Fig. 17. Partial autonomy: costs for a mixture of autonomous and mains systems.

whole question of autonomy versus collectivity, and what the hell we are trying to do anyway.

Local economies of scale

[. . .] Although inevitably amenity costs are incurred by sharing in the provision of services, there may be substantial savings in money costs that make the exchange rational; and above a certain size, clusters of buildings are favoured over large single buildings. Socially, the simplest form of such a cluster of buildings is a group of nuclear-family-size dwellings, sharing common services. Perhaps this is as good a place as any to start social experimentation into autonomous systems. Richard Merrill of the New Alchemy Institute has analysed economies of scale for this situation, and shown that different sub-systems respond differently to larger scales (Fig. 18). This is an important contribution and worth describing in some detail.

Larger, shared wind generators make a great deal of sense, because power output increases with the square of the blade length and this is a relatively cheap parameter to increase. Sharing could permit siting the mill in the most favourable place, and this would also be safer. High voltage supply would be much more feasible, and there would be considerable savings in regulation equipment. With solar systems, economies of scale are less marked, since large collectors are no more efficient than small, and a central collector could not perform any double function as roof, wall or shutter. It would perhaps make sense to share long-term heat-storage among buildings close together, although the savings in heat-loss from the storage tank would have to balance against extra heat-losses in collection and redistribution pipes.

According to Merrill (Fig. 18) methane digestors show virtually no economies of scale. This may be true in California, but in cooler

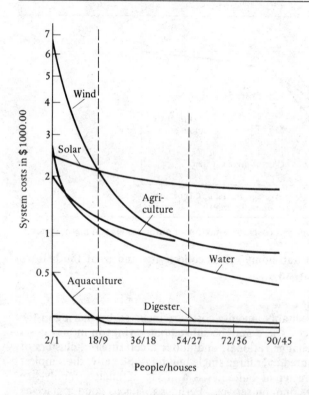

Fig. 18. Economies of scale for renewable sources of energy, estimated by Richard Merrill from various sources. Assumptions as follows: wind/water (electricity) 2 kW/2 people, 10 mph average or equivalent head and flow of water, 20-year life; solar heat: 2 people/1,000 sq. ft house, 60 per cent space heating, below 40° latitude, 20-year life; digestor (gas) 15 cu. ft/person/day, organic feedstock freely available, cooking only, 5-year life; aquaculture (food) 70 grams animal protein/ day/person, 10-year life; agriculture (food) $\frac{1}{2}$ acre of land, sufficient tools, water, seeds, etc. vegetarian diet, intensive garden farming. (From Merrill.)

climates the thermal advantages of larger systems must often outweigh the extra costs of distributing the gas – especially as digestors must be sited away from dwellings anyway. Larger digestors are also better buffered against changes of acidity, etc, arising from variations in the feed materials, which tend to upset the bacteria. Aerobic composters, too, probably work better on a larger scale. Other waste-treatment systems such as septic tanks are certainly much more economical on a larger scale.

Economies of scale in water supply must depend very much on the source, and the proximity of the buildings. Water from pump, well or stream will obviously need to be shared, and if it needs purifying, equally obviously this is best done on a collective level. Possibly 'purity B' water could be distributed in pipes, and drinking water collected by hand. If the supply depends only on precipitation, it may be found economical to arrange roof drainage to flow into a communal reservoir. From here it could be purified to various levels and wind pumped to header tanks in individual dwellings. Ideally this would avoid the need for having to recycle purity C water, but if this were necessary, again certain conditions would favour collecting dirty water and treating it in a larger communal plant.

Intensive food production, too, could benefit from a certain increase of scale, through specialisation, wider range of skills, better load factors on capital equipment (tractors, tillers, milking machines, etc), bulk purchases, smaller fluctuations of stock, and all those things you can do if there is a 'critical mass' but can't if there isn't. According to Merrill, costs for small-scale agriculture start to level off at about 60 people, while in the case of aquaculture they drop markedly to about 20 before levelling off (Fig. 18).

If all these economic benefits accrue from sharing autonomous systems, where do we stop? Why not go right on back to central servicing? This is a question that autonomists would do well to ask themselves more often. The answer depends on the reasons for which autonomy is undertaken. There are those who think they are helping conserve resources or improve the environment; those who are investing now for economies later; those who just want to be 'independent'; those who wish to survive the Great Crash; those who want to reorganise work-patterns, and so on.

[. . .] It seems to me that more solid and honourable justifications from the resource point of view are only to be found in the countryside, where network costs from central plant are high, ambient resources are abundant and are not feasibly collected, concentrated and redistributed again. The communal level would reduce *plant* costs over the private level, and reduce *network* costs over the larger public level. This would help save the concentrated resources whose existence makes feasible the functioning of central plants which are absolutely necessary in the cities. Here the primary justification of the intermediate scale – the communal level of servicing – is not technological but social.

Fig. 19. No comment. (From *Survivre et Vivre*.)

Collective-scale semi-autonomous units achieve economies over the private level through co-operation, specialisation, and in communal use patterns as well as communal production patterns. As against the public level, savings are achieved through the emergence of 'residual factors', the production of useful goods and services with little apparent cost, with hardly anyone noticing it because they are part of the social life of the community, or games, 'bees', festivals, neighbourly gestures. That these can become a major part of economic life is a basic article of faith with many radical economists. Their operation could be seen in, say Barcelona of the late 1930s, or in contemporary China. But there is no doubt that the infraction of the conventionally clean separation of public production and private consumption would strike most people in capitalist cultures as a loss of amenity.

Keeping the distinction is regarded as one of the marks of a high standard of living. Once again, therefore, the social unorthodoxy of communal arrangements prevents 'responsible' designers or planners from considering them. Perhaps this is just as well?

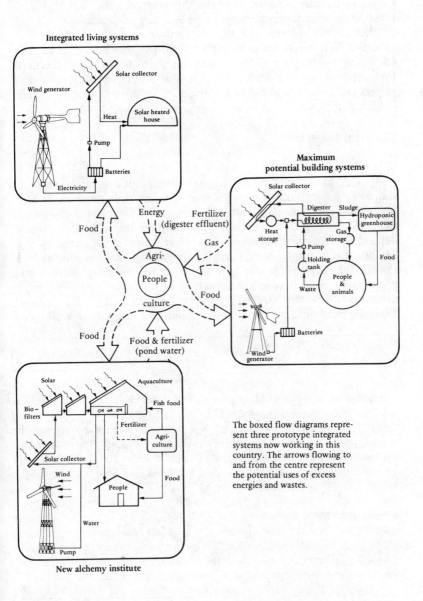

Fig. 20. A possible integrated food-and-energy economy based on three existing systems, each potentially producing a surplus. (From Merrill.)

All this is not to argue against the validity and necessity of the private and public spheres, only against their exclusive dominance. One cannot be dogmatic about the balance because circumstances vary so much. City and country demand radically different patterns. But the nettle must be grasped somewhere, and here is a rule of thumb.

Richard Merrill remarks that, according to his investigations, a group of 20 family-sized units captures most of the economies of scale for autonomous systems. This agrees fairly well with the social criteria that separate co-operation among friends from transactions among buyers and sellers, and define a 'village' or 'tribal' (?) scale as a useful intermediate level.

Practical fantasies

The country

[...] The main function of a semi-autonomous rural community should be agricultural, yielding a food surplus while requiring as little input from outside as possible. A range of technical possibilities is indicated in Fig. 20, based on three existing units. Layouts would depend on local circumstances. A possible layout is suggested by Fig. 21, but this is rather more ideal than anything likely in practice. Although the emphasis would have to be on new building, there would presumably be extensive rehabilitation of old structures. The more diversity the better. Size is a completely open matter, but 'village' gives the general idea. As an autonomous unit, the village would run

1 Meeting place, school etc
2 Workshop buildings
3 Courtyard houses for communal functions
4 Farm buildings
5 Large work-shops, buildings and light industry
6 House and garden of about ¼ acre
7 Collectively farmed land

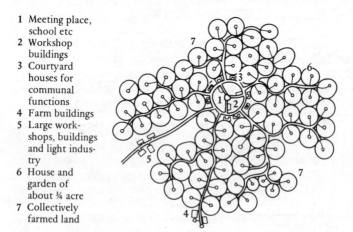

Fig. 21. A possible layout for new rural communities. The method of circular plots gives a rational but varied mixture of private and community land. Many variations are possible on this basic pattern.

its own services, and be site-specific, tuned in to the local resources as closely as possible.

Probably solar heating would best be done at the private level, perhaps with shared storage between close clusters of buildings. Other services could be shared. Electricity might well be provided by a pair of large wind-generators (e.g. 50 kW) with no storage, but backed up either by mains or by a liquid-fuelled generator whose waste heat would be used to provide communal hot water, say for laundry or bathing, or for topping up heat-storage tanks. In a basically agricultural community conditions would be ideal for producing methane gas, with plenty of animal and vegetable waste. This would be done in large central digestors (as with the wind-generators a pair would be preferable to allow for breakdowns and maintenance) and the gas piped to individual dwellings. Great care would still be needed in using gas, and back-ups of bottled gas might be necessary. Human sewage would be a small proportion of the total and would probably not be worth piping to the central point. It could be treated in smaller digestors, composters or earth closets. Grey water could be stored for use on crops, or disposed of via land drains.

Water supplies would depend on local conditions. In most rural areas streams or springs would be adequate, and a communal reservoir could be constructed to buffer peak demands. Well-water could be pumped up by windmills. Purification could be done centrally and the water piped to households. Drinking water could be provided centrally and collected by hand, or by filter-candles in individual dwellings. Food would almost all be produced locally. Herbert Giradet's plan (Fig. 21) strikes me as a good one for intensive horticulture and agriculture. The plots round each building are for use at the discretion of the occupants, but there are 'interstices' where trees, flowers and other 'free' crops are grown. Beyond the private plots is collectively worked land with heavy crops (cereals, winter feed) and animals. Elsewhere there would be glasshouses and facilities for the less orthodox food technologies if necessary (hydroponics, aquaculture). Part of the land could be used for sustainable timber-growing, partly for wood as a material, and partly as a winter back-up fuel.

Socially, the arrangements would obviously be up to the inhabitants. Little need be said about a collective meeting place, food store, medical centre, bowling green, school if the community is large enough, and any other facilities that might be required. The mixture of work inside and outside the community would have to be decided. Perhaps all work would be done 'inside' and external supplies paid for by the food surplus. There could be a certain amount of light industry, particularly that using agricultural products like hides and wool. Food could be processed (dried, etc) as well as sold or exchanged direct. Alternatively, inside and outside work could be done in rotation, or depending on skills and preferences. Much of the on-site work would be in maintaining the service systems. The legal form of landholding might be Land Trust, with no private ownership, an arrangement with promising precedents in the USA.

[. . .] What I have outlined is a mixture of the kind of community envisaged by Thompson, the kibbutz in its pristine form (as envisaged by, say, Buber), and the Chinese Production Brigade, laced with alternative technology. As yet, this form of rural life has never been widely successful in the industrial world, but its economic and social rationality seem plain enough. I could go on theorising endlessly about why it has not worked in the past, but the point is always to try again each generation, (yes, even *before* the Revolution).

One final remark needs to be made. The occupants of such a unit must remember that self-sufficiency is not enough. They can only exist by virtue of investment provided in large measure by the sweat of the wider society, and *must return a useful surplus*.

The city

The urban counterpart of the rural utopian dream has concentrated on regenerating the sense of community; of commitment to a neighbourhood, making it unique, cared-for, and a good place to be in. This must involve sharing because the sense of community is the antithesis of 'little boxes' and the private life of passive consumers.

[. . .] Autonomous units of the kind discussed in this article tend to be impractical in large cities. It is almost certainly better to concentrate on making better use of existing services, possibly supplemented by autonomous systems but chiefly by Clever Ideas and Making Do. It is necessary to find a rational mixture of mains, communal and household scale services.

By way of assumptions, let us suppose that prices of everything continue to rise faster than wages. Costs of fuel and other non-renewable resources rise even faster. Unemployment is at record levels. Balance of payments difficulties are acute. Labour and supply problems constantly threaten mains services. Under these circumstances there would be greatly increased demand for social security payments, unemployment benefits, and subsidies on essential goods and services. In other words, government and local authorities would find themselves faced with greater demands at a time when their means to meet them was stretched to the limit. The pressure could be eased by encouraging co-operative self-employment, and self-provision of services, including food.

Local authorities, statutorily obliged to provide housing, will prefer the rehabilitation of old buildings to the construction of new ones. Further, they should be willing to permit and even subsidise self-building and self-maintenance, as a way of cutting costs. Imagine, then, a block of terraced houses, emptied and awaiting demolition, but with service runs still intact – merely disconnected. A Housing Association approaches the council and offers to rehabilitate the terrace on a long-term basis. The council agrees and offers financial support. How might the terrace be organised?

Figure 22 shows the general appearance of such a terrace, and one way it might develop after a few years.

The houses could be organised as follows: two groups of four are physically collectivised, and one group of two. The remaining two become the 'Centre House' whose facilities are shared by all occupants of the terrace. Up to fifty people would live in the terrace including kids, in the three collectivised dwelling units, one housing perhaps ten and the other two twenty each. Bedrooms are private and vary in size according to need. The rest of the space is collective, some parts more regulated than others. Each unit has a kitchen and common room. Other rooms are used either for purposes of the unit itself, or of the whole terrace: playrooms, pottery, weaving, darkroom, library, games, music, storage, etc. Activities with heavy uses of energy or materials are concentrated in the Centre House: bakery, laundry, sauna, workshop, perhaps also meeting space, food store, office, etc.

Electricity. In most cases wind generators are not feasible in cities, and have other drawbacks, as discussed before. Since mains electricity is available, it is better to use it, but sparingly. In the living units, loads should be restricted to lighting and small appliances – perhaps 5 amps. The lighting should be fluorescent, or with low-wattage focused bulbs. In the Centre House higher load ratings would be needed, for tools, etc. Metering would be at the unit level, with costs shared for the Centre House.

Space heating. Heat loss would be cut by extensive external insulation, covered with weatherboarding, and double glazing. Extra insulation may be applied in communal rooms. For heat sources, various

---

Fig. 22. Autonomous terrace. This scheme is not so much an autonomous as a communalised terrace, in which shared facilities reduce demand for central services. Space inside the houses is reorganised, with groups of them being run together as a single unit. One pair of houses is used for heavy-consumption communal facilities such as the workshop, bakery, sauna and launderette, as shown here, and coffee shop. Gas, electricity and water is supplied from the mains, but the community is set up to use these very economically. It treats its own sewage and uses it as garden, greenhouse and hydroponic fertiliser.

A. Library
B. Loft hydroponics tanks and mushroom boxes
C. Shower room with composting toilets
D. Bakery
E. Sauna
F. Laundry

1. External insulation with wooden cladding
2. Rooftop solar water heaters
3. Extension greenhouses
4. Rainwater tank with overflow to pond
5. Kitchen
6. Chicken house
7. Centre House with communal facilities
8. Holding tank for soapy water
9. Reservoir/pond/swimming pool
10. Anaerobic digestor

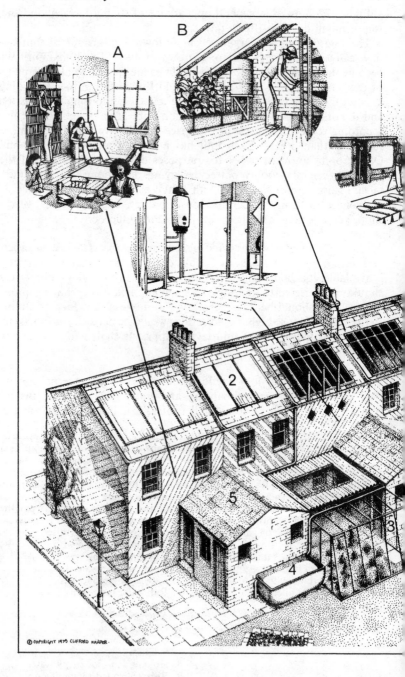

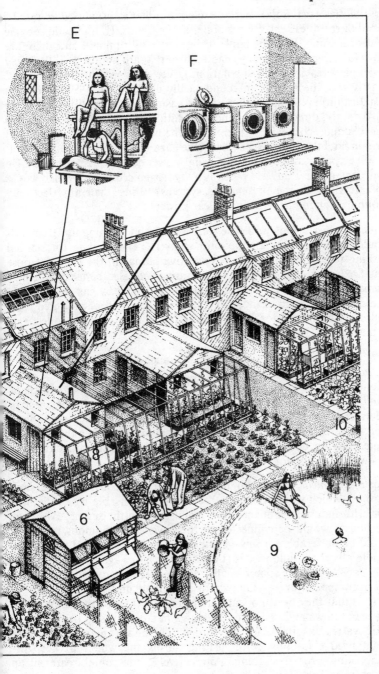

possibilities exist. Solar energy, except in rather unusual circumstances, is out of the question. A large boiler in the Centre House could provide central heating, but this tends to be too indiscriminate and therefore wasteful, keeping too many spaces warm that are not needed. Probably small gas fires are the best solution, larger ones in communal rooms. Gas is good because (a) if economically used, supplies of natural gas (for Britain) are considerable; (b) oil gasification is possible, but more particularly, direct underground gasification of coal is likely to become feasible and economic by the end of the century and coal deposits in Britain (and the US) are very large (the hazards of subsidence must not, however, be forgotten); (c) future wind-power developments may involve hydrogen generation, and possibly a 'hydrogen economy' (which would operate through the present gas systems) rather than an 'electricity economy' relying heavily on nuclear power.

Water heating. This would be for washing and washing up. Demands would be cut by using spray-mist showers. The craving for sensual bathing would be met by daily collective saunas in the Centre House (gas-fired, with cold showers). The sauna could also be used by others outside the terrace. Hot water would be provided by gas geysers, and in the summer much of the load could be taken by roof-mounted solar collectors optimised for the job. Laundry would be done collectively in the Centre House.

Cooking. This would not account for much of the gas demand, and would anyway be reduced by collective cooking. Baking is a much heavier load and would be done in the Centre House. Although methane *could* be generated for cooking, it would only allow the meanest of meals and would look quite ridiculous beside the therms tumbling in their hundreds through the gas main for space-heating. In the summer, some cooking could be done on concentrating solar collectors, but this would be just for fun.

Waste treatment. The aim here should be to conserve water and nitrogen which would otherwise be rendered unusable by contamination with industrial effluent (toxic metals, etc) in the sewers. Although the houses would be connected to the sewers, autonomous treatment would be preferable for sewage and 'grey' water, leaving the sewers to handle all other liquid wastes (i.e. not much). Sewage could be treated either aerobically or anaerobically. Aerobic treatment could be carried out in composter units – say two for each living unit. The advantage of these is that they need no water and preserve the existing connections between the wc and the sewer, leaving a handy access to the sewer for toxic wastes unsuitable for the garden. The disadvantage is that they might need extra power for heating during the winter to keep the composting processes going. Alternatively, anaerobic treatment in digestors is best done collectively, and would involve rerouting the soil-pipes across the garden. Gas output would be used exclusively to maintain optimum fermentation temperatures. The advantage of this system is that no extra power would be necessary, the disadvantage that water is needed for transport – wasting water which might anyway be too much for the digestor to handle, and need separating. A 'vacuum' system might solve this problem, but again needs extra energy. The output of composters or digestors would of course provide fertiliser for the garden.

Water supply. Water-use in the terrace would be heavier than average owing to the needs of the garden. As far as possible rainwater and grey water should be used for the garden, and mains supply for drinking, cooking and washing, since purification is costly on a small scale, and city rainwater has a high lead content. Demand would be reduced by communal laundry, shared kitchens, and showers in place of baths. Grey water could be used for flushing toilets if that were necessary, either by hand-pumping back into cisterns, from holding tanks (Fig. 12), or by using hand basins over cisterns. Water from roofs and greenhouses could be collected and stored in tanks at ground level, overflowing to a larger reservoir/swimming pool/fishpond for garden use. By such means demand for mains water could probably be reduced 70–80 per cent.

Food. Land is scarce but labour and capital in this situation is high, so the most intensive methods are favoured, particularly glasshouse cultivation. Glasshouses as extensions of the houses would have the many advantages already referred to, and could even perform better than comparable rural setups because cities are warmer – although high pollution could effect crops in some areas. Hydroponics would be ideal, and could be fed largely off the digestor effluent. Chickens and/or ducks could provide eggs and if there were a large garden it might be feasible to keep goats. Intensive aquaculture on the New Alchemy model (see interview with John Todd, and 'After the Goldfish' by John Wood) would also be a good source of primary protein economical of land. The animals might need a certain amount of supplementary feed, but they should be able to provide all the primary protein for the community. Bulk carbohydrate could be provided by potatoes. Bread costs could be reduced by buying grain direct and grinding it in the community. For this purpose a low-gear slow-speed wind machine, made out of scrap parts and operating whenever the wind was right, might be a pleasing return to a traditional pattern. Bread would be baked collectively at the Centre House. Vegetables could be grown in the usual way, with communal cultivation and proper rotations. Exotics could be grown under glass in summer. Loft-spaces could be used for germination or mushroom-growing, or, if glazed, as extra greenhouses, perhaps with hydroponics. Such a community could hardly hope to be self-sufficient in food, but it could cut its bills by a very great amount, and at some times of the year would have a surplus for sale.

Facilities. Bakery, workshop, sauna and laundry could be in the Centre House. Shared uses would require co-ordination. Other rooms in the Centre House could be used as offices, foodstores, etc. The workshop would be tooled for all routine repairs on the service systems. The living units would each contain facilities for communal use, apart from their own kitchen, common room and bedrooms – for example, weaving and clothes-making, darkroom, pottery, library, music, meditation, kids TV, games, etc.

Work.   The necessity to work outside would be greatly reduced because the community would be generating most of its own essentials. The work that *ought* to be done outside would be producing the external materials and facilities which the community used, i.e. working for the local authority in power stations, sewage and water works, roads, libraries, parks, etc.: being doctors, technicans, toolmakers; working in shops, foundries, mines, hospitals, schools – rather than banks, advertising agencies, boutiques, military installations and universities.

Conclusions

[. . .] Such a scheme as this communal terrace, in the middle of a town, dependent on mains supplies for its basic services, thoroughly embedded in the wider economy, and with not a windmill in sight, is a far cry from the brave new self-sufficiency of Fig. 9.[1] Yet the terrace still expresses the spirit of autonomous action, and is a logical outcome of the conclusions drawn during this enquiry into technical autonomy. [. . .] Social variables, however, must come to the fore. It seems that the most promising ways forward in technical autonomy, which make a tangible contribution to public as well as private problems and explore new social possibilities, are through group projects doing all their own dirty work, reducing overall demand by shared facilities, exchanging subjective amenity costs for money costs, and using a mix of technologies carefully assessed in terms of wider social criteria. Should they wish to extend the range of their autonomy to other basic requirements such as goods and social services, they would need to work in a wider community.

It is a seeming paradox that each extension of the scope of economic and material autonomy, if it is to remain honest and non-exploiting, requires commensurate measures of collective participation. If healthy autonomy can only grow through co-operation, I can think of no better moral on which to end.

Reference

1.   The two drawings sum up very nicely the change between the Alternative Technology priorities of 1972 and the Radical Technology priorities of 1975. They were both drawn by the same person, with advice from friends, including me. I wonder what 1978 will bring?

Alternative technology: possibilities and limitations

Eric Entemann, Fred Gordon, Kathy Greeley, Ray Valdes and
Peter Ward

The form technology takes is determined by the values and priorities
of the socio-economic system. As it develops, it reinforces that system.
Therefore, when we speak of technology today we must be careful to
identify it as a *capitalist* technology, one that 'represents an accumulation of past choices made for the most part by and in the interests of
employers'.[1] Those who have an interest in controlling workers in order
to increase efficiency would have us believe that the technology of
production lines, secretarial pools, pollution, hierarchical control is
good, that it is necessary, and that it is inevitable.

While 'progress' is sold to us as improving the quality of life – in the
form of products that relieve us from monotonous labour, move us
faster through the air, cook our food in seconds – it has, in fact,
alienated us and degraded our lives. Technology for most of us is
mysterious and awe-inspiring. Taught to believe in and trust a small
group of specialists who supposedly hold the golden key of knowledge,
we increasingly relinquish control over our own lives, and are left
atomized, frustrated, suffering a vague sense of loss and resentment.
Many people are aware of this process and identify technology as the
root of evil. They adopt a fatalistic, resigned attitude that this is an
inevitable development, a force that has generated a momentum beyond
human control.

However, this attitude is beginning to change. Concepts of an 'alternative technology' that would somehow restore our control over our lives
are becoming credible. For some, alternative technology means nothing
more than new inventions which would make technology less imposing
and more ecologically sound. Others, however, do not think that we
can develop a new way of life out of technology alone. They claim that,
in order to develop a meaningful concept of alternative technology, we
must determine new values and priorities and the technological forms
that would be compatible with them. We agree with this position as far as
it goes, but we would add that a struggle for new values and priorities is

From the Alternative Technology Sub-Group of the Boston Chapter of 'Science
for the People', 'Alternative Technology: possibilities and limitations', *Science
for the People*, Sept.-Oct. 1976.

not merely a matter of moral argument: it involves a political and economic struggle against those who have an interest in maintaining the system as it is.

E. F. Schumacher, author of *Small is Beautiful* and one of the most influential proponents of an alternative technology, rightly comprehends technology as part of a 'form of life', and sees that different moral outlooks would lead to different technologies. He understands contemporary advanced technology as following from a system of priorities in which work is nothing more than the means for a paycheck, and is thereby degraded. He sees the drive for profit coupled with technologies that lead to the destruction of the environment. And he recognizes that a system in which people treat others as means, and the accumulation of wealth as the end, is one which develops technologies of human surveillance and manipulation.

Schumacher's work is faulty, however, in that he does not see how both the form of technology and the moral poverty that goes with it are grounded in the economic structure. We maintain that the degradation of work, of human relations, and of the environment arises in large part from the ways that a capitalist economy *forces* people to behave. In a competitive market, each company has strong pressure on it to maximize its profits by achieving the greatest possible labor productivity at the lowest possible cost, and by maximizing total revenues (price times volume). Such a strategy is not simply the result of greed, but follows from financial necessity. If a particular company does not so behave, it will lack the capital for new investment; its products will become uncompetitive. Such a company has a precarious existence.

There are strong pressures to get work done in the fastest, cheapest manner possible: pressures toward capital intensiveness (the opposite of 'small is beautiful'), stultifying division of labor, repetitive tasks, etc. There are pressures toward the degradation of the environment: each company wants to maximize its *own* profit, and has no practical interest in the conservation of scarce energy resources or in preventing destructive materials from polluting the environment. All of this results in the moral perversion of human relations, for the capitalist must view both worker and consumer as means to capital accumulation; thus the worker is manipulated and suppressed, and the consumer lied to and plotted against by advertisers.

Although Schumacher is against private ownership, and understands it to be antithetical to the kind of society he wants, he sees the struggle primarily as a *moral* contest between the greedy and the virtuous. He does not grasp how economic structures mould values and create political power. The bulk of his book is, therefore, a moral sermon.

Schumacher's lack of understanding of the relationship between the economic structure and the values and political relations of a society is apparent in his suggested strategies for social change. Schumacher presents two schemes by which the means of production may be effectively taken from the capitalists and given to the workers and the general public. The first is based on the actual example of the Scott Bader Corporation, a British company producing sophisticated materials – polyester resins, alkyds, polymers, and plasticizers – which was given to the workers employed there by the Bader family in 1951. Since then, it has prospered enormously, while dedicating itself to the development and happiness of the workers, and supporting charitable public causes. This, apparently, is evidence that socialism can be attained through the spreading of a cooperative movement.

Schumacher's argument is, however, striking in what it omits. There have been a very large number of cooperative experiments, both in the US and in Europe. Rather than review their history, which would show that only a tiny fraction avoided collapse, and that almost all that *did* survive did so by shedding any significant social philosophy, Schumacher picks a single example of success. Schumacher never, therefore, examines the economic forces that often were important factors in the failure of earlier cooperative ventures. Nor does he consider the possibility that these forces may still threaten the Bader Commonwealth: Why, instead of its prevailing against capitalism, won't capitalism prevail against it?

What if Dupont or Monsanto, through heavy investment in productive technology, were to produce an identical product at a fraction of the cost? Or if they were to develop, through a massive program of research and development, a new product line that made Bader's plant obsolete? Or if they intentionally undersold Bader, at a loss, until Bader's limited financial resources were used up? Bader would have three alternatives: streamlining operations (which may inevitably require the 'degradation of work'); bankruptcy; or takeover by a more heavily capitalized firm. The destruction of small companies by larger and more 'rational' companies is not an unfortunate chance occurrence. It arises from pressures of capitalist development. But this pressure Schumacher does not acknowledge.

Schumacher's second scheme is a form of nationalization of all but the smallest businesses. Since in Britain and the US about half of corporate profits goes to the government in taxes, it should upset no one if the number of shares of stock is doubled, and the new shares become government property; instead of taxing the company, the government as a stockholder would get half the total dividends. Once the government has control, it can relinquish effective control to the workers and local governments, and the priorities of the company can rise to a higher moral plane.

'The transition from the present system to the one proposed', Schumacher claims, 'would present no serious difficulties';[2] the capitalists are merely giving stock instead of taxes to the government. But either the capitalists are losing power and wealth or they are not. Social welfare programs and high corporate taxes reflect power relations and were won through years of class struggle. Schumacher's scheme *either* means that the power and wealth of the capitalists will be preserved – in which case corporations will operate very much as they have in the past, maximizing efficiency and giving wealth to rich stockholders – *or* that capitalist power and wealth will be destroyed – in which case economic efficiency and maximizing return will not govern production. To believe that the capitalists will allow themselves to be dispossessed without mobilizing all their financial and political power, that the transition from capitalism to socialism 'would present no serious difficulties', is to ignore history.

Even if the social ownership of production could proceed a certain distance, as it has in Britain, so long as a country remains in the international market, forces may very well overwhelm the socialization of the economy. If a country cannot match international rates of capital accumulation, its position in the world market will decline. What ensues is the takeover of domestic industry by the heavily capitalized firms of the US and Germany. The alternative is withdrawal from the international market. Such a withdrawal has often been met by financial and possibly military sanctions by capitalist countries. Schumacher, in summary, does not fully recognize the opposition to a country's transition to socialism that would arise both domestically and internationally.

Despite the shortcomings of Schumacher and other advocates of alternative technology, the movement as a whole has value for us in that it brings out the fact that the form of technology is not invariable but is a function of the society in which it is found and tends to preserve that society; any movement for social change must include a program for changing technology. A political revolution must be accompanied by a social and technological revolution to be truly successful. The Soviet Union is a clear case where this did not occur. Although ownership of the means of production no longer lay in the hands of a few private individuals, the actual *mode* of production was never even challenged. Lenin, in fact, advocated adopting the Taylor system of management, applauding it as 'one of the greatest scientific achievements' in the field of work and production efficiency. This attitude is one of the factors that led to a state capitalism that was qualitatively little different from western capitalism.

A critique of capitalist technology might have two parts: one would proceed by accepting the predominant social values, showing that capitalism cannot or will not effectively achieve them. The second part of the critique challenges the predominant values of this society and envisions forms of technology which involve different social goals. Accepting the aims of contemporary society, it could be shown that a large number of national health problems – perhaps the majority – are created by industry, either in the plant or through pollution. Industry is able to increase production, profit and new investment because it does not have to pay to prevent these hazards. But it ruins the health of workers and nonworkers alike. To cope with the problem a huge medical empire has grown up, with the medical supply, drug, and research industries (which together amount to 10 per cent of the average American family's income[3]). If occupational health and safety and pollution abatement become major concerns of production units, it would cut direct production of these industries and hurt their profits, for a certain amount of money would have to be diverted from direct production. The resulting improved health would hurt the medical and medical-related industries. That is because one industry substantially exists to exploit the damage done by another. Other examples include the following: Factories leave the cities to cut taxes and so to maximize profits; this makes transportation by automobile indispensable, and so leads to an increase in autoproduction. Agribusiness practices extensive monoculture; this necessitates the use of chemical insecticides which supports a sizeable industry.

The second part of the critique is less familiar. To a large degree, the values and priorities of capitalism as a system have been incorporated by individuals. Capitalism is not just an economic system, narrowly defined, but a social-moral system which promotes certain human tendencies – e.g. competitiveness, materialism, individualism, the treatment of nature and people as means rather than as ends – and discourages others. The priorities of the system determine how technology will be developed.

For example, the priority of capitalism as an economic system is to maximize profits. This priority, as we mentioned earlier, determines the organization of work; work is governed entirely by efficiency. What follows is the technology of the production line, the dividing up of work into meaningless fragments, the social isolation of the worker, the maximization of the pace of work, the use of industrial processes that workers do not understand (with no effort made to make the work comprehensible to the worker), machinery which the worker cannot understand or repair, etc. To the extent that these priorities have been incorporated by the working class, the result is a consumer mentality.

A critique would point out that this is senseless, that to turn work into stultification, and then turn leisure into enjoyment without any social significance, detached from the 'real' world, is a perversion of both work and leisure. What is needed is the reorganization of work; this involves a different technology, e.g. the end of assembly lines. This part of the critique is different from the first in that it challenges values of the society which are very widely held.

The real benefits of any radical political change will not be in terms of an increase in the total number of products available to the working class, but in terms of the reorganization of the whole social and economic system in accordance with values and priorities which are different. An enormous increase in human welfare can take place without any increase in total production, or with even a sizeable decline. What is required is that instead of the criterion of capitalist profit determining what is produced and how it is produced, a standard of human need, to be arrived at through public discussion, will govern. That means the transformation of social, political and productive life, and the transformation of the material life of the society.

The primary value of alternative technology is that it is part of the vision of a good society which might help motivate a movement for political change. In addition, we recognize three ways in which demands for the development now of alternative technologies, or their actual development, might become strategies which challenge the system. We are not at all sure however that these strategies will be effective.

We can envision three strategies, involving alternative technologies, which would challenge capitalism: (1) the demand for technologies which are ecologically sound, (2) the demand for collectively managed workplaces and the technologies to go with them, and (3) the actual use of technologies of self-sufficient production.

1. The demand for technologies that are ecologically sound

Barry Commoner has argued [4] that a large portion of economic growth has been bought at the expense of the natural environment. This 'capital debt' to the environment must be paid back or else the whole ecological system will deteriorate and finally collapse, taking the economy with it. Commoner argues that this pay-back cannot occur under the present system. He argues that American industry has become too capital and energy intensive. It has purchased increased labor productivity, i.e. output per worker-hour of labor, at the cost of decreased capital productivity, i.e. output per dollar of invested capital. But in order for an economic system to survive it must regenerate its essential resources, in this case capital. The decrease in capital productivity threatens this capability.

Why has the system not collapsed thus far? As the productivity of capital has fallen, *increased* total production has provided more available capital. However since this capital is being used to finance increasingly capital-intensive production, the process is self-defeating. In addition a greater output per worker-hour and the decreasing amounts of capital available for the creation of new jobs have given us a steadily rising unemployment. Commoner then argues that this whole conflict has been cushioned by the cost of pollution being external to the marketplace. If American industry were forced to bear the cost of pollution, the result would be lower profits and consequently an even greater capital shortage. Capitalism cannot pay the debt; the strain to the economy, says Commoner, would be intolerable. If he is right, the demand for an ecologically sound technology is the demand for a technology which cannot be realized within the context of capitalist economic relations.

It would be very difficult to decide whether Commoner is right and perhaps even more difficult to calculate the implications of his thesis for alternative technology. In one sense at least, Commoner appears correct. American nonfinancial corporations do seem to be experiencing a shortage of liquid capital (e.g. money). Because of the tax structure and the high rate of inflation, many American corporations used debt financing in the late 1960s and early 1970s. With the slowdown in the economy, they were forced to turn to still more borrowing to repay old debts, to meet interest charges, and to extend credit to customers with the same problems. From 1950 to 1974 short-term debt increased from 13 per cent to 30 per cent of the gross corporate product and interest costs have risen from 2 per cent to over 20 per cent of profits.[5] This liquidity problem threatens individual corporations with either bankruptcy or takeover by sounder institutions, so they raise the spectre of a national capital shortage. The only way they can solve their problem is by increased profits, which would give them increased capital, and so the demand for an ecologically sound technology, in so far as it threatens profits, does indeed threaten them. However in some ways alternative technology may help American industry through this crisis. Alternative technology could provide a whole selection of products which can be produced by American industry. Labor-intensive technologies may increase the number of jobs (albeit low-paying ones) without the consumption of vast amounts of capital. Small-scale experiments may serve to demonstrate that ecologically sound production is efficient and adequate for people's needs, but the implementation of alternative technologies on a small scale does not seem to threaten the capitalist market system; it may even complement it, precisely because of the capital shortage and the surplus of labor.

2. The demand for collectively managed workplaces and attendant technologies

Worker dissatisfaction is the best predictor of death and disease.[6] Such dissatisfaction is correlated with lack of control as well as the boredom of repetitive work. Blumberg points to studies that show that if workers were free to discuss and decide how work is to be done, the result would be a tremendous increase in their sense of well being. At the same time, there is a lot of evidence that under these conditions productivity would actually rise significantly.

Bowles and Gintis argue that the only reason that worker's control over the work process is not implemented is that it would threaten the dominant position of the capitalists.[7] Once workers control their own productive activity, they would become intolerant of the remaining vestiges of capitalist domination. Therefore a demand to increase workers' control is a demand which leads ultimately to socialism.

Workers' control implies an entirely different technology of production. For example, the regimentation, social isolation, and extreme division of labor which is imposed by a production line is incompatible with a situation in which initiative arises from the workers themselves. From workers' control, then, there follows an 'alternative technology' of production.

Union leaders and radical organizers have not pushed the demand for workers' control; employers, however, have felt the effects of job dissatisfaction, and have become increasingly interested in programs of 'job enrichment' and 'worker participation'. Some liberal experiments in job design have stressed the factors of partial worker control and profit sharing, and have in fact increased production, sometimes by up to 40 per cent. The authors of *Work in America*, far from seeing workers' control as being a challenge to capitalism, argue that employers who institute workers' control 'will be responding directly to their obligations to shareholders'.[8] However, the success of these experiments is destined to be limited. Some have been curtailed when the workers involved, having tasted freedom, demand that employers go all the way, others because employers begin to realize the implications of extending this organization beyond a small group of carefully selected elite workers to the workforce at large. Finally, workers will realize that these enhancements are at base not serious but cosmetic, and that the criterion of profit still rules over human fulfillment.

3. The actual use of technologies of self-sufficient production

If small groups of people could create autonomous cooperative communities which produced their own food, generated their own electricity, heated their homes from the sun, produced their own tools, and in every other way were self-sufficient, these people would have effectively seceded from the market economy. No longer would they have to sell their labor to an employer who extracted a profit from it; and no longer would they have to buy products marked up to assure a retailer a profit. If a sufficient number of people formed such groups, the 'economy' as we now know it would disappear: there would be no GNP because goods and services would not be sold; money would become useless.

It is important to note that proposals for social transformation through the formation of such communities must cope with the fact that there is no way that small-scale production can provide the variety and number of goods and services which the international economy now makes available. One can argue that much of the Gross National Product is useless gadgetry and frivolous services, supported only by artificially stimulated consumption created by massive doses of advertising and media manipulation. The fact is, however, that most people have grown accustomed to certain goods and services, to the extent that they consider them vital necessities and would absolutely refuse to accept a standard of living that did not provide them.

Even the bare necessities of life – food, energy and shelter – can hardly be produced locally as cheaply as they can be bought, assuming that labor has a money value that could be realized in the market. If the aim is to maximize material wealth, these small communities are currently a poor bet.

There are, however, other factors that may go into the balance. The self-governance of work and social life might outweigh material disadvantages. Improvements in the technology of small-scale production could cut costs and raise productivity. At the same time, the costs of energy-intensive large-scale production may rise. It is therefore possible that small-scale production and cooperative consumption could become a broad-based, popular movement that challenges the present economic system. However, it would be impossible to say that this is a likely development.

Further, there are dangers in the concept of self-reliant productive groupings. To a certain extent, the present high-consumption, high-waste system is based on an insidious notion of 'self-sufficiency' that is readily exploited. A vague need for human independence and personal achievement is turned into the suburban lifestyle of individual house with individual car, pool, TV and lawnmower. This self-isolation is self-sufficiency only in that the basic consumption unit does not depend on or deal with the other consumption units but deals directly with and is individually exploited by the larger market.

Without larger support systems or a larger sense of solidarity, each consumption unit might be sold its own windmill, rotary tiller, prefab greenhouse and solar heater; radical socialist self-sufficiency will turn into isolated, bourgeois consumption. This insidious notion of self-sufficiency is a motivating force behind much of the alternative technology movement.

Further, even if relatively self-sufficient cooperative production is achieved on the scale of apartment house, city block, housing project or urban neighborhood, there is another possible pitfall: a feeling of isolation on a larger level may occur, in which the community or neighborhood sees itself as set off from, perhaps even in opposition to, not only the ruling classes and the megacorporations, but also society as a whole, decreasing solidarity among working people.

We have examined two aspects of alternative technology: its use as a vision of the future, and its use as a strategy for social change. We are not convinced that alternative technology represents an effective strategy for social change. But we think that providing a vision of the future is important for motivating a movement for social change, and alternative technologies are a crucial part of this vision. The formation of this vision remains as a task for a cooperative effort by scientists and working people.

References

1. Samuel Bowles and Herbert Gintis, 'Class power and alienated labor', *Monthly Review*, March 1975.
2. E. F. Schumacher, *Small is Beautiful*, Harper and Row, 1973, p. 290.
3. *Report of the President's Council on Wage and Price Stability*. See *New York Times*, 26.4.1976.
4. Barry Commoner, *The Poverty of Power*, Knopf, 1976.
5. P. Sweezy and H. Magdoff, 'Capital shortage, fact and fancy', *Monthly Review*, April 1976.
6. *Report on Work in America*, Report of a Special Task Force to the Secretary of Health, Education and Welfare, MIT Press, pp. 77–92.
7. Samuel Bowles and Herbert Gintis, op. cit.
8. *Report on Work in America*, p. 112.

A guide to the literature

A guide to the literature

Robin Roy

In writing this literature guide I have tried to be selective rather than comprehensive. This is because I have found that impersonal and lengthy bibliographies, even those which are well annotated, are often so overwhelming as to be almost useless.

I have tended to choose books for this guide that are suitable for the general reader from the already quite large and fast-growing literature on politics and technology. I have not attempted to cover the more specialist journal literature, partly because the best material usually seems to end up, eventually, in book form anyway.

In a field such as politics and technology it is worth making a distinction between those books written by people who display a clear commitment to a particular political viewpoint or set of values and those written by people whose commitment is less apparent, either because they have attempted to take a detached, academic view or simply because they are less critical of existing society.

Firmly in the former category is David Dickson's *Alternative Technology and the Politics of Technical Change* (Fontana, 1974). This book provides an excellent introduction to the criticisms that have been made of advanced industrialised societies and of modern technology. Dickson argues that the impetus behind technical change in both capitalist and state capitalist countries is not primarily economic but political; technology has been developed primarily to secure the power of a ruling elite and only secondarily to increase economic output. The book also provides a very useful state-of-the-art review (up to 1973) of developments in alternative technology. A much more comprehensive and up-to-date survey of alternative technology is *Radical Technology* edited by Peter Harper and Godfrey Boyle (one of the editors of this book) published by Wildwood House, 1976. *Radical Technology* is especially notable for its discussion of 'autonomy' (a brief extract of which is reprinted in this collection) and for Clifford Harper's superb illustrations of life in an alternative society.

While I am on books with which the editors of this collection have been involved, I am bound to mention two from which this one can be said to have sprung. The first is also a collection of readings entitled *Man-made Futures: Readings in Society, Technology and Design*, edited by Nigel Cross, David Elliott and Robin Roy (Hutchinson, 1974). The second is *The Control of Technology* by David Elliott and Ruth Elliott (Wykeham, 1976). *Man-made Futures*, which is the Course Reader for an Open University course of the same name, covers a similar range of topics as this collection, but with the emphasis on analysing the problems of advanced industrialised societies and on designing appropriate technologies for the future rather than on the political issues as such. *The Control of Technology* surveys critically a very wide range of topics from technocracy, to automation, technology assessment and decentralisation. The Elliotts set out to demonstrate, with a great many quotations from the literature, how the present structure of control of technology, and reforms to that structure, all tend to reinforce the power of existing institutions. A brief, but now rather out-dated survey of the literature on politics and technology from a less critical viewpoint is *Politics and Technology* by Roger Williams (Macmillan, 1971). However, a new edition is promised soon.

Of the books published around the time of the great 'limits to growth' and 'ecology' debates of the early 1970s, one of the few which sets out to explore some of the political, economic and technological dimensions of the problem is Barry Commoner's *The Closing Circle: Confronting the Environmental Crisis* (Cape, 1972). Commoner was one of the few 'eco-freaks' who argued that it is the *type* of economic growth (reflected in technological innovations such as the throwaway aluminium beer can and the nuclear reactor) that is responsible for the environmental crisis, rather than economic or population growth as such. As can be seen from the extract from *The Closing Circle* included in this collection Commoner's political programme is a reformist one, involving critical scientists and the public joining together to campaign for an environmentally sound pattern of growth.

Taking up the theme of citizen action on environmental and technical issues are several recent books. In the British context probably the best known is Richard Gregory's *The Price of Amenity* (Macmillan, 1971), which documents several case-studies in which technical projects, such as motorways, reservoirs and power lines, came up against local opposition. Two more recent books, also based on case-studies of environmental conflict in Britain, are *Campaigning for the Environment*, edited by Richard Kimber and J. J. Richardson (Routledge and Kegan Paul, 1974) and *The Politics of Physical Resources*, edited by Peter Smith (Penguin, 1975). The latter, which documents environmental conflicts over copper mining in Snowdonia, brick-making in Bedfordshire and aluminium and oil processing in Anglesey, among others, would make an excellent case-study companion volume to this collection. Also worth reading is *Politics by Pressure*, by Patrick Rivers (Harrap, 1974), which gives a useful, if rather journalistic, account of the various pressure groups in Britain concerned with technological and environmental issues. However, Rivers' main purpose is to show that neither Parliament nor the public interest pressure groups such as

Friends of the Earth, Social Audit and the British Society for Social Reponsibility in Science have much chance in competing for influence against the lavishly funded commercial and professional interest and pressure groups such as the British Roads Federation or the British Medical Association. For a practical handbook on how to organise a campaign against an unwanted project in your neighbourhood there is no better guide than *The Householder's Guide to Community Defence Against Bureaucratic Aggression*, by Antony Jay (Cape, 1972). And for the political theory of participation easily the best book is *Participation and Democratic Theory*, by Carole Pateman (Cambridge UP, 1970). Also useful is a comparative study by Dorothy Nelkin of attempts in several European countries at involving the public in science and technology policy, entitled *Public Involvement in Policies for Science and Technology* (Sage, 1977).

To the Marxist critics of limits to growth the activities of environmental campaigners do not go anywhere near to the heart of the problem. J. Ridgeway in his book *The Politics of Ecology* (Dutton, 1971) sets out to expose the 'establishment' ideology of the American environmental movement and to show that only a social and political transformation of society along socialist lines can solve environmental problems. Two useful British collections of papers from conferences which also present an analysis of environmental and resource problems from a radical socialist viewpoint are *Socialism and the Environment*, edited by Ken Coates (Spokesman Books, 1972) and *Resources and the Environment: a Socialist Perspective*, edited by Michael Barratt-Brown, Tony Emerson and Colin Stoneman (Spokesman Books, 1976). For an anarchist perspective on the same problems a very readable book is Murray Bookchin's *Post-scarcity Anarchism* (Ramparts Press, 1971) which includes Bookchin's highly influential essay, 'Towards a liberatory technology'. The liberatory possibilities of information systems and computers in the context of a libertarian socialist society is discussed in Stephen Bodington's *Computers and Socialism* (Spokesman Books, 1972).

In complete contrast, in both style and politics, to the above are the many authoritative official and semi-official reports on economic, technological and environmental questions published over the last decade by the Organisation for Economic Co-operation and Development (OECD). They are important because they reflect the changes that are taking place in certain government and administrative circles in attitudes towards science, technology and the environment. A key document here is a report entitled *Science, Growth and Society: A New Perspective* (OECD, 1971), sometimes known as the Brooks Report, after the chairman of the committee that produced it, Harvey Brooks. The Brooks Report argued that economic growth should not necessarily be the prime objective of governments, but that wider criteria for growth were now required. The consequences of economic and technological growth should be assessed and growth directed in socially desirable directions. One of the tools advocated by Brooks for aiding this new type of policy-making is technology assessment. Still the most comprehensive survey available of technology assessment and its methodology is *Society and the Assessment of Technology*, by François Hetman (OECD, 1973). This is not a book to read right through – I tried it and it is heavy going – it is best treated as a reference work.

The problems of Third-World development have not been neglected by OECD. Recently published is *Appropriate Technology: Problems and Promises*, edited by Nicolas Jéquier (OECD, 1976). This is an excellent introduction to the theory and practice of appropriate technology and includes many case-studies of appropriate technology projects in developing countries.

The political economy of technology for development is a field which, for reasons of space, we have not really covered in this collection. Fortunately there are now a number of excellent books on the subject. If you are prepared to grapple with some economic jargon a good starting point is *Science, Technology and Development* edited by Charles Cooper (Cass, 1973). Cooper is with the Science Policy Research Unit at Sussex University where many of the British experts in technology and development may be found. The Sussex group tend to be critical of the ideas of E. F. Schumacher in his now very well-known book on 'intermediate technology', *Small is Beautiful: a Study of Economics as if People Mattered* (Blond and Briggs, 1973, Abacus 1974), as failing to take sufficient account of the political situation in developing countries. They argue that both appropriate technology and political change are required. Perhaps because of the political changes that have happened there, China and the Chinese approach to technology and development, are of particular interest to many people in the West. A virtual flood of books has recently appeared about China, but still one of the best is E. L. Wheelwright and B. McFarlane's *The Chinese Road to Socialism* (Penguin, 1970).

No bibliography on the politics of technology would be complete without some mention of the literature on science and technology in government administration and in conventional (party) politics. A classic work on science and technology in Whitehall's 'corridors of power' is C. P. Snow's fascinating *Science and Government* (OUP, 1961). Then there is Norman Vig's *Science and Technology in British Politics* (Pergamon, 1968), which gives a detailed, historical account of the science policy debates inside and outside Parliament in the period 1959–64. A more up-to-date account by Vig of British science policy can be found in *Science Policies of the Industrial Nations*, edited by T. Dixon Long and Christopher Wright (Praeger, 1976). *Governing Science and Technology*, by W. H. Lambright (OUP, 1976) discusses how the American administrative agencies have gained control of science and technology policy. The international politics of science and technology are well covered in *European Technology: the Politics of Collaboration*, by Roger Williams (Croom Helm, 1973) and in *Science and Policy: the International Stimulus* by Alexander King (OUP, 1974).

Finally I should like to recommend a philosophical book which is not directly concerned with politics and technology in the same sense as the others in this guide, but which I think is highly relevant to the problems. The book has the unlikely title of *Zen and the Art of Motorcycle Maintenance*, by Robert Pirsig (Bodley Head, 1974; Corgi, 1974). One of the many aspects of this book is its discussion of ways in which the individual can overcome his or her feelings of alienation from modern technology by ceasing to be afraid of it and regaining a sense of craftmanship in relationship to it – hence the 'art of motorcycle maintenance'. But even if you disagree with its politics and the philosophy, 'ZAMM' makes an excellent read, which surely accounts for its place among the best-sellers of 1976.

Biographical notes

François Hetman is a member of the Secretariat of the Organisation for Economic Co-operation and Development (OECD) in Paris. His writing has been largely in the field of forecasting, futures research and technology assessment, and includes *The Language of Forecasting* and *Society and the Assessment of Technology* (1973).

Shivaji Lal has been a lecturer in physiology at the Chelsea College of Science and Technology. He was a founder member of the British Society for Social Responsibility in Science (BSSRS).

David Elliott is a lecturer in the Faculty of Technology at the Open University. He is a member of BSSRS and contributes regular articles to *Undercurrents* magazine.

Ruth Elliott has done research in the fields of industrial relations and industrial sociology at the National Institute of Economic and Social Research, and at the London School of Economics. She is currently working on industrial democracy for the trade union movement.

Roger Williams is Professor in Liberal Studies in Science at Manchester University. His publications include *Politics and Technology* (1971) and *European Technology: the Politics of Collaboration* (1973).

Mike Cooley is a senior design engineer at Lucas Aerospace's Willesden plant. He is a former national president of AUEW-TASS, a leading member of the Lucas Aerospace Combine Stewards Committee, and editor of *Combine News*.

Ken Coates is Director of the Bertrand Russell Peace Foundation, and a member of the Institute for Workers' Control. He is an ex-miner and has taught sociology in the Adult Education Department of Nottingham University.

Barry Commoner is Professor of Plant Physiology at Washington University in St Louis and Director of the Center for the Biology of Natural Systems which he founded in 1966. He is the author of *Science and Survival* (1966), *The Closing Circle: Confronting the Environmental Crisis* (1972) and *The Poverty of Power* (1976). He is a member of the Board of Directors of the American Association for the Advancement of Science and Chairman of the Board of Directors of the Scientists' Institute for Public Information.

Hazel Henderson is a director of the Council for Economic Priorities, New York and Washington, which prepares reports on the performance of business in the areas of pollution, minority hiring, military contracting and foreign investments. She is also co-director of the Centre for Alternative Futures, Princeton, New Jersey.

Christopher Freeman is Professor of Science Policy at the Science Policy Research Unit, Sussex University. His main work has been in the areas of research and development, and industrial innovation and his publications include *The Economics of Industrial Innovation* (1974).

John Jewkes was Professor of Economic Organisation at the University of Oxford from 1948 to 1969 and is now Director of the Industrial Policy Group and Economic Adviser to Arthur Guinness, Son & Co. Ltd. Professor Jewkes' publications include *Ordeal by Planning* (1948); *The Sources of Invention* (1958); and *Public and Private Enterprise* (1965).

The Council for Science and Society was formed in 1973 with the objects of 'promoting the study of, and research into, the social effects of science and technology' and stimulating informed discussion in the field of 'the social responsibility of the scientist'. Its membership consists of lawyers, philosophers and experts in many fields of science and technology.

Laurence H. Tribe is a lawyer and ex-director of the Technology Assessment Panel of the National Academy of Science in the United States.

Marlan Blissett lectures at the Lyndon B. Johnson School of Public Affairs, The University of Texas at Austin.

Michael S. Baram is an attorney and an associate professor in the Department of Civil Engineering at the Massachusetts Institute of Technology (MIT), where he specialises in legal and institutional aspects of planning and technology.

Tony Benn is the Member of Parliament for Bristol South-East and former Minister of Trade and Industry and Minister of Technology.

He is currently (1977) the Secretary of State for Energy in the Labour Government.

Leslie Sklair is lecturer in sociology at the London School of Economics. He was the International Secretary of BSSRS in 1973. His books include *The Sociology of Progress* (1970), and *Organized Knowledge* (1973).

Joseph F. Coates is Assistant to the Director of the Office of Technology Assessment of the United States Congress. He has written widely on technology assessment and related issues.

Dorothy Nelkin lectures at Cornell University where she has been closely involved with a course on the management and control of technology, and the program on science, technology and society. Her publications include *Nuclear Power and its Critics* (1971) and *Public Involvement in Politics for Science and Technology* (1977).

Jeremy Mitchell is the London correspondent of the *International Social Science Journal*. He was formerly deputy research director of the Consumers' Association and Secretary of the United Kingdom Social Science Research Council. His books include *Social Science Research and Industry* (with associates), and *Betting*.

Stuart Umpleby is a researcher in communications at the University of Illinois where he works for the Computer-Based Education Research Laboratory.

Sherry R. Arnstein is an urban planning consultant who has worked for a variety of firms, government agencies and community groups in the United States, including the Arthur D. Little Public Interest Group Advisory Scheme project.

David Morris is co-director of the Institute of Local Self-Reliance, an organisation that investigates the potential for cities to become productive, and for decentralisation in economic, political and manufacturing sectors. His publications include *We Must Make Haste Slowly: the Process of Revolution in Chile* (1973).

Karl Hess is a former editor of *Newsweek* and a founding editor of *National Review*. He is the author of *Dear America* (1975) and is currently experimenting with rural self-sufficiency.

Barry Stein is economic consultant to the Center for Community Economic Development, Cambridge, Massachusetts, and associate director of the Center for Social and Evaluation Research at the University of Massachusetts. His publications include *Size, Efficiency and Community Enterprise* (1974).

Colin Ward is education officer of the Town and Country Planning Association. He has written and edited a number of books, including *Anarchy in Action* and *Utopia*, and is a former editor of the magazine *Anarchy*.

Peter Harper is one of the founders of *Undercurrents* magazine. He has worked as a consultant on alternative technology for a number of government institutions both in the UK and abroad. His publications include *Radical Technology* (1976).

Eric Entemann, Fred Gordon, Kathy Greeley, Ray Valdes and Peter Ward are members of the Boston 'Science for the People' Chapter's Alternative Technology sub-group.

Index